773

PEPTIDES:
Chemistry and Biochemistry

PEPTIDES:
Chemistry and Biochemistry

PROCEEDINGS OF THE FIRST AMERICAN PEPTIDE
SYMPOSIUM, YALE UNIVERSITY, AUGUST, 1968

Editor: Boris Weinstein

DEPARTMENT OF CHEMISTRY
UNIVERSITY OF WASHINGTON
SEATTLE, WASHINGTON

Associate Editor: Saul Lande

SCHOOL OF MEDICINE
SECTION OF DERMATOLOGY
YALE UNIVERSITY
NEW HAVEN, CONNECTICUT

MARCEL DEKKER, INC., New York   1970

Preface

The papers presented in this volume were delivered at the American Peptide Symposium held at Yale University on August 13–18, 1968. This conference brought together, for the first time in the United States, physical, organic, biological, and pharmaceutical chemists with a common interest in peptides. Publication of these proceedings makes available a permanent record of research in peptide chemistry for 1968, and may be of particular interest to scientists not present at the meeting.

The topics covered can be grouped into several broad areas— these include classical and solid-phase peptide synthesis, theoretical and experimental work on peptide conformation, correlations of structure or conformation with biological activity, properties of analogs, and characterization and synthesis of new peptide natural products.

Among the many subjects discussed in detail are applications and development of new coupling reagents, the relationship between structure and activity in angiotensin, calcitonin, and certain gastrointestinal hormones, as well as methods for the detection, control or study of mechanisms of racemization in peptide chemistry. Studies involving unusual amino acids, peptide antibiotics, cystine peptides, γ-glutamyl peptides, and others are also covered.

We are indebted to both European and Japanese colleagues, after whose symposia our own was fashioned and whose high standards we hope to attain. The success of these earlier gatherings sets an example to the world of internal accord based on mutual interest and respect. Fortunately, we need not be concerned in America with political barriers. However, to encourage optimal progress in our field, we must strive to eliminate communication barriers between the many separate disciplines now working in peptide chemistry.

This series will be continued by a second American Peptide Symposium, which will be held in the summer of 1970.

SAUL LANDE
BORIS WEINSTEIN

Contributors to This Volume

Okitoshi Abe, *Laboratory of Biochemistry, Faculty of Science, Kyushu University, Fukuoka, Japan*

George W. Anderson, *Lederle Laboratories, American Cyanamid Company, Pearl River, New York*

Christian B. Anfinsen, *Laboratory of Chemical Biology, National Institute of Arthritis and Metabolic Diseases, National Institutes of Health, Bethesda, Maryland*

Haruhijo Aoyagi, *Laboratory of Biochemistry, Faculty of Science, Kyushu University, Fukuoka, Japan*

Ernest Bayer, *Department of Chemistry, University of Houston, Houston, Texas*

E. R. Blout, *Department of Biological Chemistry, Harvard Medical School, Boston, Massachusetts*

Miklos Bodanszky, *Department of Chemistry, Case Western Reserve University, Cleveland, Ohio*

H. Bossert, *Research Laboratories, Sandoz Ltd., Basle, Switzerland*

F. M. Bumpus, *Research Division, Cleveland Clinic Foundation, Cleveland, Ohio*

Nancy M. Cladel, *Department of Biochemistry, Indiana University, School of Medicine, Indianapolis, Indiana*

C. M. Deber, *Department of Biological Chemistry, Harvard Medical School, Boston, Massachusetts*

S. W. Fox, *Institute of Molecular Evolution and Biochemistry Department, University of Miami, Coral Gables, Florida*

U. R. Ghatak, *Department of Chemistry, St. John's University, Jamaica, New York*

B. F. Gisin, *The Rockefeller University, New York, New York*

A. H. Goldkamp, *Chemical Research Department, G. D. Searle & Company, Skokie, Illinois*

C. Glaser, *Department of Chemistry, Polytechnic Institute of Brooklyn, Brooklyn, New York*

J. W. Goodman, *Department of Microbiology, University of California School of Medicine, San Francisco, California*

M. Goodman, *Department of Chemistry, Polytechnic Institute of Brooklyn, Brooklyn, New York*

Norman H. Grant, *Research Division, Wyeth Laboratories, Radnor, Pennsylvania*

Erhard Gross, *National Institutes of Health, Bethesda, Maryland*

S. K. Gupta, *Department of Biochemistry, Indiana University, School of Medicine, Indianapolis, Indiana*

St. Guttmann, *Research Laboratories, Sandoz Ltd., Basle, Switzerland*

Kaoru Harada, *Institute of Molecular Evolution and Biochemistry Department, University of Miami, Coral Gables, Florida*

T. Hayakawa, *Institute of Molecular Evolution and Biochemistry Department, University of Miami, Coral Gables, Florida*

Richard G. Hiskey, *Venable Chemical Laboratory, University of North Carolina, Chapel Hill, North Carolina*

Nobuo Izumiya, *Laboratory of Biochemistry, Faculty of Science, Kyushu University, Fukuoka, Japan*

P.-A. Jaquenoud, *Research Laboratories, Sandoz Ltd., Basle, Switzerland*

R. H. Johnson, *Department of Chemistry, St. John's University, Jamaica, New York*

W. C. Jones, Jr., *Venable Chemical Laboratory, University of North Carolina, Chapel Hill, North Carolina*

E. C. Jorgensen, *Department of Pharmaceutical Chemistry, School of Pharmacy, University of California, San Francisco, California*

A. Kapoor, *Department of Pharmaceutical Chemistry, College of Pharmacy, St. John's University, Jamaica, New York*

Tetsuo Kato, *Laboratory of Biochemistry, Faculty of Science, Kyushu University, Fukuoka, Japan*

D. S. Kemp, *Department of Chemistry, Massachusetts Institute of Technology, Cambridge, Massachusetts*

P. A. Khairallah, *Research Division, Cleveland Clinic Foundation, Cleveland, Ohio*

J. Kovacs, *Department of Chemistry, St. John's University, Jamaica, New York*

G. Krampitz, *Institute of Molecular Evolution and Biochemistry Department, University of Miami, Coral Gables, Florida*

T. C. Lee, *Department of Physiology, School of Medicine, University of California, San Francisco, California*

Satoro Makisumi, *Laboratory of Biochemistry, Faculty of Science, Kyushu University, Fukuoka, Japan*

Garland R. Marshall, *Departments of Physiology and Biophysics and of Biological Chemistry, Washington University Medical School, St. Louis, Missouri*

Hiroshi Matsubara, *Department of Entomology and Space Science Laboratory, University of California, Berkeley, California*

Kazuo Matsumoto, *Institute of Molecular Evolution, University of Miami, Coral Gables, Florida*

Hisayauki Matsuo, *Department of Entomology and Space Science Laboratory, University of California, Berkeley, California*

G. L. Mayers, *Department of Chemistry, St. John's University, Jamaica, New York*

R. H. Mazur, *Chemical Research Department, G. D. Searle & Company, Skokie, Illinois*

J. Meienhofer, *The Children's Cancer Research Foundation, The Children's Hospital Medical Center, and Harvard Medical School, Boston, Massachusetts*

R. B. Merrifield, *The Rockefeller University, New York, New York*

A. R. Mitchell, *Department of Biochemistry, Indiana University, School of Medicine, Indianapolis, Indiana*

Nobuo Mitsuyasu, *Laboratory of Biochemistry, Faculty of Science, Kyushu University, Fukuoka, Japan*

John L. Morell, *National Institutes of Health, Bethesda, Maryland*

Masako Muracka, *Laboratory of Biochemistry, Faculty of Science, Kyushu University, Fukuoka, Japan*

T. Nakashima, *Institute of Molecular Evolution and Biochemistry Department, University of Miami, Coral Gables, Florida*

H. D. Niall, *National Heart Institute, National Institute of Health, Bethesda, Maryland, and Endocrine Unit, Massachusetts General Hospital, Boston, Massachusetts*

D. E. Nitecki, *Department of Microbiology, University of California School of Medicine, San Francisco, California*

Miguel A. Ondetti, *The Squibb Institute for Medical Research, New Brunswick, New Jersey*

David A. Ontjes, *Laboratory of Chemical Biology, National Institute of Arthritis and Metabolic Diseases, National Institutes of Health, Bethesda, Maryland*

R. P. Patel, *The Children's Cancer Research Foundation, The Children's Hospital Medical Center, and Harvard Medical School, Boston, Massachusetts*

W. Patton, *Department of Pharmaceutical Chemistry, School of Pharmacy, University of California, San Francisco, California*

J. Pless, *Research Laboratories, Sandoz Ltd., Basle, Switzerland*

Josip Pluščec, *The Squibb Institute for Medical Research, New Brunswick, New Jersey*

J. T. Potts, Jr., *National Heart Institute, National Institutes of Health, Bethesda, Maryland and Endocrine Unit, Massachusetts General Hospital, Boston, Massachusetts*

Roger W. Roeske, *Department of Biochemistry, Indiana University, School of Medicine, Indianapolis, Indiana*

Daniel Rudman, *Departments of Medicine and Biochemistry, Emory University School of Medicine, Atlanta, Georgia*

E. Sandrin, *Research Laboratories, Sandoz Ltd., Basle, Switzerland*

Y. Sano, *The Children's Cancer Research Foundation, The Children's Hospital Medical Center, and Harvard Medical School, Boston, Massachusetts*

A. Scatturin, *Department of Biological Chemistry, Harvard Medical School, Boston, Massachusetts*

J. S. Schlatter, *Chemical Research Department, G. D. Searle & Company, Skokie, Illinois*

John T. Sheehan, *The Squibb Institute for Medical Research, New Brunswick, New Jersey*

R. R. Smeby, *Research Division, Cleveland Clinic Foundation, Cleveland, Ohio*

Robert L. Smith, *Venable Chemical Laboratory, University of North Carolina, Chapel Hill, North Carolina*

J. T. Sparrow, *Venable Chemical Laboratory, University of North Carolina, Chapel Hill, North Carolina*

A. M. Thomas, *Venable Chemical Laboratory, University of North Carolina, Chapel Hill, North Carolina*

V. M. Vaidya, *Department of Biological Chemistry, Harvard Medical School, Boston, Massachusetts*

T. V. Waehneldt, *Institute of Molecular Evolution and Biochemistry Department, University of Miami, Coral Gables, Florida*

Michinori Waki, *Laboratory of Biochemistry, Faculty of Science, Kyushu University, Fukuoka, Japan*

C.-T. Wang, *Institute of Molecular Evolution and Biochemistry Department, University of Miami, Coral Gables, Florida*

Roderich Walter, *Department of Physiology, Mount Sinai Medical and Graduate School of the City University of New York, New York, New York and The Medical Research Center, Brookhaven National Laboratory, Upton, New York*

Boris Weinstein, *Department of Chemistry, University of Washington, Seattle, Washington*

John W. Westley, *Genetics Department, Stanford Medical School, Palo Alto, California*

H. Willems, *Research Laboratories, Sandoz Ltd., Basle, Switzerland*

G. C. Windridge, *Department of Pharmaceutical Chemistry, School of Pharmacy, University of California, San Francisco, California*

Contents

Part I:

PEPTIDE SYNTHESIS

Part II:

RELATIONSHIPS BETWEEN STRUCTURE AND BIOLOGIC ACTIVITY OF PEPTIDES

Part III:

RACEMIZATION IN PEPTIDE CHEMISTRY

Part IV:

SPECIAL PROBLEMS IN SYNTHESIS
AND ANALYSIS

PEPTIDES:
Chemistry and Biochemistry

STRATEGIES AND PERSPECTIVES IN PEPTIDE SYNTHESIS

Miklos Bodanszky

Department of Chemistry
Case Western Reserve University
Cleveland, Ohio

Fifteen years have elapsed since the epoch-making synthesis of oxytocin (9 amino acids by du Vigneaud and his associates[1]. The many remarkable achievements of these productive years cannot be enumerated here, yet perhaps the most impressive accomplishment, the synthesis of β -corticotropin (39 amino acids) by Schwyzer and Sieber[2] should not go unmentioned. The question whether presently available methods of protection and activation are suitable for the synthesis of peptide chains of considerable length, like those in proteins naturally poses itself.

The classical approach for the synthesis of peptide chains is the condensation of fragments: an octapeptide can be prepared by coupling two tetrapeptides, which in turn are synthesized through the condensation of dipeptides. A less obvious approach, the entirely stepwise synthesis was proposed in connection with the active ester method[3] by the present author[4] and its applicability was demonstrated in a synthesis of oxytocin by Bodanszky and du Vigneaud[5].

1

In the consecutive couplings of fragments a gradual deterioration of yields can be observed[6]. No such decrease of yields was found in entirely stepwise syntheses[5, 7, 8]. Therefore, the impression gained in fragment condensations, that a limit of peptide synthesis is being approached is not felt in the entirely stepwise strategy. Also, the important principle of excess acylating agent[9, 10], which allows an escape from the difficulties caused by the increasing molecular weights of the reactants, can be utilized more systematically in stepwise syntheses than in fragment condensations where unreasonable sacrifices are needed for the application of the same principle. These considerations suggest that the stepwise approach will be the strategy of choice for the synthesis of proteins.

A more recent adaptation of the stepwise strategy is the ingenious and attractive technique of Merrifield[11]: peptide synthesis on a solid support. The simplicity of this method, in which the intermediates are not isolated, allows the mechanization and even automation of the procedure. The present paper attempts a comparison of the two alternative implementations of the stepwise strategy, the synthesis through isolated intermediates with the solid phase approach. The comparison is limited, however, to three aspects: a.) yields; b.) homogeneity of the products; and c.) planning of synthesis.

a. Yields

For a particular step of a synthetic procedure the yield usually can be stated in an unequivocal manner and no special explanation is needed. The expression 'bverall yield" can be more ambiguous. The figure expressing the overall yield is calculated from the product of the yields of the individual steps. Such a single number, however, cannot reflect the efficiency of a synthetic procedure and does not allow a comparison between different syntheses leading to the same product. For instance, in peptide synthesis through frequent condensation, the sacrifice of materials in the preparation of intermediate A is obliterated if in the condensation of A with a second fragment B, compound A is used in excess. Calculation of the yield of this coupling is based on the amount of B, the component present in limiting amount. In the case of a large peptide the repeated use of such calculations may completely obscure the efficiency of the synthetic procedure. Moreover, overall yields often do not include the yield achieved in the preparation of an intermediate if the latter is commercially available or if the excess used in its preparation is re-coverable[12]. But, unless the same principles are applied in all cases, the arbitrary nature of such calculation renders the comparison of syntheses according to "overall yields"meaningless. In the stepwise strategy the

3

calculation could be more straightforward, except that the excess on acylating agents, which is not negligible with longer chains, is not shown by the single expression "overall yield". In the solid phase synthesis excess reagents, protected amino acids and coupling reagents (usually carbodiimides)[11] are used not to correct the concentration problem caused by increasing molecular weights[9,10], but to secure the complete acylation of the amino component attached to the resin. A second important reason for the application of excesses in this case is the loss of acylating intermediates, due to a side reaction. The O-acylamino-acyl-isourea intermediates can rearrange to N-acylureas[13] that are unreactive compounds and useless from the point of view of peptide synthesis. This intramolecular and therefore concentration-independent side reaction becomes especially wasteful if the desired acylation, a bimolecular and therefore concentration dependent reaction is slow. This desired reaction might be slow if the amino component is not a particularly good nucleophile (e.g., proline as N-terminal acid), or if steric hindrance by the resin, or by the growing peptide chain is noticeable[14].

Even the expression of the amounts of excess acylating agent can be ambiguous. In syntheses through isolated intermediates 100% excess means that the number of moles of the acylating agent is twice the number of moles of the

amino component. In solid phase syntheses the expression
of 100% excess refers to the excess used in the first step --
the acylation of a single amino acid attached (through an
ester bond) to the resin. During the chain lengthening
procedure the amount of amino component slowly decreases[15]
after a certain number of steps to half or less of the (molar)
amount originally present. Nevertheless, the excess is
still expressed in the original term, which was correct
only when a single amino acid was considered. In some
solid phase syntheses[15-18] the initial excess is already
considerable, several hundred percent, sometimes as much
as 500%[15]. Therefore, in the more advanced stages of the
synthesis the excess might gradually become tenfold and
more[15], if properly calculated. The excess is completely
lost in the carbodiimide coupling, but can be recovered if
active esters are used for acylation[19].

To avoid the arbitrariness and ambiguity of the "overall
yield" expression, the term "efficiency" (E_f) could be

$$E_f = \frac{n \cdot m_{pp} \cdot 100}{m_{AA}}$$

where n is the number of amino acids in the peptide chain,
m_{pp} is the number of moles of pure product obtained and
m_{AA} is the total number of moles of amino acids used in
the synthesis. This expression of efficiency, proposed by

Professor Rydon[20], is based on the utilization of amino acids. It is meaningful and allows a not arbitrary comparison of different synthetic procedures leading to the same peptide.

It cannot be our aim to present detailed calculations based on published syntheses. Such calculations are tedious but revealing enough to warrant their use in the planning of peptide syntheses. It may suffice here to mention a (solid phase) synthesis of oxytocin[18] in which the 'extremely high" yields were emphasized and yet the calculation recommended here shows that this synthesis is of an order of magnitude less efficient that the first stepwise synthesis[5] of the same compound[21]

In our view, the efficiency of yield for the solid phase technique need not be inferior to synthesis in solution through isolated intermediates. The present shortcomings stem from the application of the carbodiimide method[22], an elegant and potent procedure but particularly unsuitable for the stepwise synthesis of long chains. Coupling reagents, which involve the rist of intramolecular side reactions such as the $O \rightarrow N$ shifts in reactive intermediates, should be expected to be wasteful.

b.   The Purity of the Products

The formation of the peptide bond in an unequivocal manner is one of the ultimate goals in the search for improved

methods of protection and activation. To obtain high yields
and pure (single) products the selectivity of the acylating
agent must be considerable. Only amino groups should be
acylated, while hydroxyl and other functional groups of amino
acid side chains should be left intact. By avoiding
"overactivation'[23] such selectivity can be achieved, but -
alas - usually only at the price of reduced reactivities and
hence reduced reaction rates. The rates can be maintained
on a practical level if the reactants are used in high enough
concentration[9, 10]. This can be done in stepwise synthesis
with active esters. Since unequivocal acylation is a pre-
requisite in the stepwise approach, the use of highly reactive
coupling reagents should be avoided and mixed anhydrides,
which even in principle yield two products, should be a
priori excluded.

For the solid phase version of the stepwise strategy the
advantages of active esters were so obvious that Merrifield[11]
considered them ideal for this purpose. Yet because of
initial difficulties caused by an unfavorable choice of solvent
the active ester method was not proposed for syntheses on
insoluble polymeric support and rather the dicyclohexylcarbodiimide method[22] was applied for coupling. This rapid and
convenient method can be used without the protection of
hydroxyls on amino acid side chains[24] but only if an excess
of acylating acid and carbodiimide is avoided. The hydroxyls

7

are poor nucleophiles to compete with a free amino group
for the acylating intermediate. In the presence of an excess,
however, after the amino groups are more or less acylated,
even the weak nucleophiles will prevail and the O —acylation
will occur. Therefore, in solid phase synthesis with carbodiimides where an excess is imperative, hydroxyl groups
should not be left without protection. On the other hand,
active esters (usually recrystallized from boiling ethanol!)
can be applied also in the presence of free hydroxyl groups.
Hydroxyl groups can be protected and the N-acylurea formation can be counterbalanced with an excess of acylating
agents, but an additional side reaction caused by carbodiimides, the dehydration of the carboxamide groups in
the side chains of asparagine and glutamine residues
cannot be eliminated. Therefore, for these two amino
acids the recommendation of Bodanszky and Sheehan[25] to
use active esters also in the solid phase version of stepwise synthesis, is usually accepted. Less attention has
been paid to the warning[26] on the O-acylation of hydroxy
amino acids. The published analytical evidence serves as
good indication for our contention that several of the complex mixtures[16,17] formed in solid phase work, some of
them[15] intractable, are caused by this neglect in
protection[27].

c. Limitations in the Planning of Synthesis.

For fragment condensation the chain has to be "dissected. " The resulting fragments are so chosen that they have glycine or proline at their C terminal[28]. Unfortunately not all sequences are equally suitable for a proper dissection, e. g. , the single chain of (porcine) secretin[29] (FIG. 1) containing twenty-seven amino acids has among these not even one proline residue and the two glycines occur in the strategically unfavorable positions 4 and 25. The entirely stepwise synthesis does not require a favorable distribution of amino acids. On the other hand, in the solid phase version of the stepwise approach new limitations are introduced by the use of carbodiimidés for coupling. Some of these limitations are connected with side chain hydroxyl or carboxamide groups and were already discussed. A different problem emerges if the chain contains aspartyl or glutamyl residues. The side chain carboxyl cannot be left free because it would then participate in the carbo-diimide mediated acylations. This is a particularly serious

His-Ser-Asp-Gly-Thr-Phe-Thr-Ser-Glu-Leu-Ser-Arg-Leu-Arg-
Asp-Ser-Ala-Arg-Leu-Gln-Arg-Leu-Leu-Gln-Gly-Leu-Val-NH$_2$

FIG. 1

The Sequence of (Porcine) Secretin.

9

restriction in the case of aspartic acid. The side chain
carboxyl of this amino acid is rather inert if free but reacts,
if esterified, with the formation of aminosuccinyl derivatives
which in turn can be opened to β -aspartyl residues. This is
a disconcerting possibility, the more because it is rather
difficult to predict. In the synthesis of secretin, out of concern
for the aspartyl-amino-succinyl-β-aspartyl rearrangement,
some synthetic intermediates which contained the aspartyl
residue in position 15 were carefully scrutinized. Their
nmr spectra clearly showed that the benzyl group of the
ester used for the protection of this carboxyl has not been
lost and therefore no rearrangement should be feared[30]. It
was therefore even more disappointing to find that such a
rearrangement did occur with the aspartyl residue in
position 3. It is rather obvious (in retrospect) that ring
closure is prevented in residue 15 because of the hindering
effect of the bulky side chain of the O-benzyl-L-serine
moiety in position 16. The aspartyl residue in position 3,
however, is followed by glycine. This is a unique amino
acid in more than one respect. It can accept two acyl groups
on its amino group[31] and therefore offers no obstacle against
the formation of an aminosuccinylglycine sequence. Such
sequence dependent side reactions make it questionable
whether the convenience of rapid synthesis without the isolation of intermediates is a real advantage or not. In the

synthesis of secretin[8] the availability of the isolated intermediates allowed the recognition of this side reaction.

An additional limitation of the solid phase technique was
found in attempted synthesis of secretin by the Merrifield
method. The peptide chain, ending with valine, could not
be removed as the desired amide[26]. Ammonolysis was
hindered by the combined steric effects of the bulky side
chain of valine and the resin lattice. With short chains
ammonolysis in methanol resulted in ester exchange; with
the growing chain the steric hindrance increased and the
chain was removable only in the usual way in the form of a
carboxylic acid at its C terminal. With glycine as the C
terminal acid no such difficulty was observed and ammonolysis yielded the amide of the assembled peptide[25].

Peptide synthesis can 1) provide proof for a proposed
structure, 2) can lead to analogs which allow the study of
the relationships between structure and activity in biologically
active peptides and, 3) can produce peptides for medical
purposes. Synthesis through isolated intermediates might
render an additional, until now unexplored service. A study
of the rotational spectra of secretin and of its synthetic
intermediates[32] resulted in surprisingly detailed information
on the conformation or secondary structure of this peptide
hormone. This 'anatomical" approach to the three dimensional arrangement of a peptide chain revealed that a short

helical stretch is present between residues 6 and 13 and that the helical region lacks stability unless it is stabilized by the proximity of the C terminal portion of the molecule. This C terminal is particularly rich in amino acids with non-polar side chains and with a general folding of the molecules they can create a region poor in water and thereby stabilize the very short helix.

CONCLUSIONS

For the synthesis of long peptide chains, like those of proteins the entirely stepwise strategy[4] is the more promising approach. The execution of this approach on an insoluble polymeric support[11] is still beset with several difficulties. Part of the shortcomings of the solid phase method can be eliminated if exclusively active esters are used for acylation. Only when the underlying chemistry is already sufficiently sound will the automation of the procedure be fully justified. For the synthesis of long chains the entirely stepwise strategy through isolated intermediates offers significant advantages.

REFERENCES

1. V. du Vigneaud, C. Ressler, J. M. Swan, C. W. Roberts, P. G. Katsoyannis and S. Gordon, J. Am. Chem. Soc., 75, 487 (1953).

2. R. Schwyzer and P. Sieber, Helv. Chem. Acta., 49, 134 (1966).

3. M. Bodanszky, Nature, 175, 685 (1955).

4. M. Bodanszky, Ann. N. Y. Acad. Sci., 88, 655 (1960).

5. M. Bodanszky and V. du Vigneaud, Nature, 183, 1324 (1954); M. Bodanszky and V. du Vigneaud, J. Am. Chem. Soc., 81, 5688 (1959).

6. M. A. Ondetti, V. L. Narayanan, M. V. Saltza, J. T. Sheehan, E. F. Sabo and M. Bodanszky, J. Am. Chem. Soc., 90, 4711 (1968).

7. M. Bodanszky and N. J. Williams, J. Am. Chem. Soc., 89, 685 (1957).

8. M. Bodanszky, M. A. Ondetti, S. D. Levine and N. J. Williams, J. Am. Chem. Soc., 89, 6753 (1967).

9. M. Bodanszky and A. A. Bodanszky, American Scientist, 55, 185 (1967).

10. M. Bodanszky, Proceedings of the Symposium of the University of Houston Conference on Proteins and Nucleic Acids. In press.

11. R. B. Merrifield, J. Am. Chem. Soc., 86, 304 (1964).

12. E. g., the yield in the preparation of the amino acid esterified with the resin is often left out from consideration perhaps because acylamino resins are commercially available, or because the unreacted acylamino acid potentially could be recovered.

13. H. G. Khorana, Chem. and Ind., 1955, 1087.

14. Even in acylations with active esters (ref. 25) steric hindrance might play a not negligible role. In this case bulky ester groups much as in pentachlorophenyl esters (G. Kupryszewski and M. Kaczmarek, Roczniki Chem., 35; 935 (1961), N-hydroxyphthalimide esters (G. H. L. Nefkens and G. I. Tesser, J. Am. Chem. Soc., 83, 1263 (1961) as N-hydroxysuccinimede esters (G. W. Anderson, J. E. Zimmerman and F. Callahan, J. Am. Chem. Soc., 85, 3034 (1963) are probably less advantageous than the less hindered p-nitrophenyl esters (ref. 3).

15. E. Bayer, G. Jung and H. Hagenmaier, Tetrahedron, 74, 4853 (1968).

16. P. Jolles and J. Jolles, Helv. Chem. Acta., 51, 980
(1968).

17. J. M. Stewart, J. D. Young, E. Benjamin, M. Shimizu
and C. Y. Leung, Biochemistry, 5, 3396 (1966).

18. E. Bayer and H. Hagenmaier, Tetrahedron Letters,
1968, 2037.

19. Alternatively, the "excess" can be utilized if the acylation
is carried out in a countercurrent manner. Promising
experiments in this direction are being carried out in
the author's laboratory.

20. H. N. Rydon, personal communication.

21. In the two syntheses (refs. 5 and 18) the strategy is the
same, only the protecting groups and the coupling methods
are in part different. Therefore, the comparison of the
two procedures is fully justified and desirable. In the
comparison between the solid phase synthesis of an
analog of angiotensin and its synthesis in solution
(W. K. Park, R. R. Smeby and F. M. Bumpus,
Biochemistry, 6, 3458) the strategies are different and
therefore the comparison is not necessarily meaningful.
The advantages of the solid phase approach could be
shown only if a stepwise synthesis in solution would be
used for comparison.

22. J. C. Sheehan and G. Hess, J. Am. Chem. Soc., 77, 1067
(1955).

23. M. Brenner, in Proc. of the Eighth European Peptide
Symposium, 1966 (H. C. Beyerman, A. van de Linde
and W. Maassen-van den Brink, eds.), North Holland,
Amsterdam (1967), p. 1.

24. J. C. Sheehan, M. Goodman and G. P. Hess, J. Am.
Chem. Soc., 78, 1367 (1956).

25. M. Bodanszky and J. T. Sheehan, Chem. and Ind.,
1964, 1423.

26. M. Bodanszky and J. T. Sheehan, Chem. and Ind.,
1966, 1597.

27. The preventive measures proposed by H. Zahn, T. Okuda and Y. Shimunishi, in Proc. of the Eighth European Peptide Symposium, 1966 (H. C. Beyerman, A. van de Linde, and W. Maassen-van den Brink, eds.), North Holland, Amsterdam (1967), p. 103. are not sufficient to prevent O-acylation of threonine in solid phase synthesis. Already during the introduction of the threonine residue, if this is not protected on its hydroxyl group, O-acylation should be expected (conf. ref. 26) and similarly O-acylation of threonine and serine residues should occur in subsequent steps, if not active esters but carbodiimide is used for acylation (conf. ref. 15).

28. M. Bodanszky and M. A. Ondetti, Peptide Synthesis, J. Wiley, New York, 1966, p. 165.

29. V. Mutt and E. J. Jorpes, presented at the Fourth International Symposium on the Chemistry of Natural Products, Stockholm, Sweden, 1966. Conf. also V. Mutt and E. J. Jorpes, Pharmacology of Hormonal Polypeptides and Proteins, Plenum Press, 1968, p. 569.

30. For nmr spectroscopy of peptides CD_3COOD can be used as a solvent with considerable advantages (conf. M. Bodanszky, J. Fried, J. T. Sheehan, N. J. Williams, J. Alicino, A. I. Cohen, B. T. Keeler and C. A. Birkhimer, J. Am. Chem. Soc., 86, 2478 (1964); M. Bodanszky and M. A. Ondetti, Antimicrobial Agents and Chemotherapy, 1963, p. 360.

31. T. Wieland and B. Heinke, Ann., 599, 70 (1956); K. D. Kopple and R. J. Renick, J. Org. Chem., 23, 1565 (1958).

32. M. Bodanszky, M. A. Ondetti, V. Mutt and A. Bodanszky, in preparation.

15

APPLICATION OF PENTACHLOROPHENYL ACTIVE ESTERS IN THE SYNTHESIS OF PEPTIDES AND SEQUENTIAL POLY-PEPTIDES FROM THE C-TERMINAL RESIDUES OF AMINO ACIDS

A. Kapoor

Department of Pharmaceutical Chemistry
College of Pharmacy
St. John's University
Jamaica, New York

Pentachlorophenyl active esters, which were first reported in the literature in 1961[1], afford an excellent method for the synthesis of peptides and polypeptides with an ordered sequence of amino acids. Pentachlorophenyl active esters have the following advantages: (a) they are among one of the most active esters[2], (b) they are generally higher melting compounds than other active esters, which leads to their easy crystallization and purification[3,4], (c) they are stable to controlled hydrogenation conditions and make an excellent combination with N-carbobenzoxy and t-butyl protecting groups when the incorporation of trifunctional amino acids in peptides is desired[3]. Previously, peptide chains were lengthened by coupling pentachlorophenyl active esters of N-carbobenzoxy amino acids or peptides with C-methyl protected amino acids or peptides. C-methyl protection at each activation stage and at the end of the synthesis was removed by saponification[3,4]. Alkali treatment of peptides is associated with a number of problems, e.g., racemization[5], transpeptidation[4,6], etc. In addition, removal of C-methyl protection by alkali becomes more difficult as the number of amino acids increases in the peptide chain[7]. MacLaren reported the formation of urea or hydantoin derivatives when N-carbobenzoxy peptides were treated with alkali[8].

Avoiding racemization of optically active centers in the synthesis of peptides with biological activity is a major concern and new approaches for the synthesis which would limit the degree of racemization in synthetic peptides are under continual investigation. In order to overcome racemization and other problems associated with alkali treatment, the ideal approach would be to carry out the coupling of C-activated N-protected amino acids or peptides with amino acids or peptides C-protected by suitable salt formation, which can easily be removed by mild acid.

As the pentachlorophenyl active esters (OPCP) are among the most active esters, it was considered worthwhile to systematically study their coupling with amino acids or peptides, C-protected by suitable salt formation. Dicyclohexylamine (DCA) afforded a satisfactory base for C-protection and for optimal yields, coupling was carried out in methylene chloride or in a mixture of methylene chloride and dimethylformamide. These results are shown in Table 1.

TABLE 1

Yields and Melting Points of N-Protected Dipeptides, Made Through Coupling of N-Protected-OPCP Esters of Amino Acids with DCA, C-Protected Amino Acids[9,10].

OPCP Derivative	Amino Acid DCA Salt	Dipeptide Formed	Yield,%	M.p., °C.
Z-Ala-OPCP	H-Phe-OH	Z-Ala-Phe-OH	62	121-122
Z-Ala-OPCP	H-Ala-OH	Z-Ala-Ala-OH	61	152
Z-Ala-OPCP	H-Gly-OH	Z-Ala-Gly-OH	60	132-133
Z-Gly-OPCP	H-Gly-OH	Z-Gly-Gly-OH	55	178
Z-Gly-OPCP	H-Ileu-OH	Z-Gly-Ileu-OH	59	115
Z-Gly-OPCP	H-Ala-OH	Z-Gly-Ala-OH	62	120
Z- Gly-OPCP	H-Phe-OH	Z-Gly-Phe-OH	62	125-126
Z-Gly-OPCP	H-Asp-(OBzl)-OH	Z-Gly-Asp(OBzl)-OH	58	99-100
Z-Phe-OPCP	H-Gly-OH	Z-Phe-Gly-OH	61	154-155
Z-Gly-OPCP	H-Pro-OH	Z-Phe-Pro-OH	63	110-111

It is interesting to note that N-protected OPCP active esters of amino acids could not be coupled with glutamic or aspartic acids with DCA protection on both carboxyl groups. However, the coupling of N-protected-amino acid-OPCP active esters, was found to proceed in satisfactory yields with monoaminodicarboxylic acids, when one of the carboxyl groups was protected with DCA and the second carboxyl group was protected with a suitable ester, such as benzyl or t-butyl, which can be removed without alkali. Z-Gly-OPCP was coupled with β-benzyl asparate C-protected with DCA, and Z-Gly-Asp (OBzl)-OH was isolated in 58% yield. It was further observed that the pentachlorophenyl active esters of N-protected amino acids, coupled in better yields when the dipeptides or tripeptides C-protected by DCA were used. It can be also noted that the reverse is true, that is, OPCP active esters of N-protected dipeptide or tripeptide coupled in relative poor yields with amino acids C-protected by DCA. However, the N-protected dipeptide active esters coupled in slightly better yields with the dipeptides C-protected by DCA in comparison to the monomer. From the results in Table 2 it can be concluded that when the OPCP esters are to be used for coupling with amino acids or peptides C-protected by DCA, the peptide chains should be lengthened from the C-terminal instead of N-terminal amino acid residues.

TABLE 2

Yields and Melting Points of N-Protected Tri- and Tetrapeptides, Made Through Coupling of N-Protected OPCP Esters of Amino Acids and Peptides, With DCA, C-Protected Amino Acids and Peptides.

OPCP Derivative	DCA Protected Component	Peptide Formed	Yield,%	M.p., °C
Z-Gly-OPCP	H-Gly-Phe-OH	Z-Gly-Gly-Phe-OH	68	145-146
Z-Phe-OPCP	H-Gly-Phe-OH	Z-Phe-Gly-Phe-OH	67	151-152
Z-Ala-OPCP	H-Phe-Gly-OH	Z-Ala-Phe-Gly-OH	68	171
Z-Gly-OPCP	H-Ala-Phe-Gly-OH	Z-Gly-Ala-Phe-Gly-OH	75	174-175
Z-Gly-Ala-OPCP	H-Ala-OH	Z-Gly-Ala-Ala-OH	43	173-174
Z-Gly-Gly-Phe-OPCP	H-Phe-OH	Z-Gly-Gly-Phe-Phe-OH	38	140-142
Z-Gly-Ala-OPCP	H-Phe-Gly-OH	Z-Gly-Ala-Phe-Gly-OH	54	175-176
Z-Gly-Ala-Phe-OPCP	H-Gly-OH	Z-Gly-Ala-Phe-Gly-OH	40	175

It was previously reported[11,12] that a combination of mixed anhydride (isobutyl chloroformate) and pentachlorophenyl active ester methods, provided a suitable approach for step-wise incorporation of amino acids in peptides with an ordered sequence. In the light of above results, two possible schemes for lengthening the peptide chains without using alkali may be considered. In Scheme 1, as already indicated, the yields will decrease as we go from stage A to C.

In Scheme 2, one will observe a steady increase in the yields from stage a to c. In addition to affording relatively better yields, Scheme 2 would further limit the degree of racemization as the active ester component used would always be a monomer. This is now almost an established fact that during coupling of N-protected, C-activated peptides, racemization of C-activated amino acid residues takes place probably through an oxazolone[13,14].

Tetrapeptide sequences of glycyl-aspartl-seryl-glycine is a frequent repeating unit in enzymes such as chymotrypsin.

A. $Z-A_1-OPCP + H-A_2-OH \xrightarrow{\text{DCA}} Z-A_1-A_2-OH$

B. $Z-A_1-A_2-OH + HCl. H-A_3-OPCP \xrightarrow[\substack{\text{Isobutyl} \\ \text{Chloroformate}}]{} Z-A_1-A_2-A_3-OPCP$

C. $Z-A_1-A_2-A_3-OPCP + H-A_4-OH \xrightarrow[\text{DCA}]{} Z-A_1-A_2-A_3-A_4-OH$

SCHEME 1

SYNTHESIS OF PEPTIDES AND SEQUENTIAL POLYPEPTIDES

a. $Z-A_3-OPCP + H-A_4-OH \xrightarrow{DCA} Z-A_3-A_4-OH$

a_1 $Z-A_3-A_4-OH \xrightarrow[Pd/C]{H_2} H-A_3-A_4-OH$

b. $Z-A_2-OPCP + H-A_3-A_4-OH \xrightarrow{DCA} Z-A_2-A_3-A_4-OH$

b_1 $Z-A_2-A_3-A_4-OH \xrightarrow[Pd/C]{H_2} H-A_2-A_3-A_4-OH$

c. $Z-A_1-OPCP + H-A_2-A_3-A_4-OH \xrightarrow{DCA} Z-A_1-A_2-A_3-A_4-OH$

SCHEME 2

A_1, A_2, A_3 and A_4 represent amino acid residues in a peptide sequence.

$Z = C_6H_5- CH_2-O-\overset{O}{\overset{\|}{C}}-$ OPCP $= -OC_6Cl_5$ DCA $=$ Dicyclohexylamine

In order to investigate the usefulness of above procedure,
phenylalanine, which is more sensitive to racemization,
was substituted for C-terminal glycine and the tetrapeptide
glycyl-aspartyl-seryl-phenylalanine was synthesized both
from the C-terminal (FIG. 1) and the N-terminal residues
(FIG. 2). As expected, in the case of C-terminal synthesis
over-all yields were about 14% more. It may be noticed that
in both these routes of synthesis, the use of alkali was
avoided.

In order to observe the effect of alkali on the degree of
racemization, the same tetrapeptide was synthesized by
using C-methyl protection at three different stages of the
synthesis (FIG. 3) and C-methyl protection was removed by
the use of alkali at all these stages.

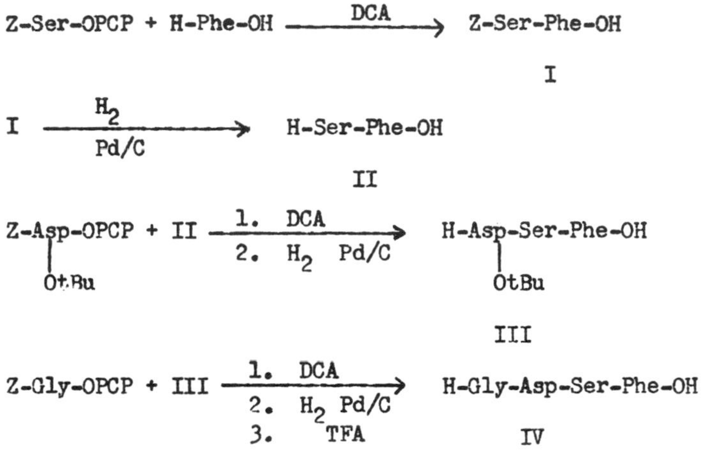

Z-Ser-OPCP + H-Phe-OH $\xrightarrow{\text{DCA}}$ Z-Ser-Phe-OH

I

I $\xrightarrow[\text{Pd/C}]{\text{H}_2}$ H-Ser-Phe-OH

II

Z-Asp-OPCP + II $\xrightarrow[\text{2. H}_2 \text{ Pd/C}]{\text{1. DCA}}$ H-Asp-Ser-Phe-OH
| |
OtBu   OtBu

III

Z-Gly-OPCP + III $\xrightarrow[\substack{\text{2. H}_2 \text{ Pd/C} \\ \text{3. TFA}}]{\text{1. DCA}}$ H-Gly-Asp-Ser-Phe-OH

IV

FIG. 1

Synthesis from C-Terminal Residue

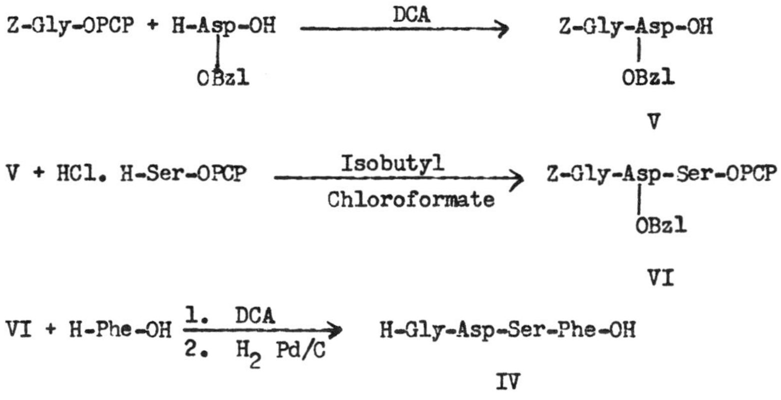

Z-Gly-OPCP + H-Asp-OH $\xrightarrow{\text{DCA}}$ Z-Gly-Asp-OH
| |
OBzl   OBzl

V

V + HCl. H-Ser-OPCP $\xrightarrow[\text{Chloroformate}]{\text{Isobutyl}}$ Z-Gly-Asp-Ser-OPCP
|
OBzl

VI

VI + H-Phe-OH $\xrightarrow[\text{2. H}_2 \text{ Pd/C}]{\text{1. DCA}}$ H-Gly-Asp-Ser-Phe-OH

IV

FIG. 2

Synthesis from N-terminal Residue

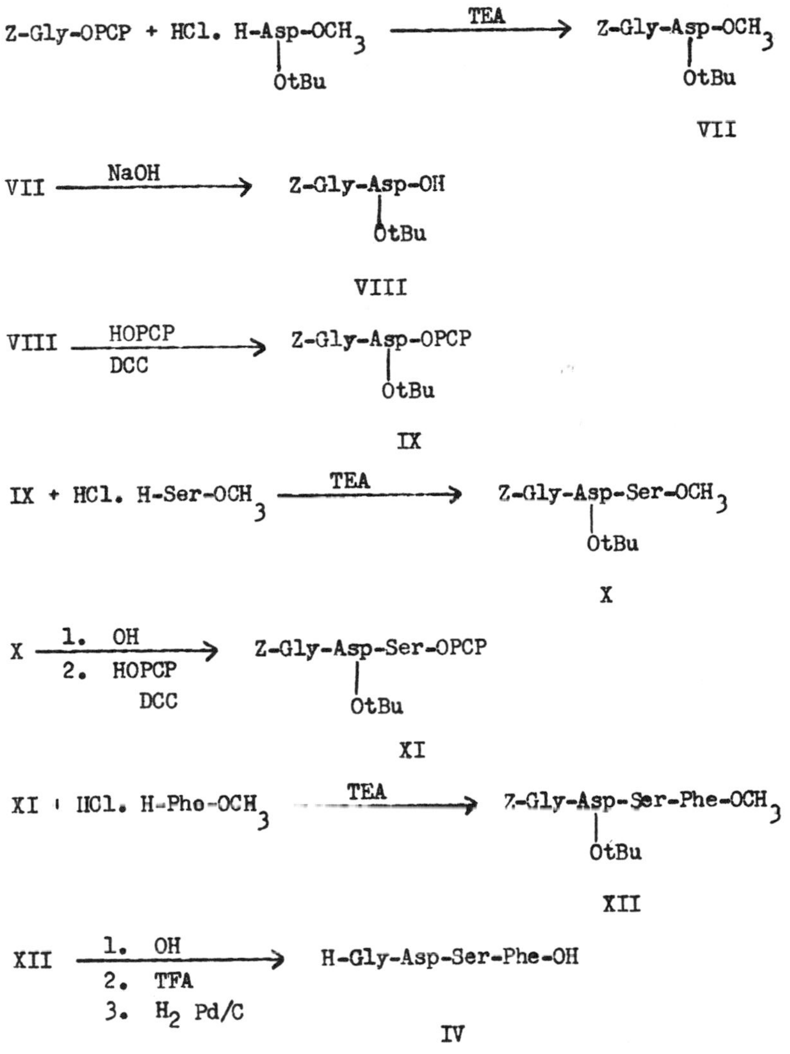

Z-Gly-OPCP + HCl. H-Asp-OCH$_3$ $\xrightarrow{\text{TEA}}$ Z-Gly-Asp-OCH$_3$
                          | |
                         OtBu   OtBu

                                                           VII

VII $\xrightarrow{\text{NaOH}}$ Z-Gly-Asp-OH
                                          |
                                        OtBu

                                        VIII

VIII $\xrightarrow[\text{DCC}]{\text{HOPCP}}$ Z-Gly-Asp-OPCP
                                           |
                                      OtBu

                                        IX

IX + HCl. H-Ser-OCH$_3$ $\xrightarrow{\text{TEA}}$ Z-Gly-Asp-Ser-OCH$_3$
                                                            |
                                                        OtBu

                                                    X

X $\xrightarrow[\substack{\text{2. HOPCP} \\ \text{DCC}}]{\text{1. OH}}$ Z-Gly-Asp-Ser-OPCP
                                               |
                                            OtBu

                                        XI

XI + HCl. H-Phe-OCH$_3$ $\xrightarrow{\text{TEA}}$ Z-Gly-Asp-Ser-Phe-OCH$_3$
                                                                   |
                                                       OtBu

                                                    XII

XII $\xrightarrow[\substack{\text{2. TFA} \\ \text{3. H}_2 \text{ Pd/C}}]{\text{1. OH}}$ H-Gly-Asp-Ser-Phe-OH

                                                  IV

FIG. 3

Synthesis with C-methyl Protection

Total hydrolysis by 6 N HCl of this tetrapeptide made from three different routes as indicated above showed the least racemization when the synthesis was carried out from C-terminal residue. To indicate the comparative figures, the tetrapeptide synthesized from C-terminal residue was approximately 98% optically pure, the tetrapeptide synthesized from N-terminal residue was approximately 95% optically pure and the tetrapeptide synthesized with C-methyl protection and where the alkali was used at three states was about 87% optically pure. The tetrapeptide was tested for acetylcholine estrase type of hydrolysis of acetylcholine and did not show any interesting results.

The role of Histidine and Serine in the tertiary structure of acetylcholine estrase has received considerable attention recently[15,16]. In order to provide Histidine at a suitable distance to Serine, a pentapeptide glycyl-aspartyl-seryl-glycyl-histidine was synthesized from C-terminal residue (FIG. 4) and the penta peptide is at present under biological investigation for the possible hydrolysis of acetylcholine.

So far, our discussion has been focused on the synthesis of peptides with free C-terminal residue of amino acids. The above approach was extended in the synthesis of poly-peptides with known sequence of amino acids by introducing C-terminal residues of amino acids as pentachlorophenyl active ester hydrochlorides and peptide chains were lengthened

Z-Ser-OPCP + H-Gly-His-OH $\xrightarrow{\text{DCA}}$ Z-Ser-Gly-His-OH

XIII

XIII $\xrightarrow[\text{H}_2 \text{ Pd/C}]{}$ H-Ser-Gly-His-OH

XIV

Z-Asp-OPCP + XIV $\xrightarrow{\text{DCA}}$ Z-Asp-Ser-Gly-His-OH
| |
OtBu   OtBu

XV

XV $\xrightarrow{\text{H}_2 \text{ Pd/C}}$ H-Asp-Ser-Gly-His-OH
                                          |
                                          OtBu

XVI

Z-Gly-OPCP + XVI $\xrightarrow{\hspace{2cm}}$ Z-Gly-Asp-Ser-Gly-His-OH
                                                        |
                                                        OtBu

XVII

XVII $\xrightarrow[\text{TFA}]{\text{H}_2 \text{ Pd/C}}$ H-Gly-Asp-Ser-Gly-His-OH

XVIII

TFA = Trifluoracetic Acid

FIG. 4

Synthesis of H-Gly-Asp-Ser-Gly-His-OH

through mixed anhydride coupling. While the yields in the
case of mixed anhydride coupling of N-protected amino acids
with single amino acid pentachlorophenyl active ester hydrochlorides were quite satisfactory, an appreciable loss in

yields was noted when the mixed anhydride coupling was attempted with di- or tripeptide pentachlorophenyl active ester hydrochlorides[11]. This was attributed to the possible formation of diketopiperazine derivatives or cyclic and linear polypeptides. In order to resolve this problem it was only natural to work out the suitable reaction conditions which would afford satisfactory coupling of di- or tri-peptide OPCP active esters with N-protected amino acids through mixed anhydride. Though not very much identical, homologs of glycine OPCP esters were selected and their mixed anhydride coupling with N-protected glycine was studied. FIG. 5 shows that as the number (n) increases, the cyclization of the hydrochloride portion would become more probable and this actually was observed under the conditions which we were previously using for coupling by mixed anhydride as indicated by the yields. It may be interesting to observe that delta amino valeric acid which would cyclise into six membered valero lactam, the yields of mixed anhydride coupling were the lowest.

The yields of this reaction, that is, the coupling of Z-Gly-OH with delta-aminovaleric acid OPCP ester hydrochloride through mixed anhydride were considerably improved (84%) by keeping the reaction temperature between -5° and -10° and adding triethylamine and OPCP hydrochloride components consecutively over a period of one hour.

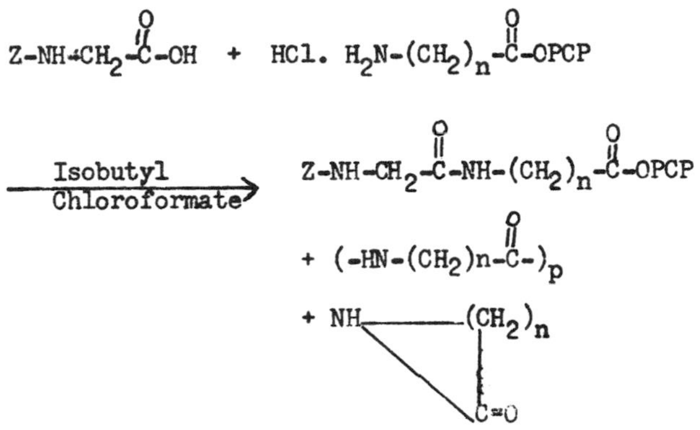

$$Z-NH-CH_2-\overset{\overset{O}{\|}}{C}-OH \;+\; HCl.\; H_2N-(CH_2)_n-\overset{\overset{O}{\|}}{C}-OPCP$$

$$\xrightarrow[\text{Chloroformate}]{\text{Isobutyl}} \quad Z-NH-CH_2-\overset{\overset{O}{\|}}{C}-NH-(CH_2)_n-\overset{\overset{O}{\|}}{C}-OPCP$$

$$+\; (-HN-(CH_2)n-\overset{\overset{O}{\|}}{C}-)_p$$

$$+\; NH\diagdown\underset{\diagdown}{\quad}(CH_2)_n$$
$$C=O$$

n =		
= (1) Glycine		83%
= (2) β-Alanine		81%
= (3) γ-Amino Butyric Acid		76%
= (4) Delta Amino Valeric Acid		65%
= (5) Epsilon Amino Caproic Acid		74%
= (7) Omega Amino Caprylic Acid		76%

FIG. 5

Comparative Yields of Mixed Anhydride Coupling
of Z-Gly-OH with Homologs of Glycine OPCP Ester
Hydrochlorides

Once this was achieved, the same reaction conditions
were extended to the mixed anhydride coupling of N-protected
amino acids with di-and tripeptide pentachlorophenyl ester
hydrochlorides. The yields at each coupling stage were
above 80% as shown in FIGS. 6 and 7.

29

Z-Gly-OH + HCl. H-Ala-OPCP $\xrightarrow[83\%]{\text{IBC}}$ Z-Gly-Ala-OPCP

XIX

XIX $\xrightarrow[93\%]{\text{H}_2\text{ Pd/C HCl.}}$ HCl. H-Gly-Ala-OPCP

XX

Z-Gly-OH + XX $\xrightarrow[81\%]{\text{IBC}}$ Z-Gly-Gly-Ala-OPCP

XXa

FIG. 6

Synthesis of Z-Gly-Gly-Ala-OPCP

Z-Ala-OH + HCl. H-Ala-OPCP $\xrightarrow[84\%]{\text{IBC}}$ Z-Ala-Ala-OPCP

XXI

XXI $\xrightarrow[91\%]{\text{H}_2\text{Pd/C HCl.}}$ HCl. H-Ala-Ala-OPCP

XXII

Z-Gly-OH + XXII $\xrightarrow[83\%]{\text{IBC}}$ Z-Ala-Gly-Ala-Ala-OPCP

XXIII

XXIII $\xrightarrow[93\%]{\text{H}_2\text{ Pd/C HCl.}}$ HCl. H-Gly-Ala-Ala-OPCP

XXIV

Z-Ala-OH + XXIV $\xrightarrow[83\%]{\text{IBC}}$ Z-Ala-Gly-Ala-Ala-OPCP

XXV

IBC = Isobutylchloroformate

FIG. 7

Synthesis of Z-Ala-Gly-Ala-Ala-OPCP

SYNTHESIS OF PEPTIDES AND SEQUENTIAL POLYPEPTIDES

Polymerization of N-carbobenzoxy amino acid or peptide pentachlorophenyl active esters has been previously described[3]. Using the above approach, we are now in the process of synthesizing poly-glycyl-seryl-aspartyl-glycyl-histidine, for possible biological activity for the hydrolysis of acetylcholine.

ACKNOWLEDGMENTS

The author is grateful to the valuable contributions of the following colleagues: Mr. E. J. Davis, Mr. L. W. Gerencser, Miss Mary J. Graetzer, Mr. Soon M. Kang and Mr. N. Azeaz.

REFERENCES

1. G. Kupryszewski and M. Formela, Roczniki Chem., 35, 1533 (1961).

2. K. Stick and G. H. Leemann, Helv. Chim. Acta, 46, 1887 (1963).

3. J. Kovacs and A. Kapoor, J. Am. Chem. Soc., 87, 118 (1965).

4. J. Kovacs, R. Giannoti and A. Kapoor, J. Am. Chem. Soc., 88, 2282 (1966).

5. E. Schroder and K. Lubke, The Peptides, Vol. 1, Academic Press, New York, 1965, p. 56.

6. E. Katchalski and M. Sela, Adv. Protein Chem., 13, 243 (1968).

7. B. F. Erlanger and E. J. Brand, J. Am. Chem. Soc., 73, 3508 (1951).

8. J. A. MacLaren, Australian J. Chem., 11, 360 (1958).

9. Abbreviations for amino acids and peptides used in this paper are those recommended in Proceedings of the 5th European Peptide Symposium (G. T. Young, ed.), MacMillan Co., New York, 1963.

10. Amino acids used in this work were all of L configuration.

11. A. Kapoor and E. J. Davis, Experientia, 23, 253 (1967).

12. A. Kapoor, E. J. Davis and Mary J. Graetzer, J. Pharm. Sci., 57, 1514 (1968).

13. W. M. Williams and G. T. Young, J. Chem. Soc., 3701 (1964).

14. M. Goodman and J. W. McGahren, J. Am. Chem. Soc., 87, 3028 (1965).

15. R. Krupa, Can. J. Biochem., 42, 667 (1964).

16. R. W. Matthews, P. B. Sigler, R. Hendersen and D. M. Blow, Nature, 214, 652 (1967).

INVESTIGATIONS OF LIMITS AND SCOPE OF THE 7-HYDROXY-2-ETHYL-BENZISOXAZOLIUM SALT METHOD OF COUPLING PEPTIDE FRAGMENTS

D. S. Kemp

Department of Chemistry
Massachusetts Institute of Technology
Cambridge, Massachusetts

Methods for cleanly coupling peptide fragments of arbitrary size, in high yield, and with insignificant racemization have been sought for many years, and despite manifold ingenious efforts still stand for the peptide chemist as unattained, and perhaps unattainable goals. At the same time, the sheer bulk of previous effort makes it unlikely that blind application of new dehydrating agents to peptides will contribute effectively to the solution of this problem. However, much is now known of the detailed mechanisms of aminolysis and racemization, and the repetitive character of peptide synthesis suggests the possibility of applying this knowledge through guile rather than luck. We have begun to explore this prospect, and I wish here to outline the results we have obtained with an attempt to design a peptide coupling reagent which combines the desirable attributes of two hitherto unrelated types of acylating agents.

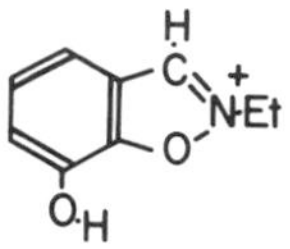

The substance, 1, is a member of the class of isoxazolium salts, explored extensively by Mumm and coworkers[1],
and later reinvestigated and applied to peptide synthesis by
Woodward and Olofson[2]. As FIG. 1 indicates, the reaction
of a carboxylic acid with an isoxazolium salt bears a
striking similarity to the preparation of phenolic esters
by means of carbodiimides, with the important difference
that while the reaction of phenol with an O-acylisourea is
an intermolecular reaction which competes poorly with
intramolecular oxazolone formation, the analogous step in
the isoxazole series is itself an intramolecular reaction, with
the result that under favorable circumstances the isoxazolium

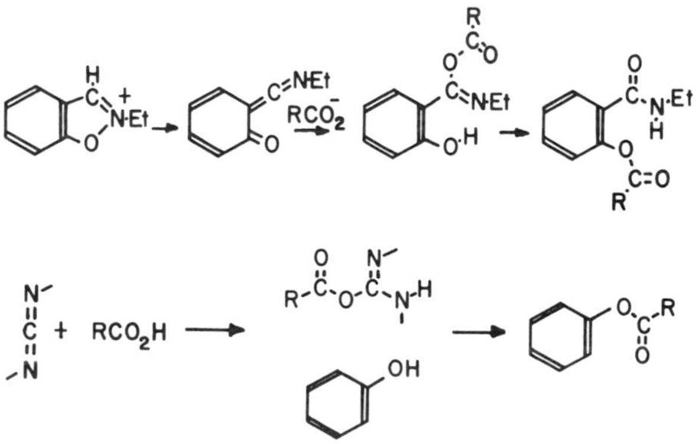

Figure 1

salts offer a racemization-free route to enolic and phenolic esters of peptide acids. Although this intramolecular "energy leak" is the primary reason why isoxazolium salts are of interest, it should be noted that the benzo system illustrated in FIG. 1 offers the additional feature of combining with carboxylate anions in water, pH 4-5, to give high yields of acylsalicylamides. Under these conditions no intermediates are detectible, and 92-98% yields of purified active esters can be isolated after 5-10 minute reaction times[3]. Unfortunately, although the acylsalicylamides obtained from these reactions are technically active esters, they are rather inferior examples of their class, being less reactive and for their reactivity, more prone to racemization than for example, p-nitrophenyl esters. An alteration of properties was clearly desired, but it was hoped that with suitable modification, the benzisoxazole framework could be used as a route to activated species with more favorable properties.

For an objective we were guided by the work of Hansen[4], Bender[5], Bruice[6] and coworkers on the hydrolysis of esters bearing an internal basic catalyst. From the work of Hansen, catechol monoacetate is known to hydrolyze nearly a thousand times more rapidly than phenyl acetate, although the two systems are of similar intrinsic reactivity. This result is most easily understood in terms of internal general base catalysis of rate-determining nucleophilic attack by water. Since aminolysis of phenyl esters is known in general to require the assistance of a general base, reaction of a catechol monoester with primary or secondary amines would be expected to be a ready process; on the other hand oxazolone formation, for geometric reasons, should be unassisted and should proceed at a rate commensurate with the intrinsic activation of the ester linkage. To the extent that the catechol monester anion is the principal catechol species, specific base catalysis[7] of oxazolone formation should be strongly inhibited on electrostatic grounds. Considerations similar to these provided the motivation for the independent development of catechol esters by Young[8] and of oxine esters by Jakubke[9].

As already reported[10], 1 has been found to react as desired with carboxylic acids to yield 3-acyloxy-2-hydroxy-N-ethylbenzamides, 2. The intramolecular competition between acyl migration and oxazolone formation has been found to be particularly favorable for these reactions: activation of Z-Gly-L-PheOH under the conditions of FIG. 2 has been shown to yield less than 0.05% of oxazolone.

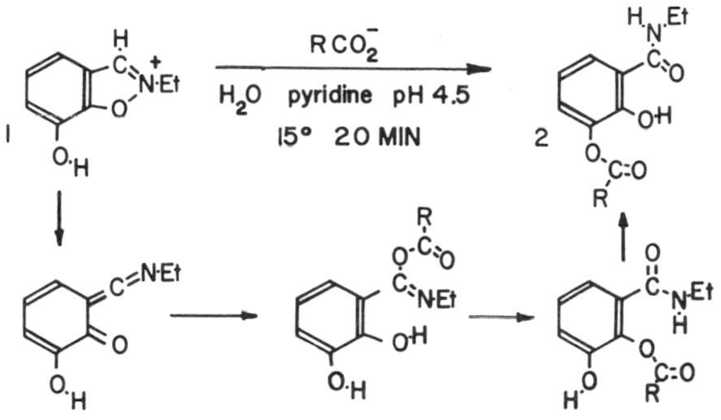

Figure 2

These activation conditions have now been applied to more than thirty N-protected peptide and amino acids; in most cases yields of 85-90% of active ester are obtained after purification, and in the cases of Z-Gly and Z-L-Ala isotopic dilution has shown actual yields to be in the range of 97-99%. Isolated yields of esters, 2, from Z-L-AsnOH and Z-L-GlnOH so far have fallen in a lower range of 75-80%, although further work is needed to reveal the nature of this discrepancy.

It has been noted previously[10] that peptide esters of structure 2 possess the features of aminolytic reactivity together with resistance to racemization during prolonged treatment with tertiary amines. An aspect of this reluctance to racemize is illustrated strikingly by the data of Table 1 which gives results of isotopic dilution modification[11] of the Anderson and Young tests, applied to coupling of esters 2 and of acylazides. To our knowledge these are the first results

TABLE 1. Racemization for Couplings with Ethyl Glycinate

Activating Agent	Bz-L-Leu-GlyOEt	ZGly-L-Phe-GlyOEt
Azide, 0°, Et_2O, 24 hr.	0.08, 0.24%	0.034, 0.011%
Azide, 0°, DMF 24 hr.	0.15, 0.50	0.040
2, 25°, DMF	0.67, 0.83	0.13, 0.12
2, 0°, DMF	0.23	0.005, 0.013, 0.011

which establish the extent of racemization for azide couplings under "least racemizing" conditions.

With amine components having basicities of normal peptide esters, the 3-acyloxy-2-hydroxy-N-ethylbenzamides thus appear to couple with optical integrity equal to or greater than that achieved with acylazides and appear to markedly increase their advantage under more strongly basic conditions in which azides are known to racemize extensively[12]. While this is itself an important result, it must be stressed that the importance of the azide coupling procedure for fragment condensation syntheses rests upon its compatibility with methyl and ethyl ester protective groups as well as on its freedom from racemization, and any new coupling procedure when applied to a fragment scheme must allow for the severe burden such a scheme places on the small group of satisfactory carboxyl protective groups.

The esters, 2, with their high integrity to bases, seemed ideally suited for reaction with the highly basic salts of amino acids and peptides, for salt couplings in the past seem to have been limited largely by the ease of racemization of peptide activated species. Coupling indeed occurs rapidly and cleanly in DMSO, DMF, tetramethyl urea, or hexamethyl-phosphoramide between esters, 2, and tetramethyl or tetra-ethylammonium salts of amino acids, but the utility of this procedure is severely limited by the necessity for using two equivalents of the amino acid salt, the first being con-sumed in forming the ammonium salt of the acidic active ester.

The need for a base capable of dissolving amino acids as their salts in dipolar aprotic solvents was met in a highly satisfactory way by tetramethylguanidine (TMG), commer-cially available as the anhydrous base. When a solution of L-phenylalanine in dry DMSO containing two equivalents of TMG was treated with 2, R $\coloneqq$ Z-Gly, a rapid reaction occurred (t 1/2 4 min, 0.2M reagents), and a 90% yield, after purification, of Z-Gly-L-PheOH was obtained; isotopic dilution analysis revealed the actual yield to be 99% after 45 min. The possibility that TMG might react as a nucleo-phile with esters 2, was discounted when 2, R $\coloneqq$ ZGly, was recovered by isotopic dilution in 100% yield after 45 min. in DMSO containing two equivalents of TMG.

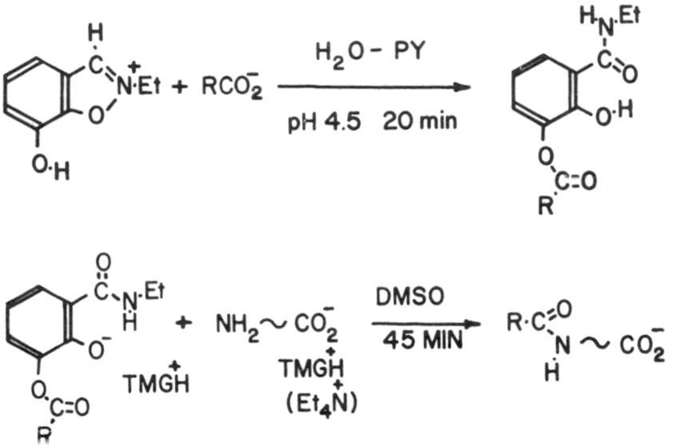

Figure 3

The general activation and coupling procedures which are now entertained are shown in FIG. 3. Since TMG in DMSO will dissolve only around half of the 20 common amino acids, salts were prepared in insoluble cases by lyophilizing a solution of the amino acid in an equivalent of aqueous tetra-methylammonium hydroxide. The resulting residue was then dissolved in DMSO containing an equivalent of TMG. This procedure has now been successfully applied to the synthesis of more than forty small peptides; all of the twenty amino acids have given satisfactory results as amine components in salt couplings, although as the data of Table 2 indicate, considerable variation in coupling rate is observed. Despite the slowness of the valine-valine coupling, after a reaction time of 12 hours a 70-80% yield of Z-L-Val-L-ValOH was isolated, and assay by isotopic

TABLE 2. Rates of Coupling Reactions of Esters 2, DMSO, $25°$[a]

Ester, 2	Amine	$K(m^{-1}min^{-1})$	Time for 50% reaction 0.2M reagents
ZGly	Gly⁻TMG⁺	~10	~0.5 min
ZGly	L-Phe⁻TMG⁺	1.3	4
Z-L-Ala[b]	L-AlaOEt	1.0	5
Z-L-Ala[b]	D-AlaOEt	0.6	9
ZGly	L-Leu⁻Me₄N⁺	0.8	6
ZGly	Sarc⁻TMG⁺	0.8	6
ZGly	L-Pro⁻TMG⁺	0.15	30
Z-L-Val	L-Val⁻Me₄N⁺	~0.1	~50

[a] Rates measured by an isotopic dilution assay
[b] Reactions run in DMF containing 1 eq. of TMG

dilution showed that less than 0.1% of the diastereometer was formed.

The issue of racemization is crucial for the salt couplings. Table 3 gives results of two independent racemization assays, and demonstrates that provided reactions are run at low temperatures, racemization levels lie below tolerable limits.

The applicability of this general procedure to practical, convenient synthesis of peptides is at least hinted at by our synthesis in 50-75% overall yields of the pentapeptides Z(-L-Ala)₅OH and ZGly-L-Leu -Gly₂OH; multigram quantities of pure samples of these substances were easily prepared

TABLE 3. Racemization for Couplings with Glycine Anion

Activating Agent, Conditions		Bz-L-Leu	ZGly-L-Phe
2, 2 eq TMG 1 eq Gly	25° DMSO	9.9%	1.0, 0.39, 0.41%
	0° DMF-DMSO	-	0.027
2, 1 eq TMG 1 eq GlyO⁻Me₄N⁺	25° DMSO	4.1, 4.3	-
	0° DMF-DMSO	0.25	0.022
2, 2 eq GlyO⁻Me₄N⁺	25° DMSO	1.1	-
	0° DMF-DMSO	0.14	0.0065, 0.0088

in two days time. Salt couplings have been found to proceed smoothly with a number of carboxyl-activated glutamine and asparagine derivatives, and clean preparations in 80% yield of the cysteine peptides Z-L-Cys(SBZ)-L-Cys(SBZ)OH and Z-L-Cys(SBZ)GlyOH have been observed. Although reactions have not been investigated carefully as yet, difficulty has been observed with couplings involving unprotected C-terminal serine, histidine, and arginine. The most serious limitation so far uncovered is the susceptibility of the esters, 2, to hydrolysis, a result which limits the useful media for salt couplings to dipolar aprotic solvents.

Although it is probably too early to predict the eventual utility of the 7-hydroxy-2-ethylbenzisoxazolium cation,

the results obtained thus far with it provide eloquent support
for the general principle which led to its development.
Other systems besides isoxazolium salts can be envisioned
as first stage activating agents, others besides catechols
as second stage tailored active esters. Whatever the eventual scope of reagent 1, it seems clear from its example that
much can be done to improve the power and delicacy of our
existing arsenal of peptide coupling reagents.

ACKNOWLEDGMENTS

I am indebted to my collaborators Dr. Shen-Wei Wang,
Mr. Julius Rebek, and Mr. Stanley Wrobel for their able
experimental assistance. Financial support from the
National Institutes of Health (GM 13453) is gratefully
acknowledged.

REFERENCES

1. L. Claisen, Ber., 42, 59 (1909); O. Mumm and G.
    Munchmeyer, ibid., 43, 3335, 3345 (1910); O. Mumm
    and C. Bergell, ibid., 45, 3040, 3149 (1912). For a
    complete tabulation of Mumm's work, see reference 2.

2. R. B. Woodward and R. A. Olofson, Tetrahedron, 57,
    415 (1966); R. B. Woodward, R. A. Olofson, and H. Mayer,
    Tetrahedron, 58, 321 (1966).

3. D. S. Kemp and R. W. Woodward, Tetrahedron, 21,
    3019 (1965); D. S. Kemp, Tetrahedron, 23, 2001 (1967).

4. B. Hansen, Acta Chem. Scand., 17, 1375 (1963). See
    also E. J. Fuller, J. Amer. Chem. Soc., 85, 1777 (1963).

5. M. L. Bender, F. J. Kezdy, and B. Zerner, J. Amer. Chem. Soc., 85, 3017 (1963).

6. T. C. Bruice and D. W. Tanner, J. Org. Chem., 30, 1668 (1965).

7. Cf. D. S. Kemp and S. W. Chien, J. Amer. Chem. Soc., 89, 2745 (1967).

8. J. H. Jones and G. T. Young, Chem. Comm., 35 (1967); J. H. Jones and G. T. Young, J. Chem. Soc., (C), 436 (1968). See also G. T. Young in Proc. Eighth European Peptide Symposium, North Holland, Amsterdam, 1967, p. 855.

9. H. D. Jakubka and A. Voigt, Chem. Ber., 99, 2419 (1966).

10. D. S. Kemp and S. W. Chien, J. Amer. Chem. Soc., 89, 2743 (1967). The reagent is commercially available from Midway Bio-Organics, P. O. Box 1804, Kansas City, Mo., 64140.

11. A preliminary report of this procedure has been given: D. S. Kemp and G. Hugel, Division of Organic Chemistry, 154th meeting, American Chemical Society, Chicago, Ill., September, 1967.

12. G. W. Anderson, T. E. Zimmerman, and F. M. Callahan, J. Amer. Chem. Soc., 88, 1339 (1966).

SYNTHETIC STUDIES OF GRAMICIDINS AND TYROCIDINES

Nobuo Izumiya, Tetsuo Kato, Haruhiko Aoyagi,
Satoru Makisumi, Michinori Waki, Okitoshi Abe
and Nobuo Mitsuyasu

Laboratory of Biochemistry
Faculty of Science, Kyushu University, Fukuoka, Japan

In order to elucidate the relationship between structure and activity in cyclic peptide antibiotics, different analogs of gramicidin S (GS) were synthesized and their growth inhibition activities were tested against some microorganisms. Several interesting chemical features were evolved in the course of this study.

FIG. 1 indicates a typical sequence for a cyclic decapeptide synthesis -- the example here is 5, 5'-Gly-GS[1]. The pMZ-group was used as the α-N-protecting group in the initial peptide active ester because the corresponding BOC-peptide active ester failed to give a satisfactory result.

When a doubling cyclization reaction was used, the protected dimer was isolated in a synthesis of GS from the linear pentapeptide active ester[2]. If the valine residue was replaced with glycine, then the corresponding linear pentapeptide active ester yielded only one product, the cyclic monomer[3]. When glycine

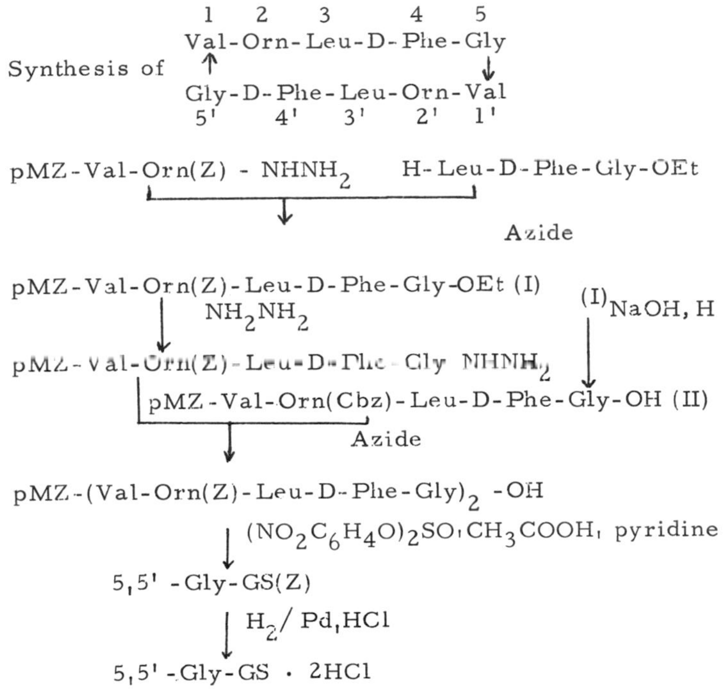

Synthesis of

$$
\begin{array}{ccccc}
1 & 2 & 3 & 4 & 5 \\
\text{Val-} & \text{Orn-} & \text{Leu-} & \text{D-Phe-} & \text{Gly} \\
\uparrow & & & & \downarrow \\
\text{Gly-} & \text{D-Phe-} & \text{Leu-} & \text{Orn-} & \text{Val} \\
5' & 4' & 3' & 2' & 1'
\end{array}
$$

pMZ-Val-Orn(Z) - NHNH$_2$ H-Leu-D-Phe-Gly-OEt

$\xrightarrow{}$ Azide

pMZ-Val-Orn(Z)-Leu-D-Phe-Gly-OEt (I)

(I) $\downarrow$ NH$_2$NH$_2$ (I) $\downarrow$ NaOH, H$^+$

pMZ-Val-Orn(Z)-Leu-D-Phe-Gly-NHNH$_2$

pMZ-Val-Orn(Cbz)-Leu-D-Phe-Gly-OH (II)

$\downarrow$ Azide

pMZ-(Val-Orn(Z)-Leu-D-Phe-Gly)$_2$ -OH

$\downarrow$ (NO$_2$C$_6$H$_4$O)$_2$SO, CH$_3$COOH, pyridine

5,5' -Gly-GS(Z)

$\downarrow$ H$_2$/ Pd, HCl

5,5'-Gly-GS · 2HCl

FIG. 1.   Sequence of Reaction for 5,5'-Gly-GS Synthesis

pMZ = CH$_3$OC$_6$H$_4$CH$_2$OCO-

Z = C$_6$H$_5$CH$_2$OCO-

occupied the place of D-phenylalanine, the pentapeptide active ester produced the dimerized cyclodecapeptide exclusively[4]. The GS pentapeptide active ester and some of its analogs were found to furnish a mixture of cyclic penta- and decapeptides. Separation was usually achieved by column chromatography using Sephadex LH-20 for the protected cyclopeptides and carboxymethyl-cellulose for the naked peptides. The semi-form of GS was isolated for the first time by the LH-20

procedure[5]. The protected semi-GS is very soluble and
difficult to crystallize.

A summary of results on the cyclization reaction for
various linear pentapeptide active esters is shown in Table
1[3-9]. The specific activity of the cyclodecapeptides is given
in Table 2. None of the cyclopentapeptides had antibacterial
activity.

Hodgkin and others[10] have suggested an antiparallel
β-pleated sheet structure for GS (FIG. 2). This conformation
seems to agree with the results of GS analog's activity test.
For example, replacement of the valine residues with glycine
may disturb a possible hydrophobic interaction with bacteria
and thereby yield an inactive product.

Apart from analog synthesis, a preparation of retro-GS
was achieved, also[11]. The occurrence of retro-GS in Nature
has not been reported, yet a molecular model of this compound
in the β-sheet structure revealed the proline side chains were
directed towards the hydrophilic ornithyl side. This may
weaken any interaction between the cationic portion of the
molecule and bacteria. The synthetic sequence for retro-GS
was similar to the GS analog as shown in FIG. 1. Pure retro-
GS and the semi-form of the peptide were obtained in good
yield. The retro-GS was found to be only one-tenth as active
as GS.

TABLE 1

Ratio of Protected Cyclic Pentapeptide and Decapeptide after Cyclization of Various Linear Pentapeptide Active Esters.

p-Nitrophenyl ester of	1	2	3	4	5	Ratio of Compound in Product Cyclic monomer	Cyclic dimer	References
H-Val-Orn(Z)-Leu-D-Phe-Pro-OH						32	63	(5)
	"	"	"	"	Gly	79	21	(6)
	"	"	"	"	Sar	85	15	(7)
	"	"	"	Gly	Pro	0	100	(4)
	"	"	"	"	D-Ala	25	75	
	"	"	"	"	D-Leu	+	+-	
	"	Lys(Z)	"	D-Phe	"	29	71	(8)
	"	Dbu(Z)	"	"	"	30	70	(8)
H-Gly	Orn(Z)	"	"	"		100	0	(3)
H-Ala	"	"	"	"		91	9	(3)
H-Leu	"	"	"	"		78	22	
H-Gly	Lys(Z)	"	"	"		100	0	
H-Gly	Orn(Z)	"	"	Gly		100	0	(9)
H-Orn(Z)	Leu	D-Phe	Gly	Gly		100	0	(9)

TABLE 2

Specify Activity of GS Analogs

1	2	3	4	5	
Cyclo(Val-	Orn-	Leu-	D-Phe-	Pro-)$_2$	100
Gly	"	"	"	"	0
Ala	"	"	"	"	100
Leu	"	"	"	"	50~100
Val-Lys	"	"	"	"	100
"	**Dbu**	"	"	"	50~100
"	Orn	"	Gly	"	0
"	"	"	L-Phe	"	0
"	"	"	D-Val	"	100
"	"	"	D-Leu	"	100
"	"	"	D-Phe	Gly	500
"	"	"	"	Sar	100

Formation of a hydantoyl derivative was found in the course of the synthesis of retro-GS. Saponification of the pMZ-pentapeptide ethyl ester, followed by chromatography with Sephadex LH-20, gave a mixture of the corresponding pentapeptide and the dicarboxylic acid of a hydantoyl derivative, as shown in FIG. 3. The byproduct formation derives occasionally from a poor yield in the saponification of several pentapeptide esters. The formation of similar compounds has been reported by others.[12]

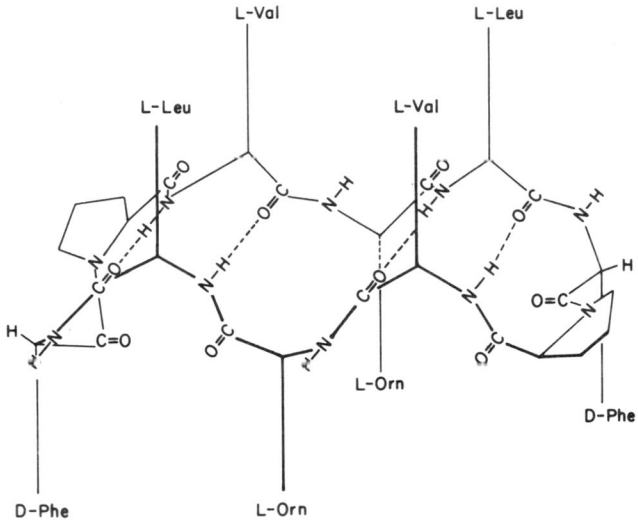

FIG. 2. β -Sheet Conformation of GS

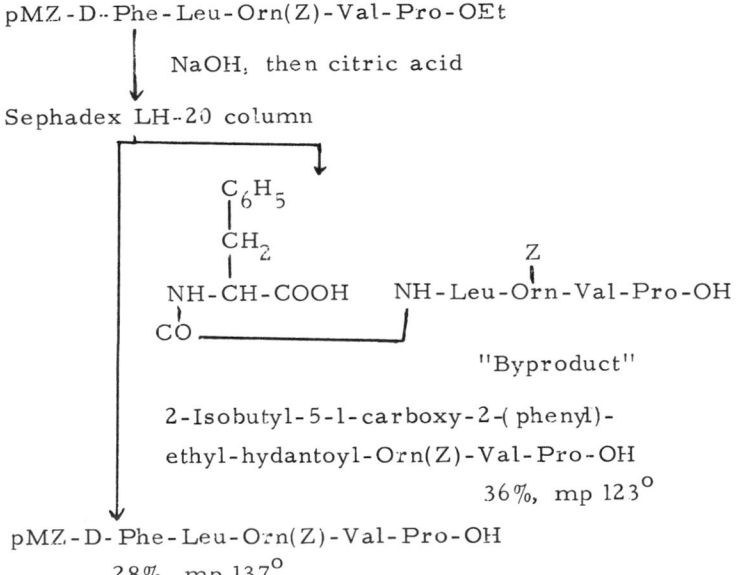

FIG. 3.   Formation of a Byproduct

It will be noted that gramiciden A has a structure equivalent to a formyl-pentadecapeptide ethanolamide[13]. Interestingly,
a biosynthetical precursor of GS, possessing a formyl decapeptide ethanolamide structure, was isolated recently[14].
These findings suggest the possibility of new, linear active
analogs. Several such linear pentapeptide derivatives were
prepared, but were found to be inactive; more such decapeptide
derivatives are under preparation now.

Additionally, tyrocidine A was synthesized and identified
with the natural peptide[15]. A cyclic peptide hydrochloride
having the supposed structure of tyrocidine E was prepared,
too, and a comparison to the natural product will be performed soon.

In another portion of this study, several related peptides
have been prepared, containing some smaller ring structures,
such as cyclo-di-[16], hexa-[17] and related heptapeptides with
plausible amino acid sequences. In the cyclic framework the
presence of basic amino acids and D-amino acids appear to
be the characteristic feature of these peptide antibiotics.
Although all of these new compounds were devoid of activity,
syntheses in this series will be continued towards the ultimate
decapeptide structure.

REFERENCES

1. H. Aoyagi, T. Kato, M. Ohno, M. Kondo, M. Waki, S. Makisumi and N. Izumiya, Bull. Chem. Soc. Japan, 38, 2139 (1965).

2. R. Schwyzer and P. Sieber, Helv. Chim. Acta, 41, 2186 (1958).

3. M. Kondo and N. Izumiya, Bull. Chem. Soc. Japan, 40, 1975 (1967).

4. R. Nagata, M. Waki, M. Kondo, H. Aoyagi, T. Kato, S. Makisumi and N. Izumiya, ibid., 40, 963 (1967).

5. M. Waki and N. Izumiya, ibid., 40, 1687 (1967).

6. H. Aoyagi, M. Kondo, T. Kato, S. Makisumi and N. Izumiya, ibid., 40, 1685 (1967).

7. H. Aoyagi, and N. Izumiya, ibid., 39, 1747 (1966).

8. M. Waki, O. Abe, R. Okawa, T. Kato, S. Makisumi and N. Izumiya, ibid., 40, 2904 (1967).

9. M. Kondo, H. Aoyagi, T. Kato and N. Izumiya, ibid., 39, 2234 (1966).

10. G. M. J. Schmidt, D. C. Hodgkin and B. M. Oughton, Biochem. J., 65, 744 (1957); R. Schwyzer in CIBA Foundation Symposium on Amino Acids and Peptides with Antimetabolic Activity (G. E. W. Wolstenhome and C. H. O'Conner, eds.), Little, Brown, Boston, 1958, p. 171.

11. M. Waki and N. Izumiya, Tetrahedron Letters, 3083 (1968).

12. M. Bodanszky, J. T. Sheehan, M. A. Ondetti and S. Lande, J. Am. Chem. Soc., 85, 991 (1963).

13. R. Sarges and B. Witkop, ibid., 87, 2011 (1965).

14. L. W. Pollard, N. V. Bhagavan and J. B. Hall, Biochemistry, 7, 1153 (1968).

15. M. Ohno, T. Kato, S. Makisumi and N. Izumiya, Bull. Chem. Soc. Japan, 39, 1738 (1966).

16. N. Izumiya, T. Kato, Y. Fugita, M. Ohno and M. Kondo, ibid., 37, 1809 (1964); M. Winitz and N. Izumiya, Arch. Biochem. Biophys., 108, 292 (1964).

17. T. Kato, M. Kondo, M. Ohno and N. Izumiya, Bull. Chem. Soc. Japan, 38, 1202 (1965); T. Kato and N. Izumiya, ibid., 39, 2242 (1966).

SYNTHESIS OF CYCLIC PEPTIDE ENZYME MODELS

Roger W. Roeske, A. R. Mitchell, Nancy M. Cladel, S. K. Gupta

Department of Biochemistry
Indiana University
School of Medicine
Indianapolis, Indiana

It is conceivable that relatively small cyclic or bicyclic peptides could be designed to bind substrates and catalyze a reaction of the substrate, thus functioning as small enzymes. We are attempting to synthesize such peptides; this progress report describes our efforts in that direction. Our first approach is to prepare compounds of the general structure shown in FIG. 1, consisting of two residues of p-aminobenzoic acid joined by peptide bridges. When the bridges are tripeptides, the cavity is elliptical, measuring about 4 x 5 Å, the exact size depending on the conformations of the peptide bridges.

In an aqueous solution, the hydrophobic part of a substrate should be attracted to the cavity of the cyclic peptide, and amino acid side chains in one of the bridges would form the catalytic site of the model. This model bears an obvious resemblance to the cycloamyloses studied by Cramer[1] and Bender[2] and their co-workers.

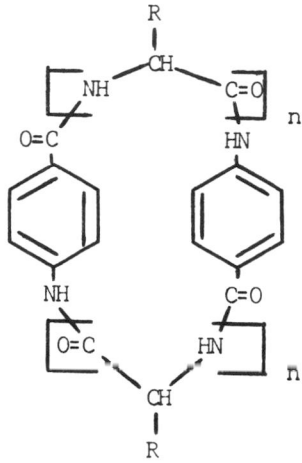

FIG. 1

We have prepared one cyclic peptide related to the above structure and have two others complete except for removal of the protecting groups. Binding studies have just begun and will not be described here.

In the first peptide (FIG. 2) the bridges are glycyl-L-histidylglycyl and ε-aminocaproylglycyl. Pab and Eac designate p-aminobenzoyl and ε-aminocaproyl, respectively. The linear peptide corresponding to the above sequence was prepared by Merrifield's solid phase method using 2% crosslinked polystyrene. t-Butoxycarbonyl-ε-aminocaproic

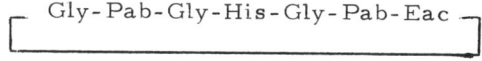
Gly-Pab-Gly-His-Gly-Pab-Eac

FIG. 2

acid was attached to chloromethylated polystyrene by refluxing
in ethanol in the presence of triethylamine to give a polymer
containing 0.62 millimoles of ε-aminocaproic acid per gram.
The protecting group was removed, as in subsequent cycles,
by treatment with trifluoroacetic acid in methylene chloride.
The dipeptide t-butoxycarbonyl glycyl-p-aminobenzoic acid
was then added as a unit because we were unable to prepare
t-butoxycarbonyl-p-aminobenzoic acid conveniently.
Addition of the dipeptide as a unit made it possible to monitor
the coupling at this stage by amino acid analysis, using the
glycine content, since p-aminobenzoic acid does not give a
positive ninhydrin test. The coupling of the dipeptide to the
polymer-linked ε-amino-caproic acid did not proceed
smoothly, perhaps because the resin was highly substituted.
Tetrahydrofuran was found to be the best solvent for the
reaction and we were finally able to acylate 80% of the
aminocaproyl residues using a 4.2-fold excess of the dipeptide
of N, N'-dicyclohexylcarbodiimide (hereafter designated DCC)
for a period of twenty hours. The resin was treated with
acetic anhydride to acetylate the unreacted amino groups.

Subsequent couplings also were carried out for twenty
hours using a four-fold excess of the protected amino acid
and of DCC. t-Butoxycarbonyl-imino-benzyl-L-histidine
was coupled in dimethylformamide, t-butoxycarbonyl glycine in methylene chloride and the final t-butoxycarbonyl

glycyl-p-aminobenzoic acid in tetrahydrofuran. The completed heptapeptide was cleaved from the resin by treatment
with anhydrous hydrogen bromide in trifluoroacetic acid for
thirty minutes. Amino acid analysis of the residue (Gly:
BzHis: Eac:3. 3:1. 0:1. 4) reflected the incomplete coupling
at the first stage and subsequent acetylation of the unreacted
aminocaproic residues. The crude peptide was purified
by column chromatography over Sephadex LH-20 in methanol.
The peptide dihydrobromide thus obtained gave satisfactory
amino acid and nitrogen analyses and weighed 0. 56 g. ,
representing a 30% conversion of polymer-linked ε-amino-
caproic acid to peptide.

Preliminary attempts to cyclize the heptapeptide using
Woodward's reagent K in dimethylformamide or DCC in
pyridine were unsuccessful. The reactions, monitored by
thin layer chromatography, showed considerable unreacted
starting material after several days. The use of a ten-fold
excess of DCC in a millimolar solution of the peptide in
80% methanol-water as described by Wieland and Ohly[3]
proved satisfactory. After purification on a Sephadex LH-20
column, the cyclic peptide crystallized in 28% yield. Removal
of the imino-benzyl group from histidine by treatment with
sodium in liquid ammonia for thirty seconds resulted in the
complete destruction of this compound and the formation of
about one equivalent of glycine. The cleavage of an N-terminal

p-aminobenzyl group from lysine vasopressin by sodium in liquid ammonia has been noted recently[4]. Fortunately the imino-benzyl group could be removed completely in sixty-six hours by catalytic hydrogenolysis using 5% Pd/C. The deblocked cyclic peptide (FIG. 2) was obtained in 80% yield after chromatography on cellulose. After long standing in an acetic acid-water solution, the peptide gave crystals which, on the basis of unit cell and density determinations, had a molecular weight of about 600. Both the cyclic peptide and the protected precursor decompose in the mass spectrometer before a parent m/e peak can be obtained. Both have satisfactory carbon, hydrogen and nitrogen analyses, assuming one mole of methanol crystallizes with the protected peptide and one mole of water with the final product.

The solubility of the cyclic heptapeptide was determined by measuring its ultraviolet absorption using glycyl-p-amino-benzoyl glycine as a reference compound. In 0.01 M phosphate buffer at pH 7.19, its solubility is only about 1 mg./liter (1.6×10^{-6} M solution), which will limit its usefulness as an enzyme model.

The synthesis of the second cyclic peptide is outlined in FIG. 3. All of the coupling steps were carried out with 1-ethyl-3(3-dimethylaminopropyl)carbodiimide hydrochloride (EDC) and the deblocking steps with trifluoroacetic acid. The N-protected peptides were all crystalline.

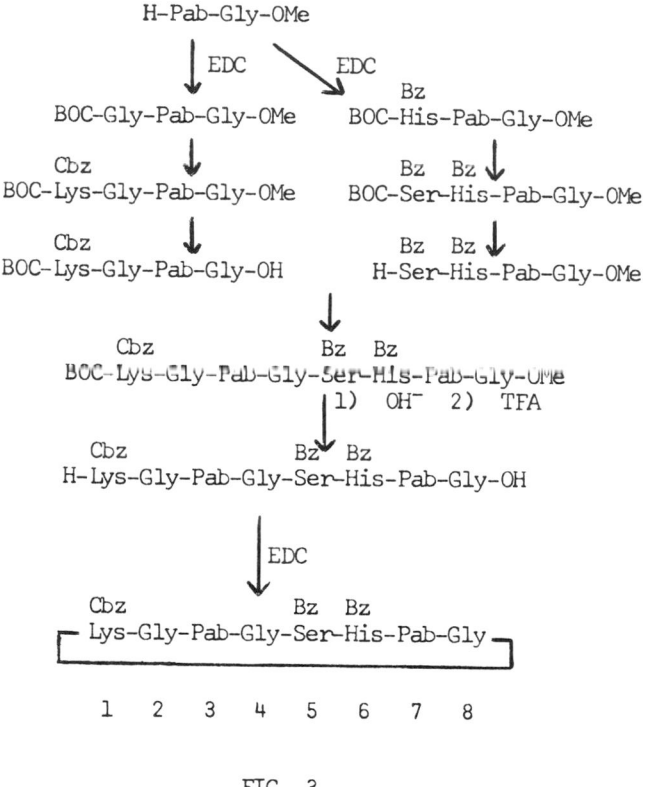

FIG. 3

Since peptides containing p-aminobenzoic acid residues are quite sensitive to aqueous base[5], the alkaline hydrolysis of the methyl esters of sequences 1-4 and 1-8 had to be carried out as gently as possible. Cyclization of the octapeptide took place in pyridine, using a 15-fold excess of EDC. The product was purified by ion-exchange chromatography on Amberlite OG-400 and by preparative thin layer chromatography on silica gel, and obtained as a white powder. The C, H, N and

O analyses indicate four moles of water of crystallization.
Molecular weight determinations by osmometry gave values
of 1020 and 1035 (calculated, 1148). We are now engaged in
preparing more of this compound and in trying to remove
the protecting groups.

The third peptide, now under preparation, contains two
residues of cis-4-aminocyclohexanecarboxylic acid(Acc) in
place of the two p-aminobenzoic acid residues of the general
structure shown in FIG. 1. The bridges are triglycyl and
histidylseryllysyl. The synthesis is outlined in FIG. 4.

Cis-4-aminocyclohexanecarboxylic acid was prepared
by hydrogenation of p-aminobenzoic acid in the presence of

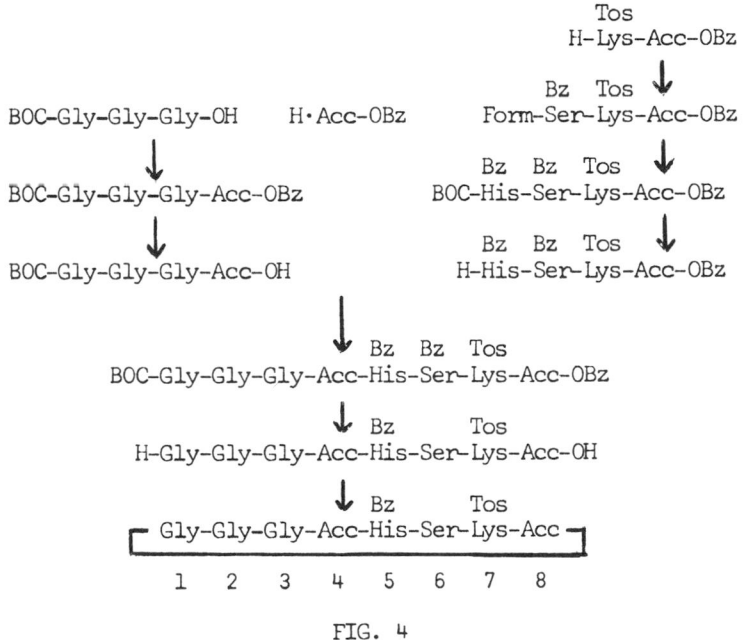

FIG. 4

5% ruthenium on charcoal[6]. Its benzyl ester formed the C-terminal end of both sequences 1-4 and 5-8. The coupling of t-butoxycarbonyl-triglycine with Acc benzyl ester by EDC gave the crystalline tetrapeptide benzyl ester which was hydrogenated to the acid. Sequence 5-8 was built up one residue at a time, using the nitrophenyl ester method for addition of lysine, DCC and two equivalents of N-hydroxysuc-cinimide for the N-formyl-O-benzyl-L-serine, and EDC for histidine. Anhydrous HCl in ethyl acetate was used to deblock sequences 7-8 and 5-8. Complete removal of the N-formyl group from sequences 6-8 by reaction with anhydrous NCl in benzyl alcohol required five days at room temperature, but the hydrochloride was obtained in 80% yield. Sequences 1-4 and 5-8 were coupled by EDC in methylene chloride. After preparative thin-layer chromatography, the yield of pure product was 66%. Simultaneous removal of protecting groups from residues 1, 6 and 8 was accomplished by treat-ment with anhydrous HBr in trifluoroacetic acid for 1 1/2 hours. The dihydrobromide was not crystalline but had a satisfactory C, H and N analysis. Cyclization was first attempted with DCC which gave several products, and then by the mixed anhydride method described by Wieland, Faesel and Faulstich[7]. After chromatography on cellulose, the peptide was obtained as a powder and had a satisfactory amino acid analysis. The elemental analysis indicated four moles of bound methanol after drying at 120° for one minute. This is noteworthy because the previous cyclic peptide held four moles of water very tightly. We are presently studying the binding properties of this peptide and are working on the removal of the protecting groups.

ACKNOWLEDGMENTS

This work was carried out during the tenure of a Research Career Development Award to Roger W. Roeske from the United States Public Health Service. The work was supported by grants from the Public Health Service and the National Science Foundation.

We wish to thank Dr. William Hargrove and Mr. Jack Campbell of Eli Lilly and Company for their work on the mass spectrometry and the high-pressure hydrogenation, respectively.

Special thanks are due Miss Anne Kask and Mrs. Holly Carlin for their technical assistance.

REFERENCES

1. F. Cramer and G. Mackensen, Angew. Chem. Internat. Ed., 5, 601 (1966).

2. R. VanEtten, J. Sebastian, G. Clowes and M. Bender, J. Am. Chem. Soc., 89, 3242 (1967).

3. T. Wieland and K. Ohly, Ann., 605, 179 (1957).

4. R. Geiger, K. Sturm, and W. Siedel, Ber., 101, 1223 (1968).

5. W. Langenbeck and D. Weisbrod, J. Prakt. Chem., 28, 78 (1965); Ibid., 31, 92 (1966).

6. W. Schneider and R. Dillmann, Ber., 96, 2384 (1966).

7. T. Wieland, J. Faesel and H. Faulstich, Ann., 713, 201 (1968).

SOLID PHASE SYNTHESIS OF VALINOMYCIN[1,2]

B. R. Gisin and R. B. Merrifield

The Rockefeller University
New York, New York

In 1955 Brockmann[3] in Göttingen isolated an antibiotic

from Streptomycines fulvissimus which was, unlike other

antibiotics, insoluble in water but very well soluble in organic

solvents. It was named valinomycin because the only amino

acid found in the compound was valine. Based on data obtained

from hydrolyses and determination of the molecular weight,

Brockmann[4] proposed valinomycin to be a cyclo-octadepsi-

peptide[5]. In 1963 this formula was corrected after Shemyakin

and coworkers[6] in Moscow synthesized first the octa-, then

the dodeca-depsipeptide that had the same acid composition

and sequence. The latter (FIG. 1) proved to be identical with

the natural product.

Valinomycin is a typical representative of the cyclo

depsipeptides. Depsipeptides are compounds that consist

of residues of amino acids and hydroxy acids joined by amide

and ester bonds. They do not necessarily have to be cyclic

but most of the naturally occurring ones are. As a rule,

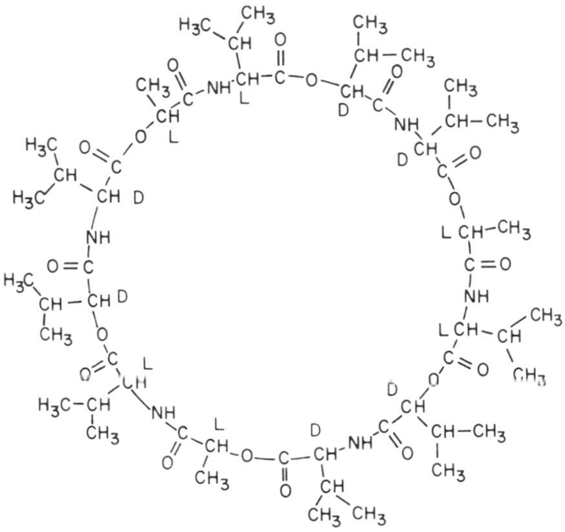

┌ L-Val-D-Hyv-D-Val-L-Lac-L-Val-D-Hyv-D-Val-L-Lac-L-Val-D-Hyv-D-Val-L-Lac ┐

FIG. 1

Valinomycin

Valinomycin consists of the residues of L-lactic acid, which is the hydroxy-analog of L-alanine; of D-valine; of D-α -hydroxyisovaleric acid, which is the hydroxy-analog of D-valine and of L-valine. This sequence of four residues is repeated three times in the 36-membered ring. In the structure initially proposed by Brockmann[4] one of these tetradepsipeptide units was missing.

these compounds are built up in a way that amide bonds alternate with ester bonds as in the case in valinomycin.

In recent years valinomycin has attracted the attention of several groups of investigators not only for its antibiotic but

66

for other rather unusual properties. It causes uncoupling of oxidative phosphorylation in isolated mitochondria[7,8], it makes natural[9,10] and artificial[10-13] lipid membranes selectively permeable to potassium ions and it is even able to form a complex with potassium ions, but essentially not at all with sodium ions[14,15]. When the hydrophobic side chains of the macrocycle are turned outwards and the hydrophilic atoms are turned towards the center, the potassium ion may be accomodated within the hole that forms. The molecule therefore could act as a carrier, enabling the cation to overcome the barrier to small charged particles which lipid membranes exhibit.

A rapid way to prepare analogs of this interesting compound for use in structure-activity studies[16] was required. For that purpose, a method involving the principles of solid phase peptide synthesis[17,18] was adapted to the synthesis of valinomycin.

The solid phase method was first used to make a disipeptide by Semkin, Smirnova and Shchukina[19] in Moscow, who prepared an angiotensin analog containing one hydroxy acid. They have also synthesized a tetradepsipeptide containing three α-hydroxy acids[20]. In each instance the ester bond was formed in pyridine by activation with benzene sulfonyl chloride and with a reaction time of one or two days. The formation of ester bonds requires much stronger activation than for peptide bonds and is therefore far less satisfactory.

The highly regular and repetitive structure of valinomycin suggested a different strategy for its synthesis on the resin. Instead of coupling the residues stepwise in 11 alternating amide- and ester- forming steps to a resin-bound residue the task was reduced to five peptide bond-forming steps by pre-forming all ester bonds in solution. Therefore dipepsi-peptides with an amino end and a carboxyl end were used in the stepwise synthesis.

Amino acids of the type $H_2N\text{-}CH\text{-}C\text{-}O\text{-}CH\text{-}COOH$ could be substituted for α-amino acids in the standard procedure of solid phase peptide synthesis[18]. In contrast to dipeptides, the carboxyl could be activated without the likelihood of racemization via an oxazolone intermediate.

FIG. 2 shows how the fragments of valinomycin were prepared. D-valine was butyloxycarbonylated with Boc-azide at constant pH according to Schnabel[21]. Lactic acid was protected by converting it into its benzyl ester. The free hydroxyl was then acylated with the Boc-valyl-residue by means of carbonyl diimidazole. With a 30% excess of acid and coupling agent the yield of protected didepsipeptide was over 95%. It was then debenzylated to give the crystalline Boc-D-valyl-L-lactic acid. The other fragment (Boc-L-valyl-D-α-hydroxyisovaleric acid) was prepared by exactly

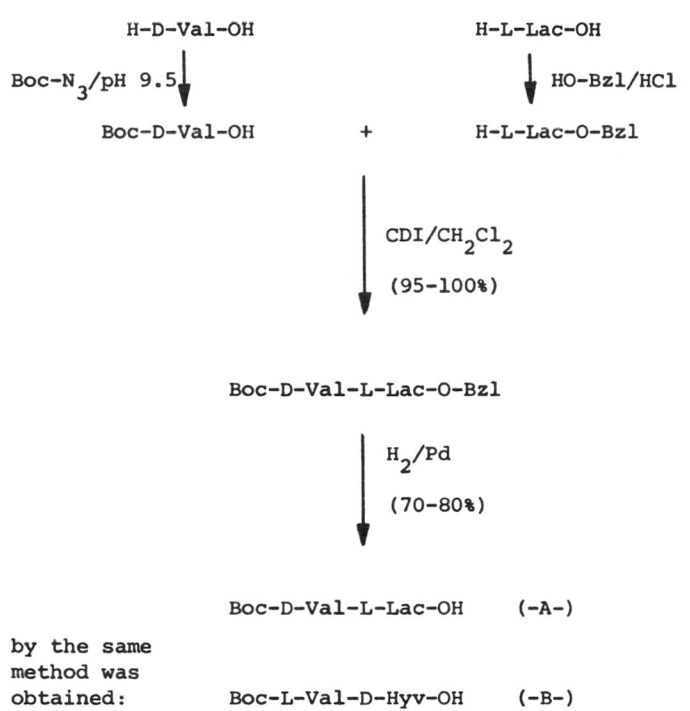

FIG. 2

Synthesis of fragments of valinomycin.

the same method. To make ester bonds in dipsipeptides the benzenesulfonyl chloride method is frequently used[22-24]. However, for the preparation of these two compounds it proved to be unsatisfactory, giving yields of less than 25%.

Now, having ready the two fragments from which valinomycin could be built up, there was still one decision left to be made: Which one to start with at the carboxyl end. In either case we would have ended up with the bulky valine at the amino end of the straight chain. But beginning with fragment A, we could expect less steric interactions in the ultimate cyclization step; for the side chain of lactic acid is only a methyl group and the side chain of α -hydroxy-isovaleric acid is an isopropyl group. Accordingly, D-valyl-L-lactate was chosen as the C-terminal fragment.

After the didepsipeptide resin was prepared it was transferred to an instrument for the automated synthesis of peptides developed by Merrifield, Stewart and Jernberg[25]. The machine was programmed and equipped to perform automatically all of the steps involved in the remainder of the synthesis. Dicyclohexylcarbodiimide was used as coupling agent. The excess of acylating agent was 2-fold and the coupling was allowed to proceed for four hours at room temperature. The cycle was repeated five times to give the protected linear dodecadepsipeptide with the sequence of valinomycin. The peptide was then cleaved from the resin with hydrogen bromide in trifluoroacetic acid, a procedure which specifically cleaves benzyl esters. It also removed the Boc-group, but did not damage the ester bonds within the chain. The crude product had already a remarkable purity and was once precipitated in water from acetic acid. After this one purification step the linear depsipeptide was homogeneous by thin

layer chormatography in three different systems, each of
which could separate lower homologs of the series.

After each coupling step a sample of the peptide resin
was cleaved, and the liberated depsipeptides were subjected
to thin layer chromatography. FIG. 3 shows schematically the
result of this analysis. The peptides showed distinct Rf-
values and were practically homogeneous. We conclude
that in each step coupling had taken place essentially quantitatively since there were no lower nomologs found in the chromatograms. Only the tetradepsipeptide was contaminated by
approximately 5% of D-valyl-L-lactic acid.

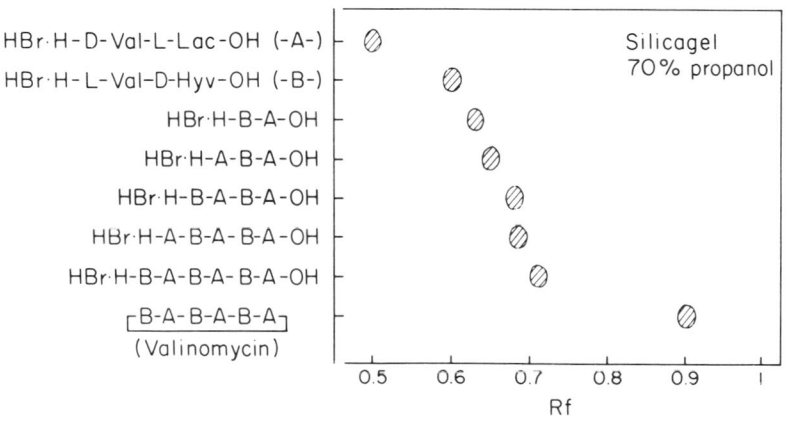

FIG. 3

The cyclized product, has, as one would expect, in all
systems used, a much higher Rf-value than the linear intermediates. It did not contain any ninhydrin-positive material
and therefore was free of possible linear contaminants.

71

In the first synthesis of valinomycin Shemyakin and coworkers[6] converted the linear dodecadepsipeptide with C-terminal hydroxyisovaleric acid to the acid chloride with thionyl chloride. They cyclized at high dilution under basic conditions to yield 10% of the macrocycle. In the present experiments the same method was used but the linear peptide had lactic acid at the carboxyl end, therefore forming a lactyl-valine-bond instead of the more hindered hydroxy-isovaleryl-valine-bond. Cyclization by this scheme resulted in a 51% yield of pure, crystalline valinomycin. Some analytical data on the synthetic and natural antibiotic are summarized in Table 1.

On the basis of these data we conclude that the synthetic material was pure and was identical with natural valinomycin. Based on the amount of didepsipeptide initially present on the resin the yields were 64% for the linear dodecadepsipeptide and 51% for the cyclization step, which gives an overall yield of about 33%. Thus, working on a one gram scale of resin about 250 mg of pure valinomycin could be obtained.

The product was subjected to a qualitative test of its influence on the electrochemical properties of a lipid bilayer[26] (FIG. 4). A lipid membrane was formed over a small hole of about one millimeter in diameter in a plastic partition sepa-rating two chambers with identical aqueous solutions of potas-sium chloride. The only way of exchange of electrical charges

TABLE 1

	Natural		Synthetic	
	Reported by Brockmann[3]	Sample(a)	Sample(b)	Reported by Shemyakin[6]
Crystal shape, from Bu$_2$O	Prisms	Prisms	Prisms	o.k.
Infra red	Identical spectra			o.k.
Spec. rot. in benzene	+31.0		+31.8	+32.8
Melting point	190°	186-186.5	186.5-187	187°
Mixed melting point depression with nat. sample	-	-	None	None
Elemental analysis	o.k.		o.k.	
Valine content, calculated, 5.90 mmole/g			5.89	
Yields		Open chain	64%(c)	10%
		Cyclization	51%	
		Overall	33%	

(a) Through Dr. M. Tieffenberg, Duke University. (b) Present work. (c) Based on Boc-didepsipeptide resin as starting material.

73

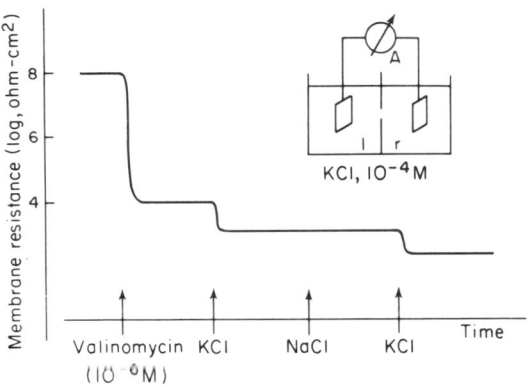

FIG. 4

Cation selectivity of synthetic valinomycin

between the two chambers was through the membrane. Two electrodes were connected with an instrument to register changes in the resistance of the membrane. Lipid membranes of this kind - they are only about 70 Angstrom thick - have a very high electrical resistance of approximately 10^{8} ohm-cm^{2} [10].

When valinomycin was added to the left chamber, the resistance fell about 10'000 fold. Addition of more potassium chloride to the left chamber resulted in a further drop of resistance. When the same amount of sodium chloride was added there was no change. But another batch of potassium chloride again lowered the resistance. These findings clearly demonstrate the ability to make membranes selectively permeable to potassium ions which is characteristic for valinomycin[13].

SOLID PHASE SYNTHESIS OF VALINOMYCIN

We have described a new way to synthesize dipsipeptides based on the principles of solid phase peptide synthesis.
The value of the method was illustrated by the successful
synthesis of valinomycin. This approach is expected to be
useful for the synthesis of analogs of this interesting biologically active dipsipeptide.

REFERENCES

1. Supported by Contract 14-01-001-1309, Office of Saline
   Water, U.S. Department of Interior, and in part by
   USPHS grant AM 1260.

2. For experimental details see: B. F. Gisin, R. B.
   Merrifield and D. C. Tosteson, J. Am. Chem. Soc.,
   in press.

3. H. Brockmann and G. Schmidt-Kastner, Chem. Ber.,
   88, 57 (1955).

4. H. Brockmann and H. Geeren, Ann., 603, 216 (1957)

5. For a review article on cyclodepsipeptides, see:
   D. W. Russell, Quart. Rev., 20, 559 (1966).

6. M. M. Shemyakin, N. A. Aldanova, E. I. Vinogradova
   and M. Feigina, Tetrahedron Letters, 28, 1921 (1963).

7. W. C. McMurray and R. W. Begg, Arch. Biochem. Bio-
   Phys., 84, 546 (1959).

8. C. Moore and B. C. Pressmann, Biochem. Biophys.
   Res. Commun., 15, 562 (1964).

9. D. C. Tosteson, P. Cook, T. Andreoli and M. Tieffenberg, J. Gen. Physiol., 50, 2513 (1967).

10. D. C. Tosteson, T. E. Andreoli, M. Tieffenberg and
    P. Cook, Proc. of a Symposium on Cell Membrane
    Biophysics, J. Gen. Physiol., 51, No. 5, part 2, 373ˢ
    (1968).

11. A. A. Lev and E. P. Buzhinsky, Tsitologiya, 9, 102 (1967).

12. P. Mueller and D. O. Rudin, Biochem. Biophys. Res. Commun., 26, 398 (1967).

13. T. E. Andreoli, M. Tieffenberg and D. C. Tosteson, J. Gen. Physiol, 50, 2527 (1967).

14. M. M. Shemyakin, Yu. A. Ovchinnikov, V. T. Ivanov, V. K. Antonov, A. M. Shkrob, I. I. Mikhaleva, A. V. Estratov and G. G. Malenkov, Biochem. Biophys. Res. Commun., 29, 834 (1967).

15. H. F. Wipf, Lavinia A. R. Pioda, Z. Stefanac and W. Simon, Helv. Chim. Acta, 51, 377 (1968).

16. Shemyakin and coworkers have prepared a large number of compounds related to valinomycin and have tested them for antimicrobial and ion transport inducing properties: M. M. Shemyakin, E. I. Vinogradova, M. Yu. Feigina, N. A. Aldanova, N. F. Loginova, I. D. Ryabova and I. A. Pavlenko, Experientia, 21, 548 (1965).

17. R. B. Merrifield, J. Am. Chem. Soc., 85, 2149 (1963); J. Am. Chem. Soc., 86, 304 (1964); Science, 150, 178 (1965); Recent Progr. Hormone Res., 23, 451 (1967).

18. For a comprehensive review on solid phase peptide synthesis see the book: J. M. Stewart and J. D. Young, Solid Phase Peptide Synthesis, to be published by W. H. Freeman, San Francisco, 1969.

19. E. P. Semkin, A. P. Smirnova, L. A. Shchukina, Zh. Obshch. Khim., 37, 1169 (1967).

20. L. A. Shchukina, E. P. Semkin and A. P. Smirnova, Khim. Prirodn. Soedin., 3, 358 (1967).

21. E. Schnabel, Ann., 702, 188 (1967).

22. M. M. Shemyakin, Yu. A. Ovchinnikov, V. T. Ivanov and A. A. Kiryushkin, Tetrahedron, 19, 581 (1963).

23. P. Quitt, R. O. Studer and K. Vogler, Helv. Chim. Acta, 47, 166 (1964).

24. G. Losse and H. Raue, Chem. Ber., 101, 1532 (1968).

25. R. B. Merrifield, J. M. Stewart and N. Jernberg, Anal. Chem., 38, 1905 (1966).

26. We wish to thank Dr. A. Cass of Rockefeller University who kindly performed this experiment.

SOLID PHASE SYNTHESIS OF A POLYPEPTIDE SEQUENCE
FROM STAPHYLOCOCCAL NUCLEASE

David A. Ontjes and Christian B. Anfinsen
Laboratory of Chemical Biology, National Institute of
Arthritis and Metabolic Diseases, National Institutes of Health
Bethesda, Maryland

The extracellular nuclease of <u>Staphylococcus aureus</u> is an enzyme particularly well suited for investigations of structure-activity relationships. Among its favorable characteristics are its ease of purification, its small size, and its ability to resume native conformation after denaturation by a variety of adverse environments. The enzyme is a phosphodiesterase which produces 3'-nucleotides from both RNA and DNA. Current knowledge of the structural basis for its catalytic activity has recently been summarized.[1]

In the presence of calcium ions and a substrate analog, 3', 5'-deoxythymidine diphosphate, nuclease becomes relatively resistant to proteolysis by trypsin, being cleaved into only three peptide fragments (Figure 1). The two largest fragments, fragment P_2 (residues 6 through 49) and Fragment P_3 (residues 50 through 149) have no significant acitivity alone, but will associate in a 1 to 1 ratio at neutral

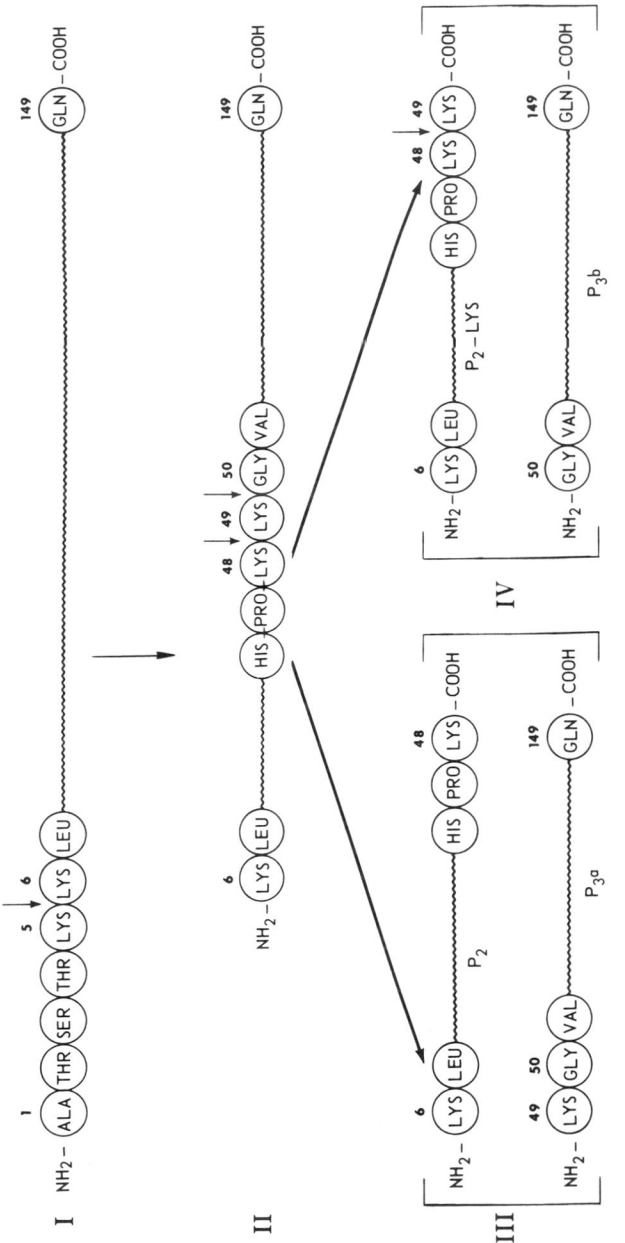

FIG. 1

Cleavage of nuclease by trypsin in the presence of 3',
5'-deoxythymidine diphosphate (10^{-3} M) and Ca^{++} (10^{-2} M).
The two species of fragment P3, with and without lysine
residue 49, are of identical activity. (Reproduced from
reference 3, with the permission of the Journal of Biological
Chemistry.)

pH to give nuclease-T, a species with approximately 8% of the activity of native nuclease.[2,3] Though less stable to denaturants than nuclease, nuclease-T has identical substrate specificity, pH and metal ion requirements. Presumably the catalytic sites of both species are quite similar. The organic synthesis of one or both of the two polypeptides constituting nuclease-T would provide valuable insights into the specific associations of the peptide chains as well as the chemistry of the catalytic site.

With this as introduction, I would like to discuss our experience in the solid phase synthesis of fragment P_2 of nuclease T. This 43-residue polypeptide is rather basic in character and contains all of the common amino acids except cysteine, serine and tryptophan. The overall scheme of synthesis, as well as the blocking groups most recently employed, are shown in Figure 2. Since the carboxyl terminal lysine residue of native P_2 may be enzymatically removed without loss of activity, the synthetic peptide was begun at proline residue 47

The synthesis of the blocked peptide chain was carried out using the principles developed by Merrifield.[4] Boc-proline was esterified to the chloromethylated polymer to yield between 0.25 and 0.30 mMoles of proline per gram of resin. The Boc group was used exclusively as the α-amino blocking group and was removed by 4 N HCl in purified

81

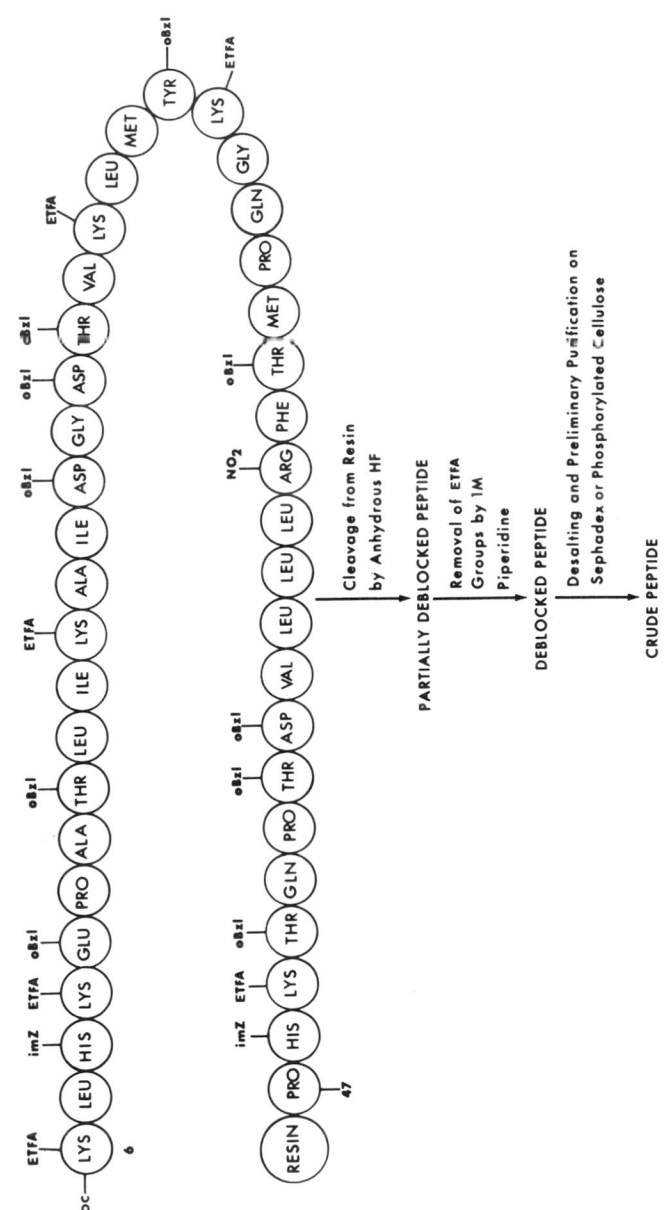

FIG. 2

Scheme for solid phase synthesis of nuclease fragment
P_2, showing blocking groups used.

dioxane. The resulting hydrochloride salt was converted to a free base with 10% triethylamine in chloroform. Coupling, using a 3-fold excess of the monomer, was generally performed in methylene chloride with DCC as the coupling agent. Glutamine and asparagine were coupled in dimethylformamide as the p-nitrophenyl esters. All reactions and rinsing operations were carried out in a shaking vessel of the type described by Merrifield, but, unfortunately for those involved, without the aid of automation.

Cleavage of the peptide from the resin was accomplished by stirring the peptidyl resin in anhydrous liquid HF at 0°C for 1 hour, using anisole as a scavenger.[5,6] In a typical cleavage procedure 400 mg of peptidyl resin was exposed to 5 ml of HF and 0.5 ml of anisole in a closed Teflon distillation apparatus similar to that described by Sakakibara.[5] After removal of HF in vacuo, remaining anisole was removed by rinsing the peptide-resin mixture with ethyl acetate. The partially deblocked peptide was then extracted from the mixture with glacial acetic acid and obtained as a white powder after lyophilization.

For a peptide such as ours, cleavage by HF is preferable to cleavage by the more widely used combination of HBr and trifluoroacetic acid. The ability of HF to remove the NO_2 blocking group of arginine is an obvious advantage in any sulfur containing peptide. In addition, we believe that the

HF procedure leads to fewer side reactions and is more compatible with the integrity of most large polypeptides and proteins. Native nuclease, for example, may be treated with HF for 2 hrs. at 0° without significant loss of activity. Recovery of such easily destroyed residues as threonine, tyrosine and methionine after HF cleavage has generally been satisfactory, and yields of crude peptide, based on the amino acid content of the starting amino-acyl resin have run from 50 to 80%.

After HF cleavage, the ε-TFA blocking groups were removed by dissolving the peptide in 1 M aqueous piperidine (pH 12) for 1 hour at 0°C. The solution was lyophilized, and the crude deblocked peptide, still containing traces of piperidine, was ready for preliminary purification, using either Sephadex G-25 or phosphorylated cellulose.

I should now like to discuss in more detail our present selection of side chain blocking groups, particularly for the ε-amino group of lysine and the imidazole moiety of histidine.

In the case of lysine, the ε-CBZ group has been commonly used in conjunction with the α-Boc group. For quantitative removal of the Boc group in solid phase synthesis, strong acids such as HCl in dioxane, HCl in acetic acid, or anhydrous trifluoroacetic acid are required. The ε-CBZ group is only relatively resistant to these acids, as shown in Table 1. After 24 hrs. in 4 N HCl in dioxane, for example, 20% of the ε-blocking groups of α-Boc-ε -CBZ-lysine have been removed. This undesirable removal also occurs when α -Boc- ε-CBZ-lysine is esterified to the usual solid phase support. Cleavage by ammonolysis after 24 hrs. of treatment with 4 N HCl in dioxane yielded a product which was a roughly equal mixture of ε-CBZ-lysine amide and lysine amide. Evidence for the formation of stable ε-peptidyl side chains under similar deblocking conditions in solid phase synthesis has been published by Yaron and Schlossman.[7] It is possible that a substituted derivative of the CBZ group may possess greater acid stability and yet be removable by HF.

Being convinced of the perils of using the CBZ group in the solid-phase synthesis of a large polypeptide, we have elected to use the ε-TFA group instead. The ε-TFA derivative of lysine shows adequate acid stability (Table 1) and may be coupled efficiently in solid phase synthesis. Hepta-ε-TFA-lysine was synthesized by the solid phase procedure. After deblocking, the product was fractionated by Dr. H. A. Sober on a carboxymethylcellulose column, using a lithium chloride concentration gradient.[8] 82% of the crude produce was true heptalysine, with hexa- and pentalysine accounting for most of the balance. Species of greater than seven residues constituted less than 2% of the total, indicating that side chain

TABLE 1

Stability of ε-CBZ Blocking Group to Acid Reagents

Lysine Derivative	Reagent	Time	Result
α-Boc-ε-Cbz-lysine	4N HCl/dioxane	15 min.	2% free lysine
		1 hr.	7% free lysine
		24 hrs.	20% free lysine
α-Boc-ε-Cbz-lysine	1N HCl/HAC	24 hrs.	39% free lysine
α-Boc-ε-Cbz-lysine	Trifluoroacetic acid	24 hrs.	Over 60% free lysine
α-Boc-ε-Cbz-lysine resin	4N HCl/dioxane (cleavage by ammonolysis)	15 min.	Major product ε-Cbz-lysine amide, trace lysine amide.
		24 hrs.	Major products lysine amide and free lysine.

Lysine was measured by quantitative amino acid analysis. ε-Cbz-lysine amide and lysine amide were estimated by thin layer chromatography (butanol 4; water 2; pyridine 1; acetic acid 1). α-Boc-ε-TFA lysine was exposed to 4 N HCl/dioxane for 24 hours with formation of less than 2% free lysine by amino acid analysis.

formation was minimal. From these data, coupling efficiency may be calculated to have been 92.2% per step.

The ϵ-TFA group may be removed under relatively mild basic conditions if aqueous piperidine is used. In many small peptides we have found deblocking to proceed quantitatively. With larger polypeptides and proteins, quantitative removal may be more difficult to achieve. Dr. Hiroshi Taniuchi has trifluoroacetylated native nuclease with recovery of 80% activity after deblocking. The recovered product, however, shows evidence of heterogeneity on an ion exchange column of phosphocellulose.[9] It is likely, therefore, that removal does not proceed quantitatively. In the piperidine deblocking of synthetic fragment P_2, there is also evidence that intact TFA groups may remain. Elemental analysis of the desalted, partially purified, deblocked product usually gives a fluorine content corresponding to 0.5 to 1.5 TFA groups per molecule of peptide. Thus, 80 to 95% TFA removal has been achieved. If conditions for more nearly quantitative removal can be developed, the ϵ-TFA group should prove very useful in the synthesis of large polypeptides.

The choice of a suitable blocking group for the imidazole function of histidine also becomes more difficult as the size of the desired peptide increases. We found that α-Boc-histidine, unprotected on the imidazole ring, gave unacceptably low coupling yields in solid phase synthesis, even when a

87

5-fold excess of the monomer was used. α-Boc-im-Bzl-histidine could be coupled efficiently, but the removal of the im-Bzl group in sodium liquid ammonia could not be carried out without simultaneous cleavage of one or more of the 4 proline bonds in the peptide. With the use of an apparatus developed by Merrifield and Marglin for Na/liquid NH_3 cleavage, the im-Bzl peptide P_2 was titrated to blue color end points lasting from 15 sec. to 45 sec. The deblocked product was then submitted to dansyl end group analysis, according to the method of Gray and Hartley.[10] In addition to the expected bis-dansyl-lysine, dansyl-proline was always detected. Amino acid analysis after Na/liquid NH_3 showed lower yields of threonine and methionine.

We have had better results with the im-CBZ group.[11] α-Boc-im-CBZ-histidine may be easily synthesized from α-Boc-histidine and carbobenzoxy chloride. In our hands the product has been an unstable oil, containing a minor impurity upon thin layer chromatography. The freshly synthesized product has been coupled to the deblocked peptidyl resin at once, using a four to five fold excess in methylene chloride, with DCC as a catalyst. Coupling efficiency in small test peptides has been 90% or better. The im-CBZ group is quantitatively removed by anhydrous HF.

Our experience with another potentially useful imidazole blocking group, the im-dinitrophenol (im-DNP) group[12]
is quite limited. However, preliminary experiments indicate that α-Boc-im-DNP-histidine may be coupled with
greater than 80% efficiency, that the im-DNP group is stable
to all of the conditions used in solid phase synthesis, and
that removal proceeds quantitatively upon treatment of the
peptide with aqueous mercaptoethanol at pH 8.

Having considered some of the blocking group problems
peculiar to the solid phase synthesis of long polypeptides, I
should like to return to the overall chemical and biological
·esults of our efforts to synthesize fragment P_2. Most of
che data I shall give pertains to a product which has been
fractionated on Sephadex G-25. With the initial passage of
the crude, deblocked peptide through the column, 20 to 30%
of the material was eluted at the excluded volume. This
peak appeared to be an aggregate of molecular weight greater
than 5,000. After removal of this fraction, the remaining
material was re-run on G-25 and divided into two fractions
as shown in Figure 3. Though the amino acid analyses of
both fractions approached that of native fragment P_2,
fraction A had a lower fluorine content. This fraction,
comprising approximately 40% by weight of the original deblocked material, was examined further.

89

AMINO ACID ANALYSIS OF
DEBLOCKED NUCLEASE P_2 PEPTIDE,
RESIDUES 6 TO 47

Amino Acid	Theory	Fraction A	Fraction B
Lysine	6	6.4	7.5
Histidine	2	1.5	2.3
Arginine	1	1.1	0.8
Aspartic	3	3.4	3.2
Threonine	5	4.2	4.6
Glutamic + Glutamine	3	2.9	3.3
Proline	4	4.0	5.0
Glycine	2	2.2	2.0
Alanine	2	2.1	2.3
Valine	2	2.1	1.9
Methionine	2	1.7	1.5
Isoleucine	2	1.9	1.6
Leucine	6	6.1	6.8
Tyrosine	1	0.7	0.7
Phenylalanine	1	0.8	0.9
TFA's per mole by analysis for Fluorine	none	0.5	1.3

ELUTION OF DEBLOCKED PEPTIDE
FROM G-25 SEPHADEX

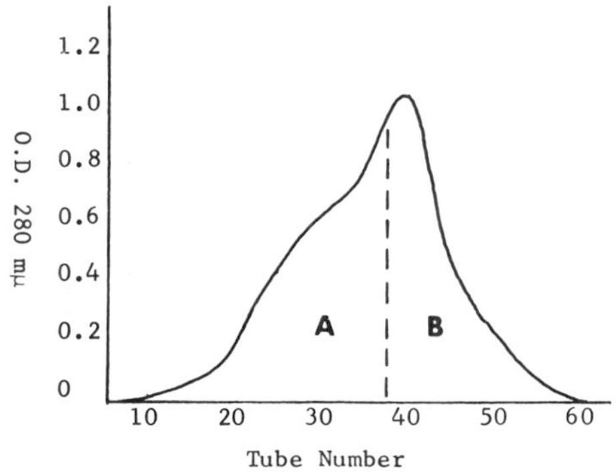

FIG. 3

Elution was from Sephadex G-25 (3 cm x 50 cm) in 0.1 M
acetic acid. Collection was begun after previously measured
excluded volume had passed through the column. Amino
acid analysis was performed on samples hydrolyzed in 6 N
HCl for 20 hours in sealed, evacuated tubes.

A sample of fraction A was digested with trypsin (1% w/w) followed by aminopeptidase M (50% w/w). Except for a 20% lower yield of proline, amino acid analysis of the proteolytic digest was similar to the analysis of the acid hydrolysate. Dansyl end group analysis showed only lysine.

Fraction A bore a structural resemblance to its native counterpart on immunologic grounds, as shown in Figure 4. The synthetic peptide was a strong inhibitor of the initial rate of the precipitin reaction between native nuclease and a nuclease antibody from immunized rabbits.[13]

This fraction of synthetic P_2 possesses a low but definite ability to activate the complementary native fragment P_3 to form an active nuclease (Figure 5). When synthetic P_2 was added in 25-fold molar excess to native P_3, the resulting mixture could promote the cleavage of heat denatured DNA in a pH stat apparatus. When added alone, neither synthetic P_2 nor native P_3 produced any effect. A similar low level of activity of the synthetic P_2-native P_3 combination has been seen in assays measuring changes in the viscosity of native DNA.

More recently we have fractionated the crude, deblocked peptide on a column of phosphorylated cellulose using a concentration gradient of ammonium acetate. Approximately one-third of the starting material was recovered as a broad peak in the ionic strength range which normally elutes native

91

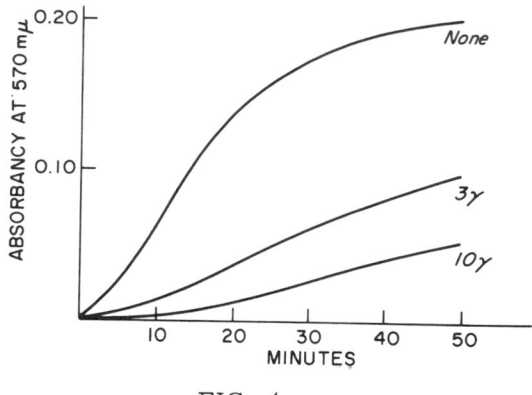

FIG. 4

Rate of turbidity development in the precipitin reaction between native nuclease and rabbit anti-nuclease gamma globulin. The precipitating mixture contained 0.02 mg. nuclease and 0.15 ml. with normal saline after addition of the synthetic peptide as inhibitor. Top curve represents development of turbidity in the absence of inhibitor. Lower curves show increasing inhibition with low levels of synthetic peptide. A trypsin digest of the peptide was without effect at the 10 λ level.

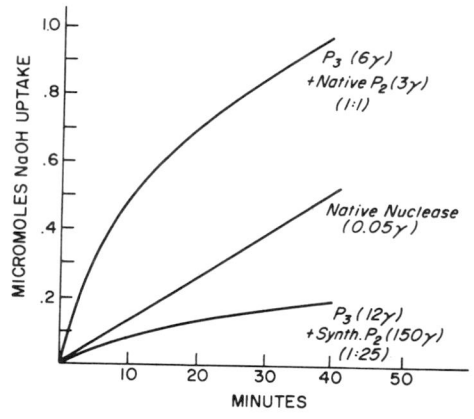

FIG. 5

Activity of the combination of native P_3 with synthetic P_2 in the cleavage of native DNA. The synthetic peptide was added in 25 fold excess to native P_3. Assay was performed in a pH stat apparatus at pH 9.0, titrating with 0.01 M NaOH.

P_2. The remainder of the material eluted earlier, over a wide range of lower ionic strength. The material eluting at the proper ionic strength was studied further. Disc gel electrophoresis of this fraction showed a single, slightly widened band with a mobility similar to that of the native polypeptide (Figure 6).

The same fraction of synthetic peptide, together with a sample of native P_2, was digested with trypsin and then submitted to paper chromatography and electrophoresis. The fingerprints of the native and synthetic materials were generally similar, with a few interesting differences. As seen in Figure 7, all of the usual tryptides of native P_2^3 are identifiable in the synthetic fraction. However, two new peptides, staining yellow with cadium-ninhydrin stain could be seen in the synthetic digest. In addition, two of the large synthetic tryptides corresponding to residues 17 through 24 and 36 through 45 appeared to give closely adjacent double spots. The chemical nature of these aberrations is not yet known. The biological activity of this synthetic material when added to native P_3, was comparable to the activity of the G-25 fractionated material described earlier.

In spite of the obvious problems, we regard the solid phase method as a promising one for the synthesis of longer polypeptides. The problems related to blocking groups will surely yield to future refinements. The achievement of

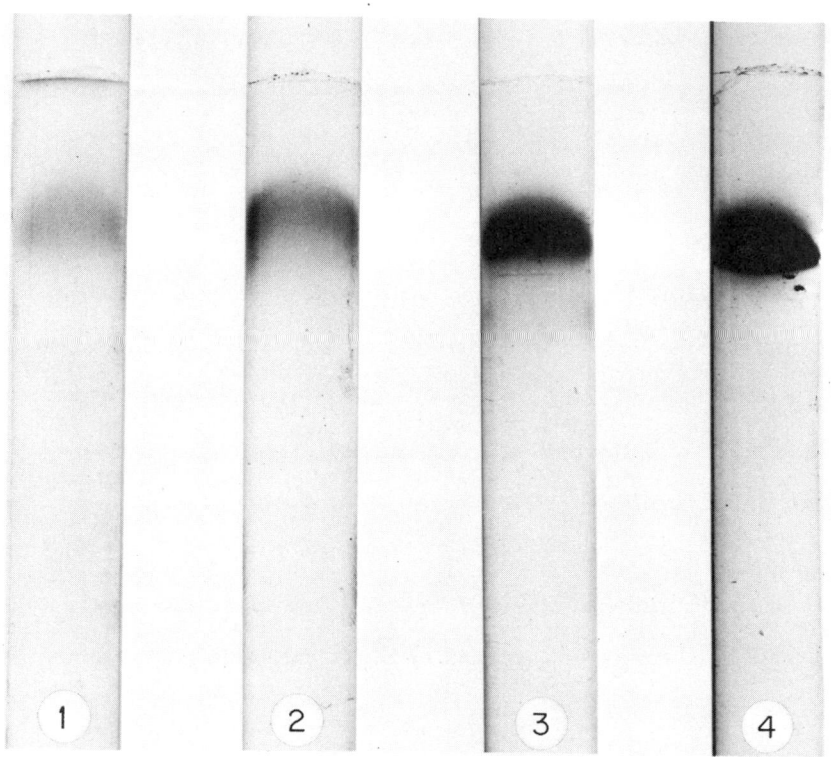

FIG. 6

Polyacrylamide gel electrophoresis of synthetic and native nuclease P_2. Tubes 1 and 2 are synthetic material eluting at low ionic strengths (see text). Tube 3 is synthetic material eluting at same ionic strength as native. Tube 4 is native P_2. All samples were applied in 50 γ quantities to a pH 2.3, 4.5% crosslinked gel and run for 2 hrs. at 2 m.a.

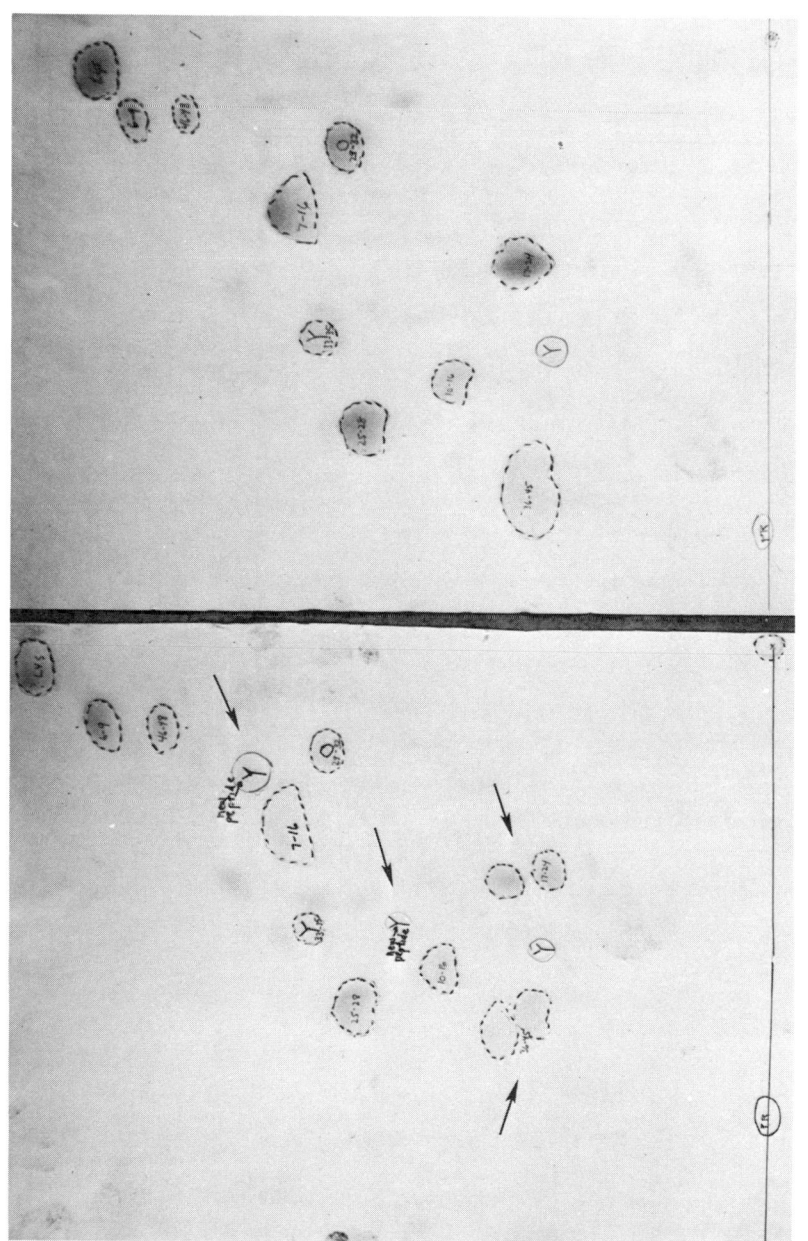

FIG. 7

Fingerprints of tryptic digests of synthetic (left) and
native (right) peptide P$_2$. Arrows indicate two new peptides
and two aberrant double peptides in the synthetic digest.

sustained perfection in the coupling of amino acids seems a much more difficult task. After 50 coupling steps with average efficiency of 98%, only a third of the product would bear the correct sequence. Such a product might have high biological activity, depending upon the tolerance of the native structure to alterations and deletions. On the other hand, the activity of the "correct" fraction might be competitively inhibited by closely related peptides in the mixture. In the case of nuclease-T there is some preliminary evidence that actual inhibition of the fruitful combination of native P_2 and P_3 does occur in the presence of synthetic P_2. Conclusions regarding structure-activity relationships would have to be made with care. Studies of the crystallographic structure of such a synthetic product would, of course, be ruled out entirely.

In assessing the heterogeneity of a large synthetic peptide, amino acid analysis is of limited value. Fingerprinting, particularly if done quantitatively on an ion exchange column, should provide a more discriminating analysis.

Purification of such a mixture exceeds the capabilities of the usual physical methods. In some cases, however, a "functional" purification, based on the affinity of the proper sequence for a complementary polypeptide or ligand, may be possible. Such fractionation is accomplished most easily if the receptor molecule is itself bound to a solid phase support. Dr. Kato, in our laboratory, has recently succeeded in purifying a heterogeneous partial sequence (residues 1-15) of ribonuclease S-peptide by passing the synthetic material through a column containing native S-protein bound to Sepharose.[14] Methods for applying this principle to synthetic nuclease-fragment P_2 are under investigation.

REFERENCES

1. P. Cuatrecasas, H. Taniuchi, and C. B. Anfinsen, Brookhaven Symp. Biol. , in press.

2. H. Taniuchi, C. B. Anfinsen, and A. Sodja, Proc. Nat. Acad. Sci. U.S. , 58, 1235 (1967).

3. H. Taniuchi and C. B. Anfinsen, J. Biol. Chem. , 243 4779 (1968).

4. R. B. Merrifield, Science, 150, 178 (1965).

5. S. Sakakibara, Y. Shimonishi, Y. Kishida, M. Okada, and H. Sugihara, Bull. Chem. Soc. Japan, 40, 2164 (1967).

6. J. Lenard and A. Robinson, J. Am. Chem. Soc. , 89, 181 (1967).

7. A. Yaron and S. Schlossman, Biochem. , 7, 2673 (1968).

8. H. A. Sober, in Polyamino Acids, Polypeptides and Proteins, (M. A. Stahmann, ed.), University of Wisconsin Press, Madison, Wisconsin (1962).

9. H. Taniuchi, personal communication.

10. W. R. Gray in Methods in Enzymology, vol. XI, (C. H. W. Hirs, ed.) Academic Press, New York, 1968, p. 139.

11. K. Inouye and H. Otsuka, J. Org. Chem. , 27, 4236 (1962).

12. S. Shaltiel, Biochem. Biophys. Res. Comm., 29, 178 (1967).

13. S. Fuchs, R. Cuatrecasas, D. Ontjes, and C. B. Anfinsen, unpublished results.

14. I. Kato and C. B. Anfinsen, unpublished results.

ADDENDUM

Since completion of the work described above, an error has been found in the originally published primary amino acid sequence of nuclease. The residue at position 43 is glutamic acid rather than glutamine. Resynthesis of the fragment P_2 polypeptide with the correct sequence has yielded a product with at least 100 times the biological activity of the incorrect sequence[1]. It appears that the glutamic acid in position 43 may play a role in the binding or catalysis of substrate.

1. D. A. Ontjes and C. B. Anfinsen, Proc. Nat. Acad. Sci., in press.

NEW RESULTS IN THE SOLID PHASE METHOD
FOR THE SYNTHESIS OF PEPTIDES

Ernest Bayer

Department of Chemistry
University of Houston, Houston, Texas

It seems to be interesting to discuss the question to which molecular weight of peptides, at the present, Merrifield's solid phase method[1-3] can theoretically be scaled up.

The primary advantage of the solid phase method is that it avoids tedious and time consuming purification procedures of the intermediate products. The most valuable product of the reaction remains always on the resin and is not subject to losses. The excess of reagents and reaction side products, which are not bound to the resin are simply filtered off. The other advantage is that the growing peptide chain always functions as protecting group for the carboxylic end. The latter advantage shares the solid phase method with every stepwise synthesis, but not with fragment techniques.

The limitations of the solid phase method are that there is no intermediate purification of impurities, which are connected with the resin during the course of the synthesis, and which can only be eliminated at the very end of the syn- thesis after the peptide has been cleaved from the resin.

If these impurities are very similar to the desired end product in respect to molecular weight and structure the separation can be very difficult or even impossible.

There may be several types of such impurifying peptides:

1) damaged peptides, where principally the sequence of amino acids is in the right order which, however, contain damaged amino acids. This can especially be the case with trifunctional amino acids as some protecting groups may not resist the repeated use of the reagents, such as acids. Tryptophane and lysine are examples of such amino acid residues where safe protecting groups are still missing which carry a synthesis over 10 - 20 steps. But such difficulties are not necessarily present in the sequence of all peptides, and more suitable protecting groups will be found so that these special problems can be overcome.

2) Optical inhomogeneous peptides may be formed. Though the synthesis of fully biologically active oxytocin[4-6] excludes that racemization is extremely high, it had to be carefully investigated.

3) Truncated sequences which may occur when the growth of the peptide chain is interrupted.

4) Failure sequences which originate from truncated sequences by the coupling of amino acids, whereby one or more amino acids are left out.

The possibilities mentioned in 3) and 4) must in principle occur in every application of the solid phase method as the yield in each coupling step is not 100% and the difference between the yield and 100% has to remain on the resin as truncated sequence, which may again react in later coupling steps and cause the formation of failure sequences. The amount of impurifying peptides decreases with increasing yields, and consequently a high yield in each coupling step is essential for solid phase synthesis. The formation of failure sequences will produce more peptides whose molecular weight is similar to that of the desired peptide. Therefore the formation of failure sequences is less favorable than that of truncated sequences. FIG. 1 and 2 demonstrate the amount of both truncated and failure sequences for the case of 90% and 99% yield in each coupling step for the synthesis of a dodecapeptide. It is evident that in the case of truncated sequences the peptides are equally distributed over the whole scale of molecular weight, whereas in the case of failure peptides there is an enrichment of higher peptides. It is also evident that the ratio of the desired dodecapeptide and contaminating undecapeptides is 10 times less in the case of any 90% yield than in the case of 99% yield.

It follows from these considerations that it is impossible to purify a 100-peptide whenever failure sequences occur. Purification, nevertheless, should still be possible

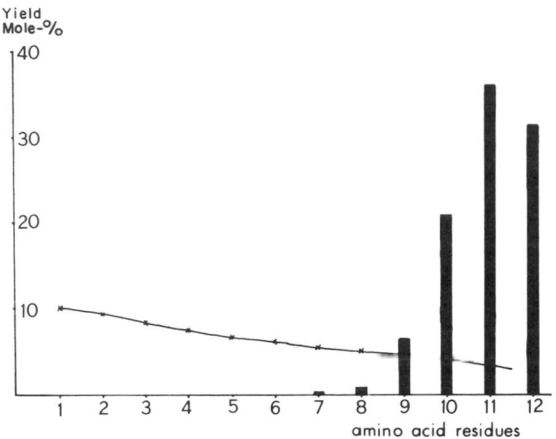

FIG. 1

Distribution of failure peptides in the synthesis of a
dodecapeptide with 90% yield in each coupling step;
Inclined line; formation exclusively of truncated sequences.
Columns: formation of failure sequences.

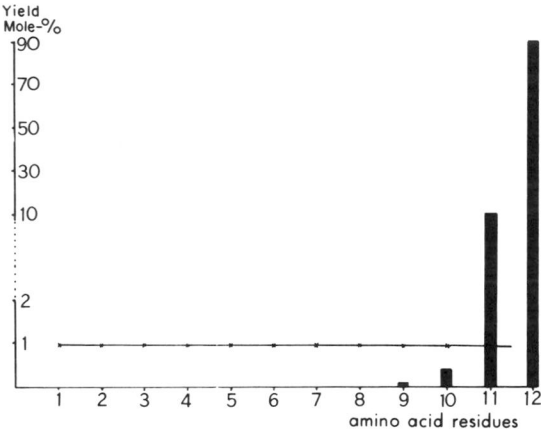

FIG. 2

Distribution of failure peptides in the synthesis of a
dodecapeptide with 99% yield in each coupling step.
Horizontal line: formation exclusively of truncated sequences.
Columns: formation of failure sequences.

when truncated sequences occur. For in the latter case there would only be one impurifying 99-peptide, whereas with the occurance of failure sequences 99 99-peptides are to be expected. Even with 99% yield in every coupling step a 100-peptide will only be synthesized with approximately 50% overall yield, and the 99 contaminating 99-peptides will amount approximately to 30% and cannot safely be separated from the desired product with the present methods of separation. When only truncated sequences are formed the single 99-peptide will amount to 1%. This and likewise the peptides of smaller size could be separated.

Therefore, it was desirable to conduct an experimental investigation into the question whether only truncated sequences or also, in addition to them, failure sequences will occur when the solid phase method is applied The purpose of the investigation was to predict up to which size polypeptides can still be successfully synthesized by this method.

In order to check the failure sequences it is of course necessary to investigate the product as it is cleaved from the resin prior to any purification procedure. For the sequence analysis a combination of mass spectrometry with gas chromatography and liquid chromatography has been used[7-10]. Any growth of wrong sequences in the first 5 - 7 coupling steps has additionally been watched by submitting the product of synthesis directly to mass spectrometry.

A mass spectrum of the pentapeptide Asn-cys (Bzl)-pro-leu-

gly which was obtained during the synthesis of ser[4]-oxytocin

and which was converted to the TFA-peptide methylester is

shown in FIG. 3 after it was split off the resin.   There is

no indication of a wrong sequence.   The mass spectrum

follows the generally accepted interpretation of fragments[8-11].

Additional evidence for the fact that there is no detectable

content of failure sequence in the case of the solid phase

synthesis of oxytocin is obtained from the sequence analysis

of the final product.   After the product was split off the

resin it was partially hydrolyzed by hydrochloric acid for

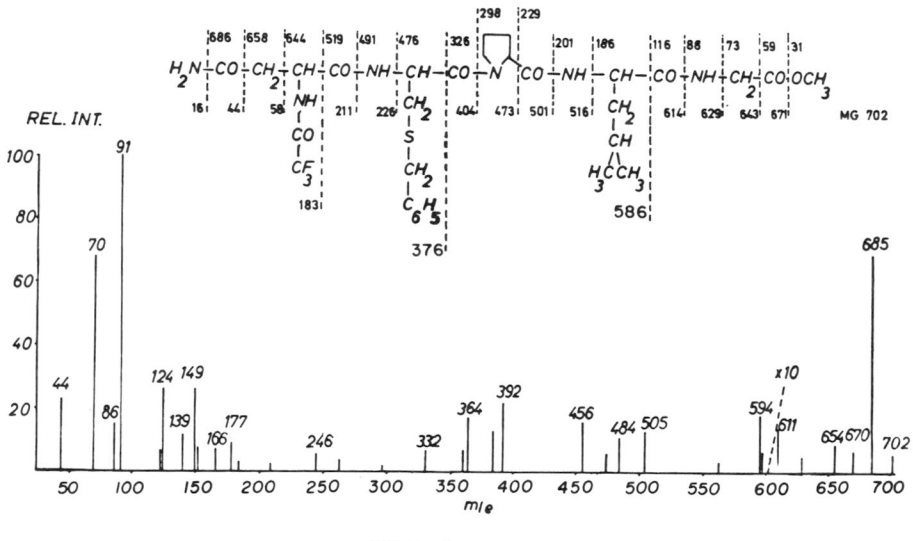

FIG. 3

Mass spectrum of TFA-ASN-CYS(BZL)-PRO-LEU-GLY-OME

LKB 9000 mass spectrometer, direct inlet system 200°C
50 eV, ion source 290°C.

72 hours at 37°C. The smaller peptides are separated by gas chromatography (FIG. 4), and the larger ones by liquid chromatography (FIG. 5). When a single peak emerges from the chromatographic column several mass spectra are taken in order to detect whether a peak represents one or more substances. All peptides which are detected and which are

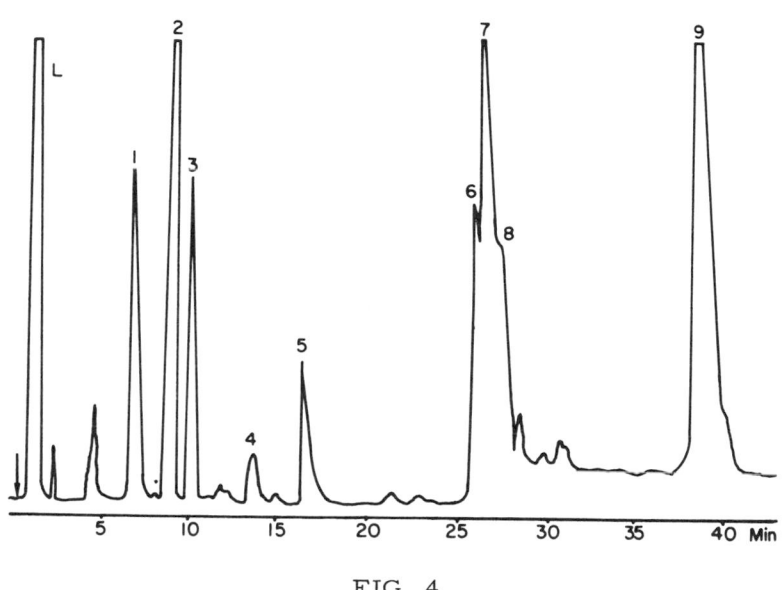

FIG. 4

Gas - chromatogram of the trifluoroacetylated peptide methylester of the hydrolysate of ser⁴-oxytocin split off the resin.

LKB 9000 (Stockholm). Column: 5% SE30 on Chromosorb P 1. 5m and 0. 3 cm∅. Temperature programmed from 130°, 3°/min. to 250°, detector: total ion current; ion source: 290°C; separator 285°C; inlet: 300°C.

L	solvent	5	TFA-ser-asp-(OMe)2
1	TFA-leu-gly-OMe	6	TFA-pro-leu-gly-OMe
2	TFA-cys(Bzl)-OMe	7	TFA-cys(Bzl)-pro-OMe
3	TFA-pro-leu-OMe	8	TFA-tyr-ile-OMe
4	TFA-ile-ser-OMe	9	TFA-cys(Bzl)-pro-leu-OMe

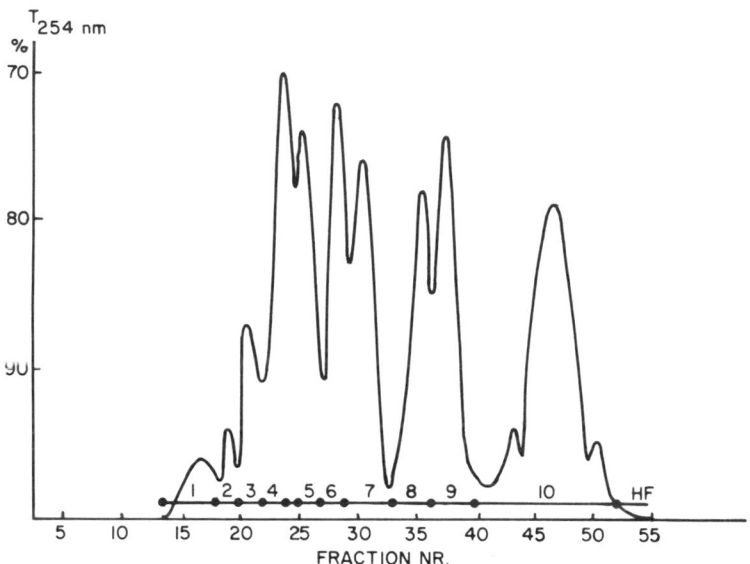

FIG. 5

Separation of Cys(Bzl)-ser^4-oxytocin hydrolysate.
Sephadex G 15 partition chromatography column:
120 x 1.5 cm. Solvent: butanol: propanol: acetic acid:
water (600 : 300 : 10.25 : 890 V/V).
Substances: 1 Asp-cys(Bzl)-pro-leu, 2 Asp-cys(Bzl)-
pro-leu, 3 cys(Bzl)-tyr-ile, 4 3, 5 cys(Bzl)-pro-leu,
6 5, 7 cys(Bzl)-pro-leu-gly, 8 cys(Bzl)-tyr,
9 cys(Bzl)-pro, 10 ser-asp-cys(Bzl), tyr-ile, pro-leu.

shown in Table 1 are in agreement with the right sequence

of the peptide. There is no failure sequence detectable

within the limits of the sensitivity of the applied method

which is about 1%. As the synthesis of ser^4-oxytocin pro-

ceeded with about 99% yield in each coupling step this was

to be expected. Therefore we had to increase the amount

of detectable failure sequences by synthesizing peptides where

repeatedly the same sequences are present.

TABLE 1

Sequence of ser^4-oxytocin and peptides identified after hydrolysis.

Cys(Bzl) - tyr - ile - ser - asn - cys(Bzl) - pro - leu - gly

Cys(Bzl) - tyr - ile

Cys(Bzl) - tyr

      Tyr - ile

        Ile - ser

          Ser - asp

          Ser - asp - cys(Bzl)

            Asp - cys(Bzl) - pro - leu

              Cys(Bzl) - pro

              Cys(Bzl) - pro - leu

              Cys(Bzl) - pro - leu - gly

                  Pro - leu

                  Pro - leu - gly

                    Leu - gly

The dodecapeptides (leu-ala -)$_5$ - leu - ala and (ala - phe -)$_5$-ala-phe have been synthesized[12]. When in these peptides failure sequences occur, dipeptides with two identical amino acids should be expected after acid hydrolysis. Due to the repetition of the sequence any failure in a couping step will add up six times, and then it should be clearly detectable with the combined method of gas chromatography - mass spectrometry down to less than 0. 3% failure in one coupling step.

After the (leu - ala -)$_5$-leu - ala has been split off the resin and after partial hydrolysis and preparation of the N-trifluoroacetyl-esters of the dipeptides, the separation and identification prove that among the dipeptides 2. 6% leu - leu and 1. 35% ala - ala are present which indicate the failure sequences, and that 96% of leu - ala and ala - leu are present which indicate the right sequences. In the region of tri - and tetrapeptides no wrong sequence was detected. Table 2 summarizes the results for (leu - ala-)$_5$- leu - ala and (ala - phe -)$_5$ - ala - phe. In the latter case no ala - ala was detected, whereas phe - phe was present in the amount of 9. 3% indicating that during this synthesis the coupling of the alanine had smaller yields.

TABLE 2

Amount of dipeptides found by gas chromatography and mass spectrometry after acid hydrolysis of dodecapeptides.

Hydrolysis of (Leu - ala)$_6$		Hydrolysis of (Ala - phe)$_6$	
Peptide	Amount %	Peptide	Amount %
Ala - ala	1. 35	Ala - ala	negative
Leu - ala	67. 50	Phe - ala	39. 7
Ala - leu	28. 53	Ala - phe	51. 0
Leu - leu	2. 62	Phe - phe	9. 3

NEW RESULTS IN THE SOLID PHASE METHOD

These results clearly prove that failure sequences
occur in the solid phase method. However, in a properly
conducted synthesis they are low, and polypeptides up to
60 - 80 amino acid residues can certainly be synthesized.
However, the purification of the end product is more important. In fact, the dodecapeptides (leu - ala)$_6$ and (ala - phe)$_6$
can be purified so that no failure sequence can be detected
anymore.

As we found that the solid phase method is restricted
by the presence of failure sequences, any additional mistake
in a synthesis creating other byproducts, which are difficult
to separate, will further lower the upper limit of a successful application of the solid phase method. Among the method-
ological mistakes the question whether racemization occurs
is therefore important. This has been investigated[13] on
several peptides by means of the method which was developed
by Gil-Av[14]. In all cases which had been investigated it
could be demonstrated that the content of D-amino acids in
the mixtures obtained after hydrolysis does not exceed 1%.
As such an amount of D-amino acids is always found during
the hydrolysis conditions of stereo homogeneous peptides
it is indicated that there is no racemization at all to be
detected. FIG. 6 shows the separation of D-amino acids
and L-amino acids which are obtained after acid hydrolysis
of (leu - ala -)$_5$ - leu - ala.

109

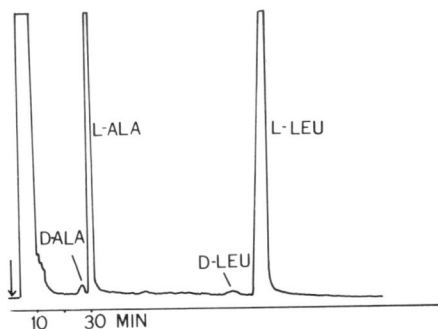

FIG. 6

Gas-chromatographic test for D-amino acids (12) hydrolysate
(concentr. HCl, 100°C, 25 hrs. i. V.) of (L-leu-L-ala)$_6$.
Column: 120m steel capillaries (0.25 mm Ø) impregnated
with TFA-L-val-L-val-cyclohexylester. Separation
temperature: 110°C. Carrier gas: helium 30 psi.
Detector: FID 300°C. Inlet temperature 300°C.

Therefore racemization does not cause any additional
restriction in the solid phase method. Thus we can conclude
from the characteristics of the method itself that it is restricted to polypeptides up to 60 - 80 amino acid residues,
whenever it is possible to solve individual difficulties which
may arise from special amino acids. At the present state
of separation techniques it seems to be impossible to apply
the solid phase methods for the synthesis of proteins. This
is due to the fact that a reliable yield in the coupling steps
which is greater than 99% has not yet been achieved, and
the presence of failure peptides imposes difficult separation
problems. It has been shown in the case of the synthesis of
the amino acid sequence of ferredoxin[15] with 55 amino acid

residues that the yield in the couping is not decreasing with the increasing number of amino acid residues.

ACKNOWLEDGMENT

We are grateful to the Robert A. Welch Foundation for the support of these investigations.

REFERENCES

1. R. B. Merrifield, J. Am. Chem. Soc., 85, 2749 (1963); ibid., 86, 304 (1968).

2. R. B. Merrifield, Biochemistry, 3, 1385 (1964).

3. R. B. Merrifield, Science, 150, 178 (1965).

4. E. Bayer and H. Hagenmaier, Tetrahedron Letters, 17, 2037 (1968).

5. D. T. Manning, J. Am. Chem. Soc., 90, 1348 (1968).

6. H. C. Beyermann, Rec. trav. chim. Pays-Bas, 87, 257 (1968).

7, F. Weygand, A. Prox, E. C. Jorgensen, R. Axen, and P. Kirchner, Z. Naturforsch., 18b, 93 (1963).

8. F. Weygand, A. Prox, H. H. Fessel, and K. Kunsun, Z. Naturforsch., 20b, 1169 (1965).

9. E. Bayer, W. Koenig, H. Hagenmaier, and H. Pauschmann, Z. Analyt. Chem., in press.

10. E. Stenhagen, Z. Analyt. Chem., 181, 462 (1961).

11. E. Bayer, W. Koenig, G. Jung, Z. Naturforsch, 22b, 924 (1967).

12. E. Bayer, H. Hagenmaier, and W. Koenig, unpublished data.

ERNEST BAYER

13. E. Bayer, E. Gil-Av, W. Koenig, S. Nakaparksin, unpublished data.

14. E. Gil-Av, B. Feibush, and R. Charles-Sigler, Tetrahedron Letters, 10, 1009 (1966).

15. E. Bayer, G. Jung, and H. Hagenmaier, Tetrahedron 24, 4853 (1968).

STRUCTURE-ACTION RELATIONSHIPS IN ANGIOTENSIN II: SOME NEW DATA ON THE CONTRIBUTION OF ASPARTIC ACID AND ARGININE TO THE BIOLOGICAL ACTIVITY

E. C. Jorgensen, G. C. Windridge, W. Patton
Department of Pharmaceutical Chemistry
School of Pharmacy

and

T. C. Lee
Department of Physiology, School of Medicine
University of California
San Francisco, California

The existence of a new substance which mediated the pressor response of renin was demonstrated in 1940 by Page and Helmer[1] and concurrently by Braun-Menendex and co-workers[2]. During the sixteen years following their observations, several groups worked on the difficult task of purifying this substance and establishing its structure. It was found that there are two forms of what we now know as angiotensin. The enzyme, renin, acts upon a substrate occurring in the α_2-globulin fraction in plasma to liberate the decapeptide, angiotensin I, with the sequence, Asp-Arg-Val-Tyr-Ile-His-Pro-Phe-His-Leu in horses[3], pigs[4] and humans[5]. In the cow, the isoleucine is replaced by valine[6]. This decapeptide has very little biological activity in isolated muscle assays but it is rapidly converted in vivo to the biologically active

113

angiotensin II by removal of the C-terminal dipeptide. This

conversion apparently occurs mainly in the lungs[7].

The first synthesis of angiotensin II was reported by

Bumpus, Schwartz and Page in 1957[8]. At the same time

Rittel and co-workers[9] synthesized the first analog of bovine

angiotensin II in which the N-terminal aspartic acid was

replaced by asparagine. Much of the impetus for the early

work on angiotensin was based upon the belief that it might

be a key factor in hypertension. Attempts to establish a

connection between angiotensin and hypertension have been

mostly unsuccessful; however, angiotensin is apparently

the most important chemical stimulus for the release of

aldosterone from the adrenal cortex and therefore plays an

important role in electrolyte balance.

One route to greater understanding of the physiological

and possible pathological roles of angiotensin would be

through studying the effects of antagonists. The same rationale

has been applied to the search for an antagonist as that used

for simpler molecules; namely a systematic study of the rela-

tionships between chemical structure and biological activity

followed by modification of those groups which appear to be

important in eliciting the biological response. Numerous

studies have provided much information on the relative

importance of the individual amino acid residues in angio-

tensin II[10]. Both the carboxyl group and the aromatic ring

of phenylalanine are important for activity although it is
not yet clear to what extent the aromatic ring may be
modified.

Proline is believed to be essential, perhaps by virtue
of its effect on conformation; however, data is too limited
at present.

Histidine is also believed to play an important role but
its exact nature is not clear.

The isoleucine or valine in position five is not essential although β-branching does give optimum activity.

The phenolic hydroxyl of tyrosine seems to be quite
important though not essential.

The valine in position three is not important.

The first two amino acids, aspartic acid and arginine,
appear to be quite unimportant despite their high degree of
functionality. The compounds shown in Table 1 clearly
illustrate that the functional groups of aspartic acid may
be modified or even eliminated without significant loss in
activity.

Table 2 shows some of the analogs of angiotensin II in
which arginine has been replaced by structurally related
amino acids.

It appears that the guanidine group of arginine is more
important than the functional groups of aspartic acid since
less variation can be tolerated; however, considerable

TABLE 1. Angiotensins Modified in Position 1[10]

Peptide	Pressor Activity
Asp-Arg-Val-Tyr-Val-His-Pro-Phe	100%
D-Asp-Arg-Val-Tyr-Val-His-Pro-Phe	100%
Asn-Arg-Val-Tyr-Val-His-Pro-Phe	100%
Gly-Arg-Val-Tyr-Val-His-Pro-Phe	50%
desamino-Asp-Arg-Val-Tyr-Val-His-Pro-Phe	50%
Arg-Val-Tyr-Val-His-Pro-Phe	50%

TABLE 2. Angiotensins Modified in Position 2[10]

Peptide	Pressor Activity
Asp-Arg-Val-Tyr-Val-His-Pro-Phe	100%
Asp-Orn-Val-Tyr-Val-His-Pro-Phe	20%
Asp-Arg(NO_2)-Val-Tyr-Val-His-Pro-Phe	50%
Asn-D-Arg-Val-Tyr-Ile-His-Pro-Phe	5%
Asn-Cit- Val- Tyr-Ile-His-Pro-Phe	2%
Val-Tyr-Val-His-Pro-Phe	<1%

variation can be made without drastically curtailing activity.

It has been suggested[11] that the amino terminal dipeptide of angiotensin II (Asp-Arg-) might stabilize some biologically important conformation of the entire molecule by

involvement of the amide groups of the extended peptide
chain. A helical conformation with stabilizing hydrogen
bonds involving the amide groups contributed by both arginine
and aspartic acid was visualized[12]. More recent physical[13, 14]
and biological[15] data indicates that the helical model is
unlikely, although the possibility exists that the extended
peptide chain may stabilize some other biologically important conformation.

To further define the relationships between chemical
structure and biological activity, additional studies on the
roles of aspartic acid and arginine were undertaken. Studies
to date had not yet explained the dramatic enhancement in
activity imparted to the relatively inactive, but structurally
specific hexapeptide, Val-Tyr-Ile-His-Pro-Phe, by the
addition of amino acid residues to the amino end. Our first
approach was to study the influence of the peptide backbone.
The simplest system for studying the effects of extension of
the basic hexapeptide structure to an octapeptide is

Gly^1-Gly^2-angiotensin II.

The first attempt at preparing Gly^1-Gly^2-angiotensin II
followed a classical fragment condensation[16]; however due
to inadequate temperature control during the reaction of
Z-Val-Tyr-N_3 with Ile-His-Pro-Phe OBzl(NO_2) the final
octapeptide contained only 36% of the expected amount of

tyrosine. This was presumably due to a Curtius rearrangement of the azide to the isocyanate resulting in an aza-
peptide[17]. Despite this apparent contamination of the
desired peptide with the aza-peptide, this preparation had
5% the pressor activity of angiotensin II. In order to prepare
a pure sample of the desired peptide and related analogs,
Merrifield's solid phase method[18] of synthesis was used.
The hexapeptide, Val-Tyr(Bzl)-Ile-His(Bzl)-Pro-Phe-Resin,
was prepared using four equivalents of BOC-amino acid and
DCCl in dichloromethane. A small sample was cleaved from
the resin using HBr in trifluoroacetic acid after each step
and tested by high voltage paper electrophoresis at pH 1.85
for the presence of unacylated amino component. Small
amounts (<5%) of the dipeptide and tripeptide were found
after the benzylhistidine and isoleucine steps. Acetylation
was used after each coupling in order to simplify purification
of the final peptide. The two glycines were incorporated
without difficulty in one step using six equivalents of Z-Gly-
Gly and DCCl in dimethylformamide. After cleavage from
the resin with HBr in trifluoroacetic acid, the product was
hydrogenated over 10% Pd/charcoal for 72 hours at 45 psi
to remove the benzyl group from histidine. The product
was then purified by chromatography on sulfoethyl cellulose
using an ammonium acetate gradient. The product was
chromatographically and electrophoretically homogeneous

and gave the expected amino acid analysis. Its steric purity was established by aminopeptidase-M degradation since the glycyl-glycyl sequence is attacked very slowly by leucine amino peptidase. The octapeptide containing benzyl-histidine was purified by the same procedure.

Gly-Gly-Val-Tyr-Ile-His-Pro-Phe showed 16% of the pressor activity of angiotensin II when assayed in nephrecto-mized, pentolinium treated rats by the method of Boucher et al[19]. The benzylated derivative, Gly-Gly-Val-Tyr-Ile-His(Bzl)-Pro-Phe, had only about 0.2% activity, and no antagonistic activity. The low activity of the benzylated peptide may be ascribed to either a requirement for a free -NH group in the imidazole ring of histidine or to other effects such as steric, electronic or solubility.

The significant enhancement in activity shown by Gly-Gly-Val-Tyr-Ile-His-Pro-Phe (16%) over the hexa-peptide, Val-Tyr-Ile-His-Pro-Phe (<1%) is consistent with the idea of conformation stabilization. However, the enhancement in activity could also be due to the contribution of the terminal amino group. In order to distinguish between these two alternatives the terminal amino group was acetylated. The resulting compound, AcGly-Gly-Val-Tyr-Ile-His-Pro-Phe showed pressor activity of 0.4 % which is in the same activity range as the hexapeptide, Val-Tyr-Ile-His-Pro-Phe. No antagonistic activity was

119

found. From this we conclude that in the absence of functional groups, the peptide backbone of the first two residues contributes nothing to the biological activity. However, the backbone might contribute a useful stabilizing influence when an essential functional group is present.

It is tempting to conclude from the activity of Gly-Gly-Val-Tyr-Ile-His-Pro-Phe that this constitutes good evidence that the functional group and indeed the entire side chain of the arginine in position two can be eliminated without drastically impairing the biological activity. However, spatial considerations indicate that the terminal amino group in Gly-Gly-Val-Tyr-Ile-His-Pro-Phe may function in place of either the terminal amino group or the side chain guanidine group of angiotensin II. FIG. 1 shows a simplified comparison of Gly-Gly-Val-Tyr-Ile-His-Pro-Phe with two heptapeptides studied by Havinga[20].

$$\overset{+}{\underset{\overset{\|}{NH_2}}{H_2N-C-NH-CH_2CH_2CH_2-}}\overset{\overset{+}{NH_3}}{\underset{\overset{\|}{O}}{CH-C}}-Val-Tyr-Ile-His-Pro-Phe$$

des-Asp^1-Ile^5-angiotensin II
Pressor Activity - 15%

$$\overset{+}{H_3N-CH_2CH_2CH_2-}\overset{\overset{+}{NH_3}}{\underset{\overset{\|}{O}}{CH-C}}-Val-Tyr-Ile-His-Pro-Phe$$

des-Asp^1-Orn^2-Ile^5-angiotensin II
Pressor Activity - 3%

$$\overset{+}{H_3N-CH_2-}\overset{\overset{O}{\|}}{C-NH-CH_2}-\overset{\|}{\underset{O}{C}}-Val-Tyr-Ile-His-Pro-Phe$$

Gly^1-Gly^2-Ile^5-angiotensin II
Pressor Activity - 16%

FIG. 1

120

It is apparent that the distance of the terminal functional group from the valine nitrogen is approximately the same in each case. Measurements on Corey-Pauling-Koltun models show that this distance is essentially identical for the fully extended forms of the diglycyl peptide and the ornithyl peptide, although glycylglycine has less rotational freedom because of the steric restraint imposed by the planarity of its amide bond. It is therefore possible that glycylglycine may be acting as an analog of arginine. For this reason, the activity of Gly-Gly-Val-Tyr-Ile-His-Pro-Phe does not eliminate the arginine side chain as an essential group.

Table 3 shows some other heptapeptides prepared by Havinga and co-workers[20,21]. In all cases studied the

TABLE 3

Heptapeptide Analogs of Angiotensin II[20,21]

Peptide	Pressor Activity
L-Arg-Val-Tyr-Ile-His-Pro-Phe	15%
D-Arg-Val-Tyr-Ile-His-Pro-Phe	20-30%
desamino-Arg-Val-Tyr-Ile-His-Pro-Phe	38%
L-Arg(NO_2)-Val-Tyr-Ile-His-Pro-Phe	1.5%
D-Arg(NO_2^-)-Val-Tyr-Ile-His-Pro-Phe	4.5%
desamino-Arg(NO_2^-)-Val-Tyr-Ile-His-Pro-Phe	7.5%
L-Orn-Val-Tyr-Ile-His-Pro-Phe	3%
D-Orn-Val-Tyr-Ile-His-Pro-Phe	23%
L-Cit-Val-Tyr-Ile-His-Pro-Phe	0.5%
D-Cit-Val-Tyr-Ile-His-Pro-Phe	11%
6-$(CH_3)_3N^+$-L-Nle-Val-Tyr-Ile-His-Pro-Phe	0.3%
6-$(CH_3)_3N^+$-Cap-Val-Tyr-Ile-His-Pro-Phe	1.5%

D-isomer was found to be more active than the L-isomer.
Limited data showed that the desamino compounds were
even more active. This was attributed by Havinga to an
unfavorable effect being exerted by the free N-terminal
a -amino group in the heptapeptides which is more pronounced
in the L-isomer and obviously absent in the desamino compound. It appears from our results that Gly-Gly-Val-Tyr-
Ile-His-Pro-Phe (16%) is a little less active than D-Orn-Val-
Tyr-Ile-His-Pro-Phe (23%). If Havinga's explanation is
correct and if our peptide is mimicking a heptapeptide then
we would expect Gly-Gly-Val-Tyr-Ile-His-Pro-Phe to have
biological activity close to the as yet unknown heptapeptide,
desamino-Orn-Val-Tyr-Ile-His-Pro-Phe which Havinga has
predicted will have high activity. Since Gly-Gly-Val-Tyr-
Ile-His-Pro-Phe is actually less potent than the D-ornithine
heptapeptide this is not in good agreement with this idea.
The acetylated peptide, AcGly-Gly-Val-Tyr-Ile-His-Pro-
Phe, on the other hand should have biological activity in
the same range as D-Cit-Val-Tyr-Ile-His-Pro-Phe since
both represent peptides in which the only functional group
at the amino end of the molecule is acylated. Since it is
much less active, this may be interpreted, in contrast
to the conclusions of Havinga, as indicating a positive
influence by the D-a -amino group in the heptapeptide.

There is some reason to question Havinga's theory.

STRUCTURE-ACTION RELATIONSHIPS IN ANGIOTENSIN II

The most dramatic difference between L, D and desamino heptapeptides is in arginine itself but other workers[22, 23] have found much higher activity from the L-arginine heptapeptide. Potentially the most interesting desamino compounds are desamino-Orn-Val-Tyr-Ile-His-Pro-Phe and desamino-Cit-Val-Tyr-Ile-His-Pro-Phe. If they prove to be less active than Havinga's theory would predict, this would constitute indirect evidence that the N-terminal free D-α-amino is exerting a positive effect. It is difficult to imagine that desamino-Cit-Val-Tyr-Ile-His-Pro-Phe will be at least five times as active as Asn-Cit-Val-Tyr-Ile-His-Pro-Phe though this is what one must predict from Havinga's theory. Indeed the difference between D-Cit-Val-Tyr-Ile-His-Pro-Phe (11%) and Asn-Cit-Val-Tyr-Ile-His-Pro-Phe (2%) is difficult to rationalize if the N-terminal α-amino group in the D-heptapeptides is exerting an unfavorable effect. It would appear more likely that in the D-heptapeptides, the α-amino group may be exerting a very favorable influence and may be primarily responsible for the activity in some cases, i.e., there may be some binding site for the heptapeptides which is not normally involved in the binding of the octapeptides. This appears to be an attractive alternate explanation for Havinga's data and it is one which we are presently investigating.

At present we can only conclude that the incorporation of a single basic group separated by five atoms from the valine nitrogen is sufficient to significantly enhance the activity of the hexapeptide.

ACKNOWLEDGMENTS

This investigation was supported in part by Research Grants AM 08066 and AM 06704 from the National Institute of Arthritis and Metabolic Diseases, and by Public Health Service Training Grant No. 5 TO1 GM 00728, from the National Institute of General Medical Sciences. We wish to thank Dr. W. F. Ganong for his interest and cooperation.

REFERENCES

1. I. H. Page and O. M. Helmer, J. Exp. Med., 71, 29 (1940).

2. E. Braun-Menendez, J. C. Fasciolo, L. F. Leloir, and J. M. Munoz, C. R. Soc. Biol., 133, 731 (1940).

3. L. T. Skeggs, K. E. Lentz, N. P. Shumway, and K. R. Woods, J. Exp. Med., 104, 193 (1956).

4. F. M. Bumpus, H. Schwartz, and I. H. Page, Circ., 17, 664 (1958).

5. K. Arakawa and M. Nakamura, Circ. Res., 21, Suppl. II, 101 (967).

6. D. F. Elliott and W. S. Peart, Nature, 177, 527 (1956).

7. K. K. F. Ng and J. R. Vane, Nature, 216, 762 (1964).

8. F. M. Bumpus, H. Schwartz, and I. H. Page, Science, 125, 3253 (1957).

9. W. Rittel, B. Iselin, H. Kappeler, B. Riniker, and R. Schwyzer, Helv. Chim. Acta, 40, 614 (1957).

10. (a) E. Schroder and K. Lubke, The Peptides, Chapter 1,
    Vol. 2, Academic Press, New York, 1966.
    (b) H. D. Law, Progr. Med. Chem., 4, 86 (1965).

11. K. Arakawa, R. R. Smeby, and F. M. Bumpus, J. Amer.
    Chem. Soc., 84, 1424 (1962).

12. R. R. Smeby, K. Arakawa, F. M. Bumpus, and M. M.
    Marsh, Biochim. Biophys. Acta, 58, 550 (1962).

13. T. B. Paiva, A. C. M. Paiva, and H. A. Scheraga,
    Biochemistry, 2, 1327 (1963).

14. L. C. Craig, Science, 144, 1093 (1964).

15. J. W. Constantine, Experentia, 20, 381 (1964).

16. K. Arakawa and F. M. Bumpus, J. Amer. Chem. Soc.,
    83, 728 (1961).

17. B. Riniker, Metab., 13, 1247 (1964).

18. R. B. Merrifield and G. R. Marshall, Biochemistry, 4,
    2394 (1965).

19. R. Boucher, R. Veyrat, J. deChamplain, and J. Genest,
    Can. Med. Assoc. J., 90, 194 (1964).

20. E. Havinga, C. Schattenkerk, G. Heymens Visser, and
    K. E. T. Kerling, Rec. Trav. Chim., 83, 672 (1964).

21. E. Havinga and C. Schattenkerk, Tetrahedron, Suppl.,
    8, 313 (1966).

22. R. Schwyzer, Helv. Chim. Acta, 44, 667 (1961).

23. F. M. Bumpus, P. A. Khairallah, K. Arakawa,
    I. H. Page, and R. R. Smeby, Biochim. Biophys. Acta,
    46, 38 (1961).

SYNTHESIS AND BIOLOGICAL PROPERTIES
OF ANGIOTENSIN II ANALOGS

F. M. Bumpus, R. R. Smeby, and P. A. Khairallah

Research Division
Cleveland Clinic Foundation, Cleveland, Ohio

The peptide, angiotensin, has been known for many years and has been suspected to play a major role in some forms of hypertension. More recently, however, since both renin and angiotensin have not always occurred in excessive quantities in chronic forms of experimental renal hypertension and in renal artery stenosis in humans, many feel that angiotensin plays a minor role in the disease. Many of us, though, feel that angiotensin, even though it is not found in large quantities in these forms of hypertension, still likely plays a major causative role in the development and maintenance of the disease. This great and prolonged interest in this polypeptide has led us to search for an angiotensin antagonist. To do this we first felt that it was necessary to study the peptide to determine which of the side groups were most important for its biologic activity.

Renin substrate protein has no myotropic activity itself while angiotensin I and the tetrapeptide substrate have low biologic activity. This suggested very early that the C-terminus of angiotensin II was biologically the more functional portion of this peptide. Removal of histidyl-leucine dipeptide seemed to be nature's way of activating the peptide. Freeing of the carboxyl group on the 8 position is necessary for activity, as borne out later by the fact that blocking this acid group by amide, ester or histidyl-leucine residue diminished or completely removed the ability of the peptide to contract smooth muscle.

Studies have now proceeded to the point where more than 100 analogs of angiotensin have been synthesized. The results still substantiate our early conclusions that side groups on amino acids 4 through 8 are the most important, while those of groups in positions 1, 2, and 3 are of much less significance.

It is interesting that aromatic groups in positions 4, 6, and 8 seem to be essential. Blocking or removing the hydroxyl group of tyrosine abolishes activity while adding an hydroxyl group on position 8 results in only minor reduction in biological activity. Removal of the five-membered ring of proline in position 7 destroys activity while the introduction of an hydroxyl group on this ring greatly reduced the pressor response to this peptide. It seems probable that the latter two substitutions are changing the conformational positions of the imidazole of histidine and the phenyl group of phenylalanine relative to one another. It has recently been suggested by Hoffmann and coworkers[1] that the stereo configuration of the imidazole rather than its basicity is the crucial feature of position 6. Schroeder and collaborators[2a, b] have shown that the 6-phenylalanine and 6-lysine derivatives are inactive. The former group have prepared an active 6-(β -pyrazolyl-3-alanine) angiotensin and have concluded that the stereo structure of five membered heterocyclic ring of histidine and not its charge is of crucial significance for high level angiotensin activity.

It is well established now that the guanido group of arginine in position 2 and the amino group of aspartic acid in position 1 are of less significance. Likewise, the carboxyl of aspartic acid can be converted to the amide and the resulting peptide retains full pressor activity. Even the total replacement of these two amino acids by a polymer made up of poly-O-acetyl serine will produce a large polypeptide which has 10% of the biologic activity of the parent angiotensin II.

Here we are going to discuss changes by the substitutions indicated by the arrows in FIG. 1[3a, b, c, d]. The phenyl group of phenylalanine in position 8 has been substituted with phenolic or phenylmethylether group. The side chain on this amino acid has also been lengthened by a methylene adjacent to the terminal carboxyl. In another substitution, the amino function of phenylalanine has been once removed by a methylene group

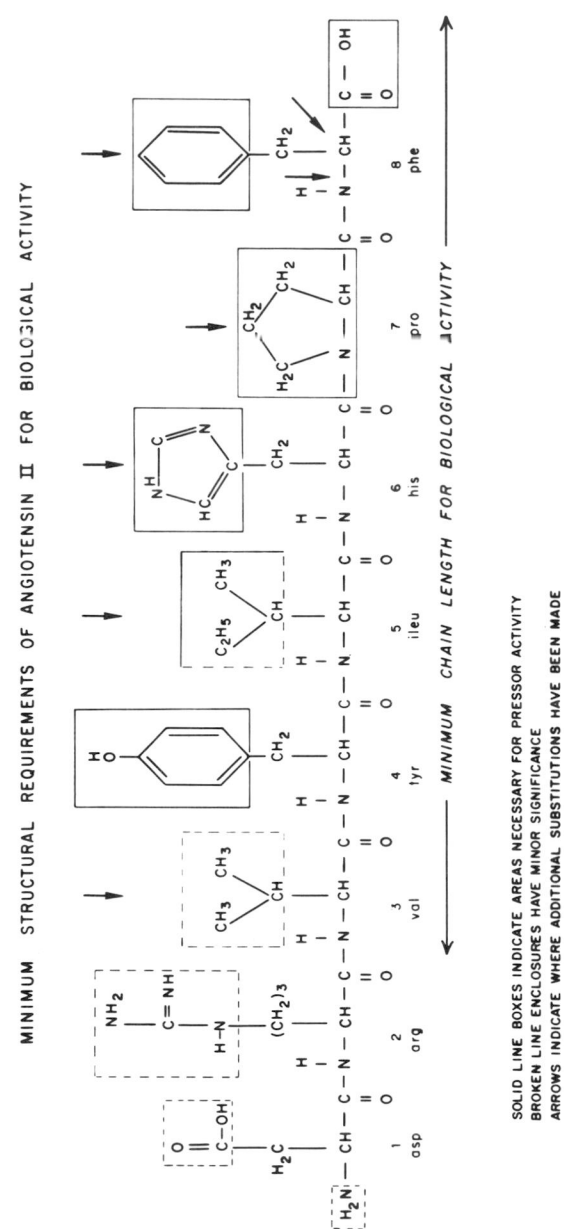

FIG. 1

from the rest of the molecule. Proline of position 7 has been substituted by hydroxyproline and the imidazole of histidine has been substituted by a thienyl group. The side chain of isoleucine in position 5 has been replaced by methyl group, and valine in position 3 has been substituted by a cyclic amino acid. Most peptides discussed here have been synthesized by the Merrifield solid-phase procedure. When using this method to synthesize a peptide of this size, we found that it is more convenient to complete a pilot synthesis and remove the peptide from the polymer before any analyses were performed. Corrections can then be made for the final synthesis. Preliminary analyses consisted of paper electrophoresis, usually in an acid medium, at pH 1.9, by paper chromatography or thin layer chromatography using butanol:acetic:water or butanol:acetic acid:water:pyridine solvent system. When electrophoresis yielded good resolution, we found that the peptides could be purified on CM cellulose or CM Sephadex using an acetic acid gradient elution system. When the chromatography methods yielded the better resolution, peptides were purified on Sephadex G-25 using one of the solvent systems for elution. All angiotensin analogs were shown to be homogeneous by the methods in FIG. 2. All angiotensin analogs prepared by the solid-phase method, except 3-proline angiotensin II, were obtained in yields between 50 and 70% and were calculated on the amount

Selection of Purification Procedure	Type of Column Used
paper electrophoresis	CM-cellulose (Seph) acetic acid gradient elution
paper chromatography or TLC	BAW on Seph -G-25

Determination of Homogeneity

paper electrophoresis, paper and thin layer chromatography optical rotation, C, H, N analysis, amino acid analysis and enzymatic degradation.

FIG. 2

of amino acid on the polymer. The preliminary synthesis of

the 3-proline derivative yielded less than 10% of the octapep-

tide. It is difficult to understand why it was so difficult to

combine arginine to proline in the angiotensin series since

it has already been shown by Merrifield et al.[4] that this bond

could be formed without difficulty in the synthesis of bradykinin.

However, in this series even when an excess of arginine was

used, a small amount of heptapeptide, which did not contain

arginine, was obtained. This indicates clearly the unpredic-

tability of this method and shows the need for very careful

analysis of the peptide after synthesis. We are not implying

that the solid-phase method is not a useful method, but sug-

gesting that we should not limit ourselves to any particular

method of peptide synthesis at present. Each method has

limitations and should be chosen carefully for each peptide to be synthesized.

Some investigators tend to overlook the metabolic breakdown of polypeptides when comparing analogs for their biological activity. Angiotensin is rapidly destroyed by plasma and tissue enzymes[5]. The metabolic breakdown of angiotensin by plasma has been well worked out as shown in FIG. 3. The major metabolism in plasma is that catalyzed by angiotensinase A, an amino peptidase activated by calcium and inhibited by EDTA. This enzyme is apparently the same as that isolated by Glenner et al.[6] from kidney tissue and called amino peptidase A. Two aminopeptidase angiotensinases occur in plasma. One cleaves aspartic acid from the N-terminus while the other removes asparagine[7]. An endopeptidase which converts angiotensin into two tetrapeptides has been reported[8]. This enzyme is similar to chymotrypsin in that it is inhibited by DFP and cleaves peptides at the carboxyl end of aromatic amino acids, but has a different pH optimum than does chymotrypsin. Since the main breakdown pathway for angiotensin is via an aminopeptidase, modifications on the amino end of angiotensin should greatly modify its rate of destruction. This has definitely been shown for β -aspartyl as well as the l-arginine and l-succinic acid angiotensin II. Indeed, the reported high activity of β -aspartyl angiotensin could

133

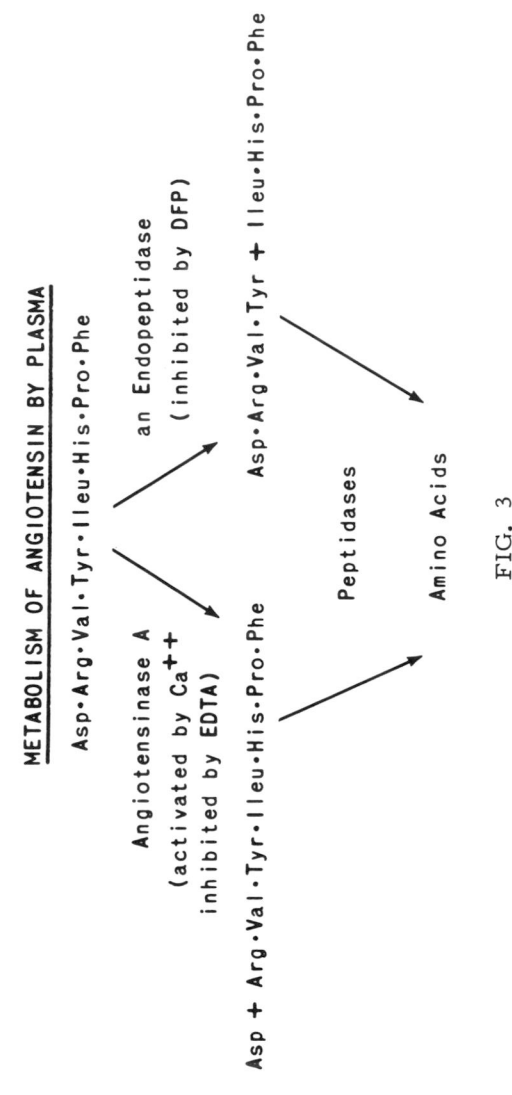

METABOLISM OF ANGIOTENSIN BY PLASMA

Asp•Arg•Val•Tyr•Ileu•His•Pro•Phe

Angiotensinase A
(activated by Ca++
inhibited by EDTA)

an Endopeptidase
(inhibited by DFP)

Asp + Arg•Val•Tyr•Ileu•His•Pro•Phe

Asp•Arg•Val•Tyr + Ileu•His•Pro•Phe

Peptidases

Amino Acids

FIG. 3

very well be due to its increased half life in the plasma.
Comparison of biological activities of peptides tested on
these very rapid degradations may very well account for
some of the discrepancies between the myotropic activity as
determined on isolated muscle preparations and the pressor
or depressor activity of peptide when injected in a living
animal.

Based upon our early work which showed that the aromatic
side groups of angiotensin and its carboxyl group were all
necessary for biological activity, we were able to construct
a model which had all of these groups upon one side that
might easily react with a receptor site[9]. The model was a
partial alpha-helix. We interpreted our ORD data to mean
that angiotensin had conformation. However, work by Paiva,
Paiva and Scheraga[10] suggested that angiotensin existed in
a random coil and could not possibly have enough energy in
hydrogen bonds to maintain this structure, our proposed
structure. We did not suggest that there was evidence for
the exclusive existence of an α -helix, but that angiotensin
did have preferred forms and the α -helical molecule constructed allowed all the important side groups to arrange
on the same side of the molecule. Craig and coworkers[11]
later showed that angiotensin dialyzed through a prepared
membrane more rapidly than did other peptides of similar
molecular weight. They, too, concluded that angiotensin

had a conformational character. We have prepared membranes similar to those prepared by Craig and compared the relative 50% escape times of numerous of the analogs of angiotensin against that for angiotensin. It was hoped that there might be some relationship between the observed escape times and the pressor activities of these various analogs. It is interesting to note in Table 1 that there is almost a three fold variation in the relative escape time for these analogs of angiotensin. However, we were rather disappointed to see that we could in no way correlate this with the pressor activity of these various peptides. This variation in escape time, however, does suggest a difference in these peptides which all had a very similar molecular weight and suggest that this variation must be due to conformation differences.

Some additional support for a hypothesis that the carboxyl end of angiotensin was extremely important for biological activity comes from some biological experiments related to the reversal of the phenomenon of tachyphylaxis[12]. In FIG. 4, demonstrated by the solid line is the phenomenon of reduced response following repeated injections of angiotensin. The broken line shows the reduced response obtained immediately even at very low concentrations of antiogensin by an artery taken from an animal that had received infusions of high levels of angiotensin for 1 hour.

TABLE 1

Peptide	Mol. Wt.	Relative 50% Escape Time	% Pressor Activity
Ileu^5-Angiotensin II	1047	1.00	100
Asp(NH$_2$)^1-val^5-Angiotensin II	1032	0.94	100
Gly^1-val^5-Angiotensin II	975	0.73	50
Ileu^1-ileu^5-Angiotensin II	1045	0.63	26
Arg^1-ileu^5-Angiotensin II	1103	0.56	33
Ala^4-ileu^5-Angiotensin II	966	0.74	0.31
Ala^5-Angiotensin II	1005	0.75	7.5
Ala^6-ileu^5-Angiotensin II	981	1.29	0.83
Ala^7-ileu^5-Angiotensin II	1020	0.65	0.83
(OH)pro^7-ileu^5-Angiotensin II	1063	0.86	9.8

It is assumed that the low response of the latter is due to the fact that the receptor sites are all filled with antiotensin or metabolites, thereby preventing additional response following injection. In FIG. 5 repeated injections of angiotensin are given for the first 6 injections at which time

137

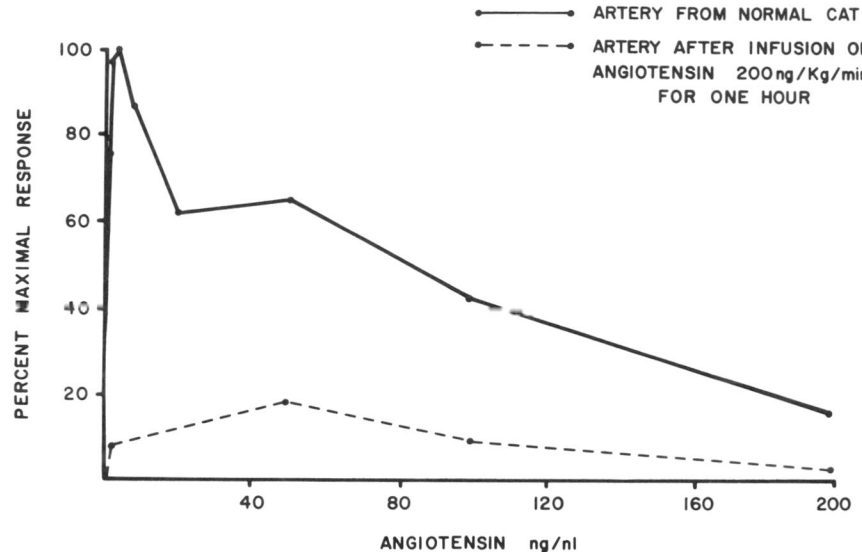

FIG. 4

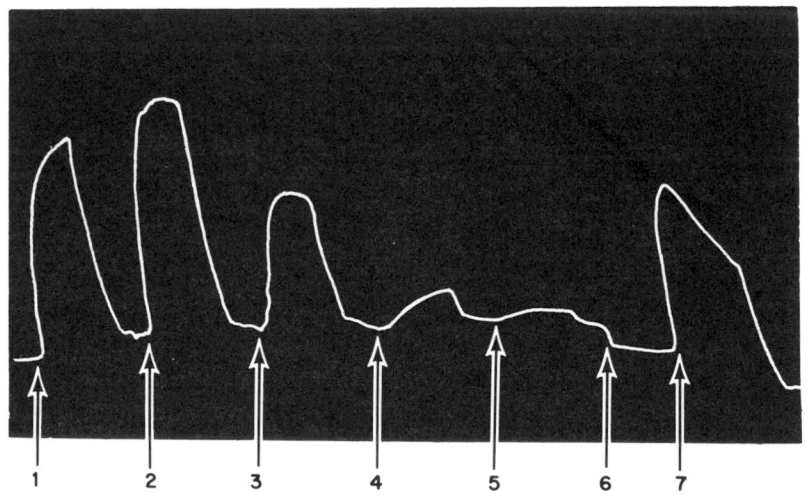

FIG. 5

repeated injection yield no response by an isolated muscle strip. Between points 6 and 7 a small sample of Dowex-50 resin, which has been pretreated with the same physiological salt solution which has been bathing the muscle, was added to the muscle bath. Here is noted that at injection 7 a complete reversal of the tachyphylaxis was obtained. A similar reversal was demonstrated by adding leucine amino-peptidase or specific aminopeptidases which are obtained in plasma, to the bath for a very brief time. The reversal of tachyphylaxis by these two aminopeptidases and by the resin has been interpreted as a removal of the peptide or its metabolites from the receptor site, thereby allowing additional angiotensin to react. We have found that car-boxypeptidase, which very rapidly destroys angiotensin in solution does not reverse this phenomenon. It seems then that the most plausible explanation for this phenomenon is that angiotensin must be coupled to its receptor site via its carboxyl end, leaving the amino end free to be acted upon by an aminopeptidase. Because of this observation and those data obtained from the optical rotatory dispersion and nmr measurements to be reported by Dr. Goodman in a later paper, we had decided to synthesize several peptide analogs with modifications at the C-terminus.

Replacement of the very rigid five membered ring in position 7 with that of a six membered nitrogen containing

ring as found in pipecolic acid should allow interpretation
with respect to the necessity of the cyclic structure in this
position. It was thought that the more flexible ring of
pipecolic acid should allow the peptide to go into a conformation similar to that obtained when alanine is in the 7 position.
L-Pipecolic acid was easily synthesized by reduction of
α -picolinic acid and resolved as its tartarate salt. Tartaric
acid was easily removed by passing the salt over an IR-45
resin yielding pipecolic acid as its hydrochloride salt which
was easily crystallized from methanol-acetone(FIG. 6).

Synthesis of L-Pipecolic Acid

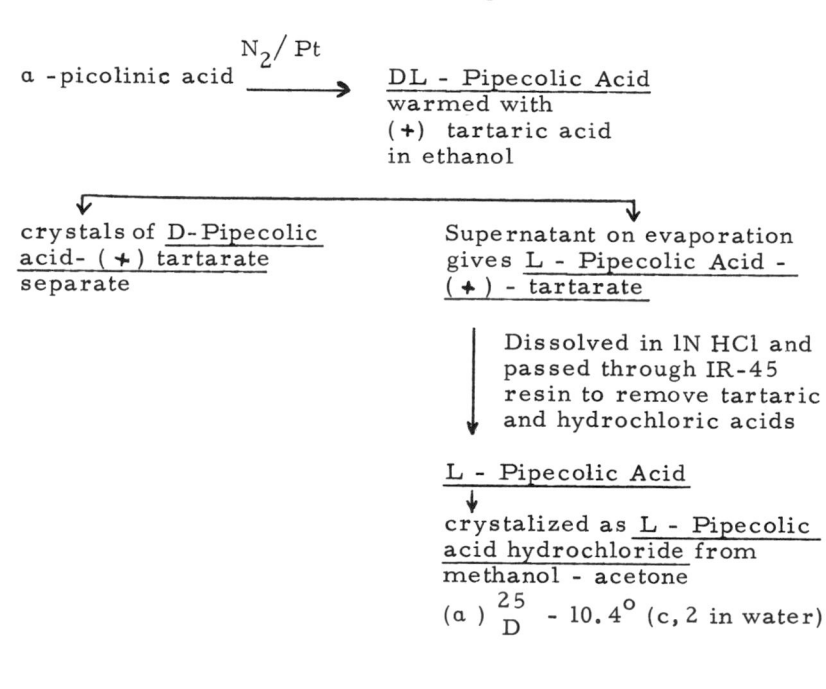

α -picolinic acid $\xrightarrow{N_2/Pt}$ DL - Pipecolic Acid
warmed with
(+) tartaric acid
in ethanol

crystals of D-Pipecolic
acid- (+) tartarate
separate

Supernatant on evaporation
gives L - Pipecolic Acid -
(+) - tartarate

Dissolved in 1N HCl and
passed through IR-45
resin to remove tartaric
and hydrochloric acids

L - Pipecolic Acid

crystalized as L - Pipecolic
acid hydrochloride from
methanol - acetone
$(\alpha)_D^{25}$ - 10.4° (c, 2 in water)

FIG. 6

To determine the importance of the position of the carboxyl group on amino acid number 8, we synthesized a butyric
acid derivative which removed the carboxyl from the amino
group by one methylene. This was easily accomplished by
converting carbobenzoxyphenylalanine to an acid chloride,
the azide, and by a Curtius rearrangement, L-3-amino-4-
phenyl butyric acid was obtained. The amino acid, 3-amino-
3' isobutyric acid represents a compound with both the phenyl
group and the carboxyl group one more methylene group
removed from the amino group of phenylalanine.

The D, L form of this amino acid was synthesized by
converting the formyl derivative to the chloro derivative
with PCl_5 and finally adding this to the sodio derivative
of 2-benzyl-diethylmalonate. Hydrolysis at high pressure
and at 175° in concentrated HCl yielded the D, L form of
this amino acid. We made no attempt, as yet to resolve
this substance (FIG. 7).

SYNTHESIS OF DL-3-AMINO-3'-PHENYL-ISOBUTYRIC ACID

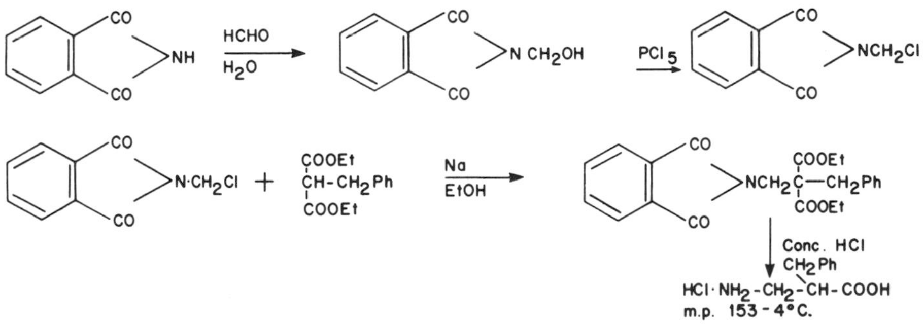

FIG. 7

The biological activities of some of these analogs are shown in Table 2. Isoleucine was substituted in the 1 position of angiotensin, since its side chain is somewhat similar

TABLE 2

1	2	3	4	5	6	7	8	Pressor Activity Vago-tomized Rat
Asp -	Arg -	Val -	Tyr -	Ile -	His -	Pro -	Phe	100
			(1-Asp, 5-Ile)-Angiotensin II					
Ile -	Arg -	Val -	Tyr -	Ile -	His -	Pro -	Phe	25
			(1-Ile, 5-Ile)-Angiotensin II					
Asp -	Arg -	Pro -	Tyr -	Ile -	His -	Pro -	Phe	40
			(3-Pro, 5-Ile)-Angiotensin II					
Asp -	Arg -	Val -	Tyr -	Ala -	His -	Pro -	Phe	7.5
			(5-Ala)-Angiotensin II					
Asp -	Arg -	Val -	Tyr -	Ile -	Ala -	Pro -	Phe	.83
			(5-Ile, 6-Ala)-Angiotensin II					
Asp -	Arg -	Val -	Tyr -	Ile -	TAla-	Pro -	Phe	1.0
			(5-Ile, 6-TAla)-Angiotensin II					
Asp -	Arg -	Val -	Tyr -	Ile -	His -	Pipe-	Phe	.18
			(5-Ile, 7-Pipecolic acid)-Angiotensin II					
Asp -	Arg -	Val -	Tyr -	Ile -	His -	Pro -	APB	10
			[5-Ile, 8-(3-amino, 4-phenyl-butyric acid)]-Angiotensin II					
Asp -	Arg -	Val -	Tyr -	Ile -	His -	Pro -	APIB	.1
			[5-Ile, 8-DL(3-amino-3'-phenyl-isobutyric acid)]-Angiotensin II					
Asp -	Arg -	Val -	Tyr -	Ile -	His -	Pro -	Tyr*	83
			(1-Asp, 5-Ile, 8-Tyr)-Angiotensin II					
Asp -	Arg -	Val -	Tyr -	Ile -	His -	Pro -	(OMe)Tyr	33
			(1-Asp, 5-Ile, 8(OMe)Tyr)-Angiotensin II					
Asp -	Arg -	Val -	Tyr -	Val -	His -	Pro -	(OMe)Tyr	33
			(1-Asp, 5-Val, 8(OMe)Tyr)-Angiotensin II					
Asp -	Arg -	Val -	(OMe)Tyr-Ile -		His -	Pro -	Phe	0.95
			(1-Asp, 4(OMe)Tyr, 5-Ile)-Angiotensin II					
Asp -	Arg -	Val -	(OMe)Tyr- Val-		His -	Pro -	Phe	0.93
			(1-Asp, 4(OMe)Tyr, 5-Val)-Angiotensin II					
Asp(NH₂)-	Arg -	Val -	(OMe)Tyr- Val-		His -	Pro -	Phe**	0.35
			(1-Asp(NH₂), 4(OMe)Tyr, 5-Val)-Angiotensin II					

* Schroeder and Hempel reported 10-20% of the pressor activity of the (5-valine-angiotensin II (1965).

** Schroeder and Hempel (1965) and Cresswell, Hanson and Law (1967) reported 0.2 and 0.1% respectively of the pressor activity of the (5-valine)-angiotensin II.

in size to that of aspartic acid. It has already demonstrated that the acidity of aspartic acid is not necessary for biological activity. However, 1-isoleucine-angiotensin has reduced activity very similar to that of the heptapeptide not containing aspartic acid. It had been assumed that the introduction of proline in the 3 position would change the conformational possibilities of angiotensin by placing aspartylarginine in a different position respective to the rest of the polypeptide chain. However, 3-proline angiotensin still retained 40% of the pressor activity of the parent compound when assayed in an intact rat. Alanine substituted in the 5 position brought about a rather significant reduction in biological activity; thus, the branched chain of isoleucine or valine in position 5 is extremely important and possibly necessary to place the aromatic group of tyrosine in the proper position relative to that of histidine and phenylalanine.

As discussed earlier, Hoffman and coworkers[1] have synthesized 6 β -pyrazolyl-3-alanine angiotensin II and showed it to possess 57% of the pressor activity of angiotensin when assayed in a nephrectomized rat and 79% of the activity when assayed in a pithed rat. We cannot agree with their conclusions. 6-Thienylalanine angiotensin was synthesized and found to be almost completely inactive. We do not agree that the stereo structure of the 5 membered heterocyclic ring of histidine is the only contributing factor to biological activity of angiotensin and suggest, in contradiction to these workers, that the basicity of this group is likewise necessary.

It is interesting that the 7-pipecolic acid angiotensin has very little biological activity since its conformation should be somewhat similar to that of 7-alanine-angiotensin. At present, we have assumed then that the 5 membered ring of proline is necessary for the conformation of angiotensin or that it may in some way enter into the reaction between angiotensin and its receptor protein.

Schroeder and Hempel synthesized 8-tyrosine angiotensin and reported a product to have 10 to 20% of the pressor activity of 5-valine angiotensin. The same analog was synthesized in our laboratory and we were amazed to find that it has no effect upon the conformation of the peptide. Introduction of a methoxyl group, however, in position 8 seems to reduce the activity to a greater degree. This being larger may prevent the aromatic group from entering the receptor site. Etherification of the hydroxyl of tyrosine in position 4 almost completely destroys the biological activity. It was shown earlier that the hydroxyl group is necessary for biological activity, and very likely enters into the reaction between the peptide and its receptor site.

Substitution of the amino acid 3-amino-4-phenyl-butyric acid abbreviated APB, into the 8 position of angiotensin reduces the biological activity to 10%. In this peptide the carboxyl group is now removed one methylene group farther from the peptide bond. This slight change in the position of the carboxyl group reduces the activity so significantly that one must conclude that the relative position of the carboxyl group and the aromatic group on the amino acid #8 is extremely important. When phenylalanine is replaced by 3-amino-3' phenylisobutyric acid, labeled as APIB, the biological activity is reduced even further. I must point out, however, that the D, L form of this amino acid was used in the synthesis of the peptide and it is highly possible that during the purification procedures we may have concentrated either the D or L form in the peptide. Here, both the phenyl group and the carboxyl group are one methylene group further removed from the peptide bond. The effects of these last two peptides on the inhibition of the uptake of norepine - phrine by coronary arteries are highly significant[13]. Studies designed to measure uptake of norephinphrine were carried out by adding tritiated norepinephrine to a perfusing solution being circulated through an isolated rabbit's heart. The addition of l-asparagine angiotensin at a concentration of 0.2 ng/ml to the perfusate reduced the uptake of norepine-phrine by 80% as well as an increase in heart rate. The naturally occurring angiotensin, i.e. the aspartic acid derivative, likewise has the same effect at the same concentration. Numerous analogs of angiotensin which had low

145

TABLE 3

Treatment	Concentration	n	% Inhibition NE Uptake	% Ang Pressor Activity
H^{3}NE	10 ng/ml	15	---	---
1-Asp(NH$_2$)-Ang II*	2 ng/ml	10	80	100
1-Asp(NH$_2$)-Ang II*	0.05 ng/ml	5	80	100
Ang II	0.2 ng/ml	5	80	100
1-Ileu-Ang II	2 ng/ml	6	25	20
1-Ileu-Ang II	10 ng/ml	6	70	20
3-Ala-Ang II	2 ng/ml	6	70	65
4-Ala-Ang II	2 ng/ml	6	0	0
6-Ala-Ang II	2 ng/ml	6	0	1
7-Ala-Ang II	2 ng/ml	8	0	2
1-Asp(NH$_2$)-Ang II(NH$_2$)	2 ng/ml	8	0	0
8-Ala-Ang II	2 ng/ml	10	80	2
8-Ala-Ang II	0.2 ng/ml	8	50	2
8-APIB-Ang II**	2 ng/ml	8	40	0.1
8-APB-Ang II+	2 ng/ml	8	80	10
8-APB-Ang II	0.05 ng/ml	6	40	10
8-Tyr-Ang II	2 ng/ml	2	80	85
8-Tyr-Ang II	0.2 ng/ml	4	20	85
Ang I (Decapeptide)	2 ng/ml	6	0	0 (Oxytocic activity)

* Hypertensin - Ciba
** 8 (D,L 3-amino-3'-phenylisobutyric acid)
+ 8 (d-amino-4-phenylbutyric acid)

pressor activity were tested for their effects upon the inhibition of norepinephrine uptake by the heart tissue. Here we note that 1-isoleucine angiotensin, which has only 20% of the pressor activity, inhibits the uptake of norepinephrine by 20%. Likewise, the 3-alanine derivative, which has 65% of the pressor activity of the parent molecule, also inhibits. The

4, 6, and 7 substituted derivatives of angiotensin, which have
very little or no pressor activity, likewise seem to have very
little effect upon the uptake of norepinephrine. From this
it first appeared as though the inhibition of norepinephrine
uptake paralleled the pressor activity. However, when modifications were made in the 8 position very different results
were obtained. The 8-alanine derivative of angiotensin,
which has less than 2% pressor activity, inhibits the uptake
of norepinephrine to the same degree as the parent angiotensin. Also, the APB and the APIB derivatives, which had
much less pressor activity than angiotensin, also inhibited
norepinephrine uptake as did the tyrosine analogs. From
this, it is clear that the receptor site on nerve terminals
which affects the inhibition of norepinephrine uptake does
not require the phenyl group in the 8 position of angiotensin.
However, since angiotensin I, which has histidyl-leucine
on the carboxyl group in the 8 position, or angiotensin dia-
mide, are both inactive in inhibiting norepinephrine uptake,
demonstrating that the free carboxyl group is necessary in
this position. It can, however, be removed by one methylene
group without greatly changing its activity on norepinephrine
uptake, while there is some reduction of the pressor activity.
This seems rather significant since for the first time we have
been able to show a difference in receptor sites for angiotensin. It, indeed, would be even more exciting to find an

147

analog which has very little pressor activity but would inhibit norephinephrine uptake and also release aldosterone. For some time we have felt that the indirect effects of angiotensin may be more significant in controlling blood pressure than the direct vasoconstriction properties. An analog with these indirect effects without the acute pressor action would be a valuable tool with which to study the sensitization mechanism which many of us believe to be extremely important during the development of hypertension.

In summary, I would like to point out that we have synthesized many angiotensin analogs in good yields and high purity by the Merrifield solid-phase method. It has been very useful in our laboratory. One analog has been extremely difficult to synthesize by this manner, and it is difficult to understand why the arginyl proline bond of 3-proline angiotensin II is so difficult to form. In this case it would have been much easier to synthesize the analog by the usual solution methods. None of our analogs have significant inhibitory activity on angiotensin; nor have we been able to correlate the differences of the dialysis rates of the various analogs with their biological activities. We are hopeful that Dr. Goodman's work with nmr and ORD will shed some light on this matter. His studies have, indeed, shown the importance of the 8 position toward the possible conformation of angiotensin, and this has led us to make numerous substitutions in this position for further tests on his part.

It is extremely interesting now that these analogs which are

substituted in the 8 position have a very different action

upon inhibition of norepinephrine uptake.

REFERENCES

1. K. Hoffman, R. Andreatta, J. P. Buckley, W. E. Hageman, and A. P. Shapiro, J. Am. Chem. Soc., 90, 1654 (1968).

2. a) E. Schoreder, Ann., 680, 142 (1964).

   b) E. Schoreder and R. Hempel, Ann., 684, 243 (1965).

3. a) W. K. Park, J. R. Seu, R. R. Smeby, and F. M. Bumpus, to be published.

   b) N. C. Chaturvedi, R. R. Smeby, and F. M. Bumpus, to be published.

   c) M. G. Khosla, N. C. Chaturvedi, R. R. Smeby, and F. M. Bumpus, Biochem., in press.

   d) W. K. Park, R. R. Smeby, and F. M. Bumpus, to be published.

4. R. B. Merrifield, Biochem., 3, 1385 (1964).

5. F. M. Bumpus, R. R. Smeby, I. H. Page, and P. A. Khairallah, Can. Med. Assoc. J., 90, 190 (1964).

6. G. G. Glenner, P. J. McMillan, and J. E. Folk, Nature, 194, 867 (1962).

7. P. A. Khairallah and I. H. Page, Biochem. Med., 1, 1 (1967).

8. D. Regoli, B. Riniker, and H. Brunner, Biochem. Pharmacol., 12, 637 (1963).

9. R. R. Smeby, K. Arakawa, F. M. Bumpus, and M. M. Marsh, Biochem. et Biophys. Acta, 58, 550 (1962).

10. T. B. Paiva, A. C. M. Paiva, and H. Sheraga, Biochem., 2, 1327 (1963).

11. L. C. Craig, E. J. Harfenist and A. C. Paladini, Biochem., 3, 764 (1964).

12. P. A. Khairallah, I. H. Page, F. M. Bumpus, and R. K. Turker, Circul. Research, 19, 247 (1966).

13. M. J. Peach and P. A. Khairallah, The Pharmacologist, 10, 182 (1968).

CONFORMATION, COMPUTERS, AND BIOLOGICAL ACTIVITY

Garland R. Marshall

Departments of Physiology and Biophysics and
of Biological Chemistry
Washington University Medical School, St. Louis, Missouri

The ability to synthesize a large number of analogs of a small peptide has become a reality, whether one is speaking of classical procedures as exemplified in the case of the gastrin tetrapeptide[1], or of solid-phase procedures as exemplified in the case of bradykinin[2]. The question which faces every investigator interested in this approach to the structure-activity relationship is which analog to synthesize next. Some 70-100 analogs of most of the small biologically active peptides have been synthesized with a relatively small gain in understanding the effects of structural change on the biological activity.

This problem is not unique to peptide chemists, but is a common difficulty even among those working with much simpler molecules with a predetermined configuration. Obviously, we are facing a multivariable problem in that many of the assay procedures would be expected to be influenced by lipid solubility, resistance to enzymatic

151

degradation, and a multitude of other factors. There have been some recent attempts to analyze simpler systems in terms of lipid solubility, dipole moments, etc. with some degree of success[3]. An attempt to apply similar ideas to oxytocin and angiotensin noted some correlations although any predictive value is questionable[4].

One parameter which we know must be affected by the chemical change is the conformation, either unique or allowed, which the molecule can assume. The question of uniqueness of conformation as a function of peptide size is an area with little experimental data and open to controversy[5]. Physical techniques, at best, would give only the conformation in a crystal or in solution. Since we are really interested in the conformation while interacting with the receptor, one must focus on the sterically allowed conformations rather than those present in the crystal, or in solution, or calculated to have the minimum energy in solution. In addition, some problems in x-ray crystallography which become particularly acute with peptides should be pointed out. First, crystal packing forces become proportionately greater as the molecular size decreases, and the problem of conformation in the crystal versus that in solution is raised. Second, peptides appear hard to crystallize in the 6-20 residue range. Third, isomorphous heavy metal replacement becomes more difficult as the

perturbation to the crystal structure becomes greater.
Other methods, so far, are not sufficiently powerful to
solve the structures directly. Solution methods are in the
process of development and the results are hard to interpret at present. Several appear quite promising, i.e.,
electron-donor acceptor complexes[6], spin-labelling[9],
and NMR[8].

One approach which we are evaluating assumes some
major similarity in the active analogs of a peptide which is
not shared by the inactive analogs and which will be reflected
in the conformation. Meister's work on glutamic analogs
has determined the conformation of glutamic at the binding
site of glutamine synthetase[9]. By determining the allowed
conformations as a function of sequence, one could compare
those resulting from active analogs with those from inactive
analogs. In selecting sets of analogs for such a study, one
must consider that certain groups will be necessary for
function and that the role of the other residues is to provide
a structural basis for a required spatial configuration of
those groups at the receptor. Ideally, one would like to
identify the functional residues and only consider analogs
which vary the other residues. One obvious means of
changing the conformation without affecting the functionally
required groups is substitution with enantiomers. Unique
spatial requirements for, at least, three groups is implied

153

in the fact that the all-D analogs of bradykinin[10],
angiotensin[11], and oxytocin[12] are inactive.

The initial problem is how to determine the effects of
changes in sequence on the allowed conformations of a
peptide. The studies begun by Ramachandran and extended
by Liquori, Scheraga, Flory, and others, provide the basic
foundations for calculating the allowed conformations.
Ramachandran plots of the allowed dihedral angles for a
dipeptide have been calculated for a given set of Van der Waal's
radii[13]. Such a diagram is shown in FIG. 1. One can extend

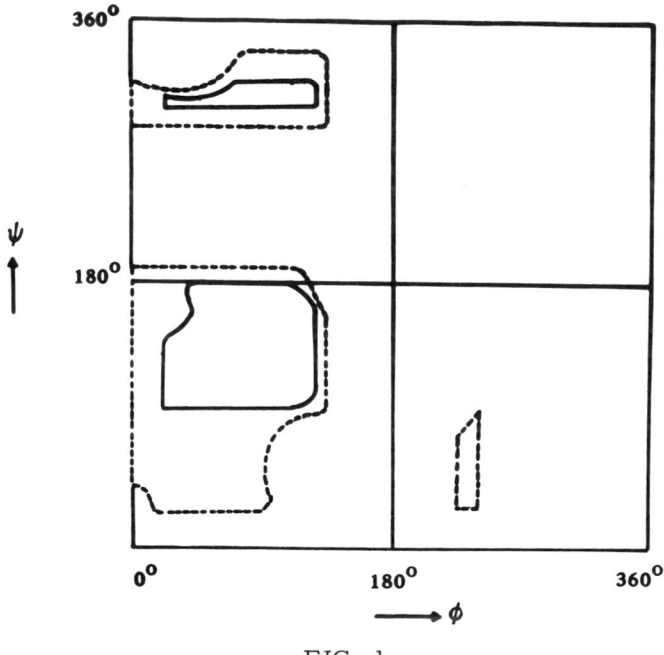

FIG. 1

Plot of the fully allowed (line) and outer limit (dash) regions
for values of backbone angles (13).

this type of calculation to any given peptide as exemplified by Nemethy and Scheraga[14] who calculated nine allowed backbone conformation for the octapeptide loop of ribonuclease. One of the major drawbacks to this approach is the strain on present-day computational facilities, especially for linear peptides where one does not have the constraint when generating the structure that the considered conformation must allow closure.

Fortunately, the need for improved computational facilities and the means of supplying them have enjoyed a dialogue at Washington University the last few years. A new concept in computer technology, namely modular computer, or macromodules, is being implemented as a means of designing specialized computers which offer enormous savings in time and computational expense[15]. This concept essentially allows the design of very efficient specialized computers for specific application with possibilities of parallel computation and hardware programming. As a means of determining which parts of such a problem would best yield to such a technique, we have been investigating the problem of calculating allowed conformation on a rather small computer, the LINC[22]. In addition, we have been interested in molecular graphics as a means of allowing the investigator to digest some of the enormous amounts of data available as computer output. FIG. 2 illustrates one step

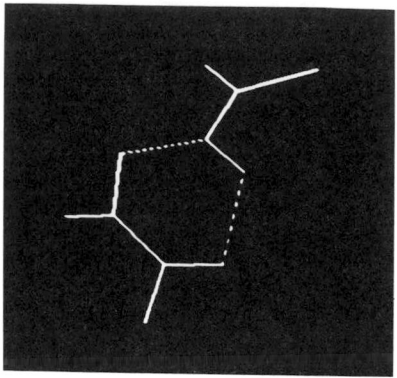

FIG. 2

Display of glycine dipeptide unit rotating about dotted bond
between α -carbon and carbonyl carbon.   Dotted line shows
collision between starting α -carbon and carbonyl oxygen.
This configuration is not allowed.

in the calculation of a Ramachandran plot as shown on our

LINC display.   FIG. 3 shows the staggered configuration of

the pentapeptide, alanyl-alanyl-alanyl-arginyl-arginine.   A

macromodular design for comparable facilities[16] which

should increase the speed of computations by a factor of

10^3 awaits the fabrication of some of the component modules

for implementation.

Another approach which we are investigating is the use of

NMR as a means of determining peptide conformation.   The

upfield shift in resonance of methyl groups due to aromatic

shielding observed in lysozyme can be explained by sidechain

interactions observable in the x-ray crystal structure accord-

ing to Sternlicht and Wilson[17].   Such shifts are indicative of

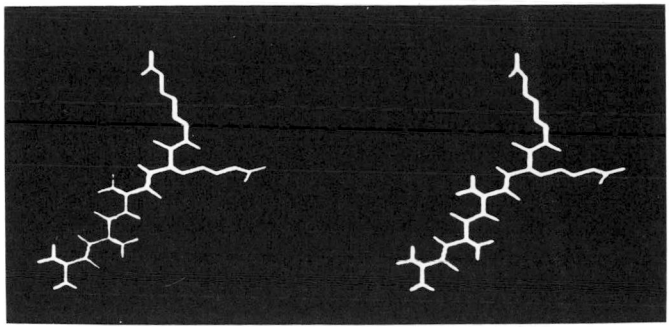

FIG. 3

Stereo display of Ala-Ala-Ala-Arg-Arg in staggered con-
figuration. Three dimensional viewers such as sold by
Stereo-Magniscope, Inc., 40-31 81st St., Elmhurst,
New York will allow viewing in stereo.

the proximity of an aromatic sidechain. In collaboration

with Dr. Leroy Johnson of Varian Associates, the 220 MHz

spectra of Asn^1-Val^5-angiotensin II and glucagon have been

examined. These are shown in FIGS. 4 and 5. FIG. 6

shows an enlarged view of the upfield spectra of angio-

tensin. Notice that the peak due to the 4 methyl groups of

the 2 valine residues do not coincide. Also note that no

resonances are shifted upfield enough in the glucagon spectra

to be distinguished from the broad spectra. This asymmetric

appearance in angiotensin has prompted us to synthesize the

following compounds in an attempt to determine if this

asymmetry is due to a conformational effect

     optical ASP-ARG-VAL-TYR-D-VAL-HIS-Pro-PHE

     optical ASP-ARG-VAL-TYR-VAL-HIS-D-PRO-PHE

     isotopic ASP-ARG-VAL-TYR-Deuterated-VAL-HIS-
           PRO-PHE

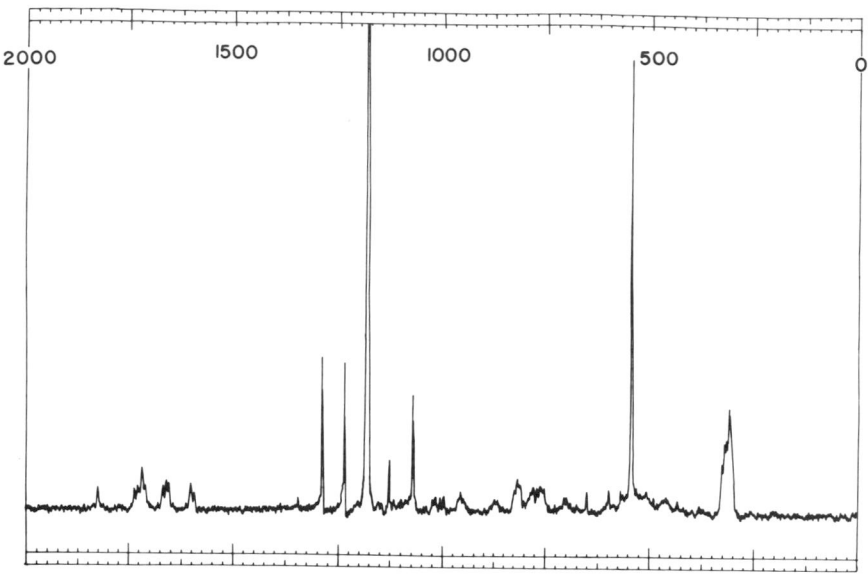

FIG. 4

NMR spectra of Asn[1]-Val[5]-angiotensin II. Aromatic residues are on the far left and valine methyl protons are on the far right.

These peptides have been synthesized[18] using essentially the described procedure of solid phase[19]. In several cases, the histidine protection was varied. Free His and DNP-His were used in additional to im-Bz-His. Free His coupling was incomplete, giving only 60-70% coupling when performed as described by Loffet[20]. This is similar to our unpublished experience with several other sequences. The BOC-DNP-His incorporation was satisfactory and the DNP group removal by β-mercaptoethanol in a mixed solvent of DMF

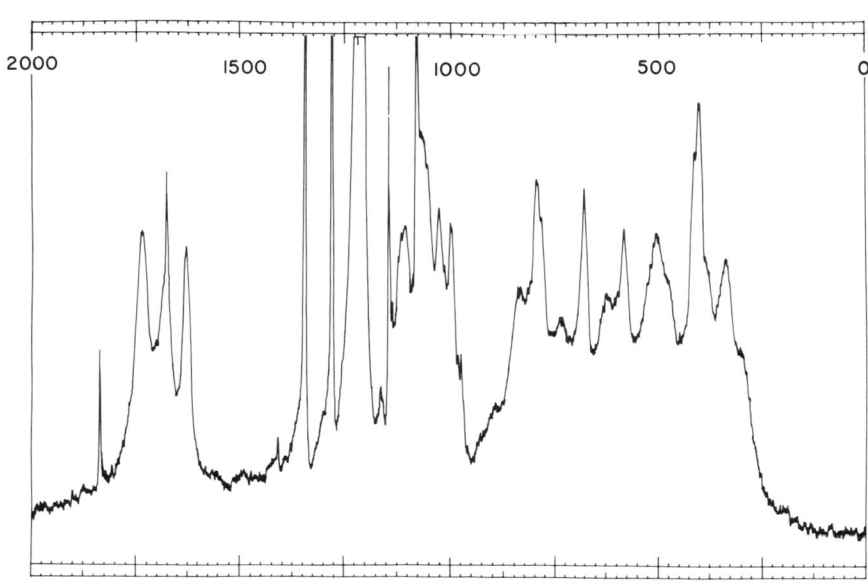

FIG. 5

NMR spectra of glucagon at pH. 9.

and Na_2CO_3 buffer, pH 8. 0,was complete after 24 hours. The peptide was desulfured and hydrogenated to give the free angiotensin analog. The NMR spectra and other physical parameters are under investigation and will be presented elsewhere[21].

Information from NMR on peptide conformation would give the location of two groups with respect to each other. This essentially imposes a cyclic constraint on a linear peptide or a bicyclic constant on a cyclic peptide. These constraints reduce enormously the number of allowed con-

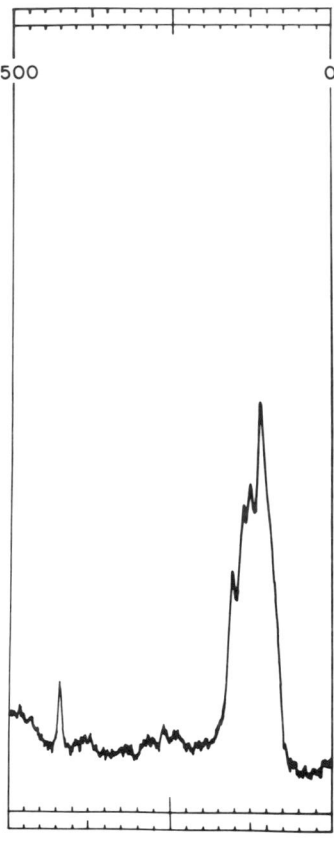

FIG. 6

Enlarged spectra of resonance due to valine methyl groups in Asn[1]-Val[5]-angiotensin II.

figurations for these structures. In the case of the ribonuclease loop, the reduction was of the order of 2 orders of magnitude[22]. We hope that our efforts in calculating allowed conformations will also be useful in determining those which will be consistent with NMR spectra and other physical methods as these develop further. One must be careful before mixing the constraints imposed by biological activity and those by measurements in solution for reasons pointed out previously. Hopefully, the combination of the various physical techniques available, combined with improved computational facilities will yield the effervescent conformational parameter. This should assist our effort to understand the role of structure in biological activity.

ACKNOWLEDGMENTS

The author wishes to acknowledge the contributions of his collaborators in this effort: computer graphics and conformational calculations, Robert A. Ellis, Susan Graesser, and Dr. C. D. Barry; nuclear magnetic resonance spectra, Dr. Leroy Johnson of Varian Associates; and chemical synthesis, Jane Welsh, Alan B. Silverberg, and Dr. Lee A. Rigg. In addition, special thanks to Dr. Charles E. Molnar for encouragement in crossing the barriers between computers and chemistry.

REFERENCES

1. J. S. Morley, Proc. Roy. Soc., B., 170, 97 (1968).

2. J. M. Stewart, Federation Proc., 27, 63 (1968).

3. C. Hansch, J. Med. Chem., 11, 920 (1968).

4. P. H. A. Sneath, J. Theoret. Biol., 12, 157 (1966).

5. K. D. Kopple and D. H. Marr, J. Amer. Chem. Soc., 89, 6193 (1967).

6. J. P. Carrion, D. A. Deranleu, B. Donzel, K. Esko, P. Moser, and R. Schwyzer, Helv. Chim. Acta, 51, 459 (1968).

7. C. L. Hamilton and H. M. McConnell, in Structural Chemistry and Molecular Biology (A. Rich and N. Davidson, eds.), W. H. Freeman, San Francisco, 1968, p. 115.

8. A. Nakamura and O. Jardetzky, Biochemistry, 7, 1226 (1968).

9. A. Meister, Federation Proc., 27, 100 (1968).

10. J. M. Stewart and D. W. Woolley, Nature, 206, 619 (1965).

11. K. Vogler, R. O. Studer, W. Lergier, and P. Lanz, Helv. Chim. Acta, 48, 1407 (1965).

12. G. Flouret and V. du Vigneaud, J. Amer. Chem. Soc., 37, 3775 (1965).

13. G. N. Ramachandran, D. Ramakrishnan, and V. Sasisekhran, J. Mol. Biol., 7, 95 (1963).

14. G. Nemethy and H. A. Scheraga, Biopolymers, 3, 155 (1965).

15. W. A. Clark, Proc. Spring Joint Computer Conf., 1967, Thompson Book Co., Washington, 1967, p. 335.

16. R. A. Ellis and G. R. Marshall, unpublished data.

17. H. Sternlicht and D. Wilson, Biochemistry, 6, 2881 (1967).

18. L. A. Rigg and G. R. Marshall, unpublished data.

19. G. R. Marshall and R. B. Merrifield, Biochemistry, 4, 2394 (1965).

20. A. Loffet, Experientia, 23, 406 (1967).

21. G. R. Marshall and D. W. Urry, work in progress.

22. W. A. Clark and C. E. Molnar, Ann. N. Y. Acad. Science, 115, 653 (1964).

SMALL CYCLIC PROLINE PEPTIDES:
ULTRAVIOLET ABSORPTION AND CIRCULAR DICHROISM

C. M. Deber, A. Scatturin, V. M. Vaidya, and E. R. Blout

Department of Biological Chemistry
Harvard Medical School, Boston, Massachusetts

The presence of proline residues in a biopolymer, particularly when their percentage is relatively high as in the
protein collagen, may confer unique conformational properties
upon the molecule, since (a) rotation around $N-C_\alpha$ bonds is
restricted[1] and (b) proline-proline peptide bonds may adopt
energetically similar cis- or trans- forms[2].

Poly-L-proline, as obtained by polymerization of L-proline-
N-carboxyanhydride in pyridine or acetonitrile[3-5] is in the cis-
form "I", [3,4] but undergoes mutarotation (as monitored by
changes in characteristic optical rotatory dispersion (ORD)
and circular dichroism (CD) spectra) to the trans-form 'poly-
L-proline II" in suitable solvent systems[4-10].

Small cyclic proline-containing peptides in which the peptide linkages are conformationally constrained to remain in the
cis -form provide a favorable situation for the study of the
spectral properties of such bonds. In this paper, we present
the results of some preliminary observations concerning the

CD and ultraviolet absorption (UV) spectra of three cyclic peptides: L-proline-L-proline diketopiperazine, cyclo (tri-L-prolyl), and cyclo(Gly-L-Pro-Gly-Gly-L-Pro-Gly).

Synthesis

Cyclo(tri-L-prolyl) was synthesized in 30-40% yield by either of two variations of the original method of Rothe:[11] cyclization under conditions of high dilution of H-L-Pro-L-Pro-L-Pro-p-nitrophenyl ester trifluoroacetate in dimethyl formamide/triethylamine or of H-L-Pro-L-Pro-L-Pro-p-nitrophenyl ester hydrochloride in pyridine. The cyclotripeptide forms beautiful crystals (from methanol), m.p. ∼ 340° with prior sublimation at ∼250°; the only band in the carbonyl region of its infrared spectrum is an intense one at 1630 cm^{-1}.

It is intriguing that the synthesis of cyclo(tri-L-prolyl) represents the only reported example of the cyclization of a tri-peptide which does not undergo the "doubling reaction" to produce a cyclohexapeptide. Factors contributing to this phenomenon may include (a) the inability of the linear prolyl tri-peptide to hydrogen bond to a second trimer in head-to-tail fashion just prior to cyclization as suggested by Schwyzer[12] as well as (b) the tendency of proline to form cis-peptide bonds which would bring the two ends of a trimer close together in space.

Cyclo(Gly-L-Pro-Gly-Gly-L-Pro-Gly) was synthesized according to Reader and Smith[13], who employed the cyclodimerization of H-Gly-L-Pro-Gly-p-nitrophenyl ester hydro-bromide in dimethylformamide/triethylamine. It had the correct amino acid analysis, m.p. $>350°$, and an infrared spectrum identical to that reported[12] containing a complex carbonyl region with several bands between 1630 and 1685 cm cm^{-1}.

L-Pro-L-Pro diketopiperazine was obtained from Cyclo Chemical Co., and displayed an infrared carbonyl absorption band at 1655 cm^{-1}.

Results and Discussion

Cyclo(tri-L-prolyl) exhibits a maximum in the UV at $\lambda = 205$ mμ ($\epsilon = 6200$) and a distinct shoulder at $\lambda = 230$ m$_\mu$ ($\epsilon = 1400$), as shown in Figure 1. The λ_{max} at 205 mμ corresponds closely to that observed for poly-L-proline I (in water) ($\lambda_{max} = 204.5$, $\epsilon = 7500$, no shoulder) while both differ somewhat from the UV of poly-L-proline II ($\lambda_{max} = 202$ mμ $\epsilon = 7000$, no shoulder)[14].

The cyclo-tri-peptide possesses a complex CD spectrum (Figure 1), containing maxima at $\lambda = 215$ mμ ($\theta' = +19,000$)and $\lambda = 190$ mμ ($\theta' = +30,000$), and minima at 233 mμ ($\theta' = -12,000$) and 202 mμ ($\theta' = +7500$). A slight shoulder at about 250 mμ is also discernible.

We suggest that the relatively large CD transition at 233 mμ as well as the UV absorption shoulder at 230 mμ represent spectral manifestations of a strong n-π^* band.

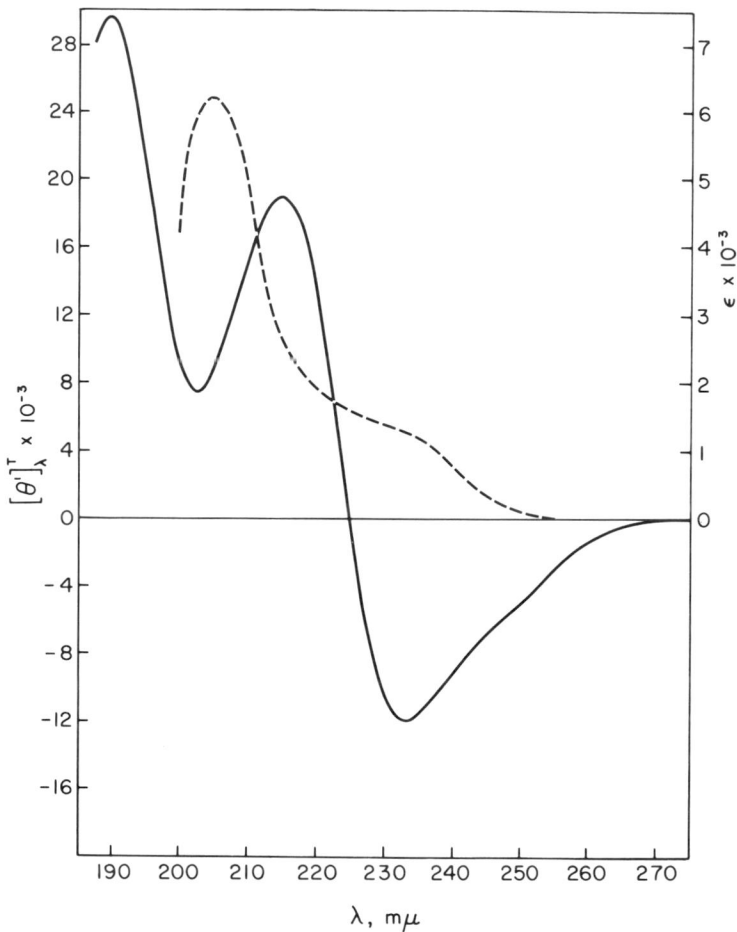

FIG. 1

The circular dichroism spectrum (solid line) and ultraviolet absorption spectrum (dashed line) of cyclo(tri-L-
prolyl, recorded in methanol at 24°. The ε scale on the
right refers to the UV spectrum.

This contention is supported by the experimental observation

that the CD band at 233 mμ in methanol red-shifts to 237 mμ

($\theta' = 16,500$) in methylene chloride.

An explanation for the remaining bands in the CD spectrum will follow a more detailed theoretical treatment of the data. It is not surprising that cyclo(tri-L-prolyl), a relatively simple molecule, limited as it is to only a few possible conformations, nevertheless exhibits a CD spectrum with bands of considerable magnitude. A possible reason for this is the absence of "compensating conformations" (normally available to linear proline oligomers) which might serve to "cancel" or reduce the magnitudes of the observed CD bands. Thus, the experimentally observed θ' values are quite large.

Calculations based on allowed bond angles by Ramachandran and Venkatachalam[15, 16] reveal that "it is impossible to close the (cyclotriprolyl) ring using three peptide units all in the trans-conformation", a fact certainly borne out by studies with molecular (CPK) models. Photographs of the "front" and "rear" views of a cyclo- (tri-L-prolyl) model built with slightly non-planar cis-peptide bonds shown in FIG. 2, confirm Venkatachalan's finding[15] that the former face (a) is "hydrophilic" in nature, while the latter face (b) has "hydrophobic" character.

The ORD spectrum of L-Pro-L-Pro diketopiperazine, reported by Schellman[17], shows an asymmetric Cotton effect (i.e., peak and trough have different magnitudes), indicating the presence of at least two optically active transitions, a result confirmed by the CD results reported herein. The

(a)   (b)

FIG. 2

Photographs of CPK molecular midels of cyclo(tri-L-prolyl), showing "front" (hydrophilic) face (a) and "rear" (hydrophobic) face (b). The black atoms are carbon, the white atoms are hydrogen, the gray atoms are nitrogen, and the grooved atoms are oxygen.

CD spectrum of this material possesses a maximum at $\lambda = 205$ mμ ($\theta' = +5000$) and a minimum at $\lambda = 222$ mμ ($\theta' = -5300$). Although L-Pro-L-Pro diketopiperazine ("cyclo(di-L-prolyl)" is a compound which must contain only cis-peptide bonds, its CD spectrum (FIG. 3) bears no obvious resemblance to the cyclo(tri-L-prolyl) spectrum. Thus, if one were hoping to discern bands in either CD spectrum which were "diagnostic" for the presence of cis-peptide bonds, one could reach no firm conclusion on this point from the available data.

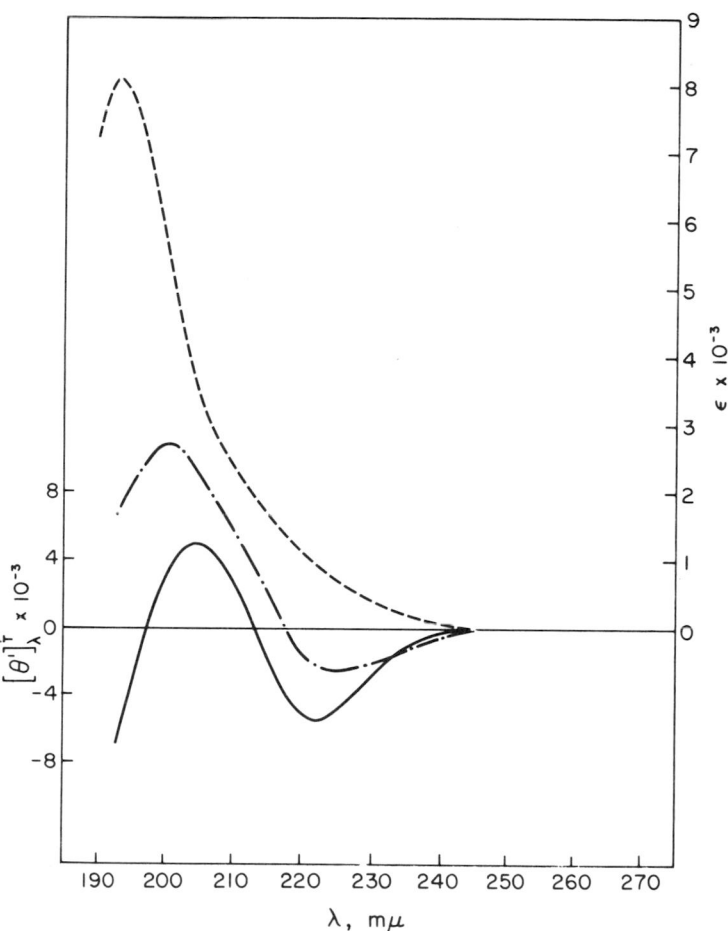

FIG. 3

The circular dichroism spectrum (——————) and the ultra-violet absorption spectrum (— — — — — —) of L-proline-L-proline diketopiperazine, and the circular dichroism spec-trum (——— • ——— •) of cyclo (Gly-L-Pro-Gly-Gly-L-Pro-Gly). The ϵ scale on the right refers only to the UV spectrum. All spectra were recorded in methanol at 24°.

Somewhat unexpectedly, the CD spectrum of the cyclo-hexapeptide cyclo(Gly-L-Pro-Gly-Gly-L-Pro-Gly) (FIG. 3) does qualitatively resemble that of the diketopiperazine, displaying a maximum at λ = 201 mµ (θ = + 11,000) and a minimum at 225 mµ (θ = -2500). One naturally assumes that a cyclic hexapeptide, particularly one containing four glycine residues, could, and should adopt the trans-conformation for its peptide linkages; it is doubtful that the actual conformation of this molecule contains any cis-bonds. Furthermore, examination of a molecular model of the compound built with cis-peptide bonds presents one with no obvious reason why the two proline residues might be spatially disposed in such a way so as to resemble the situation in the diketopiperazine. Thus, one is led to the conclusion that the CD spectra of both diketopiperazine and the cyclohexapeptide represent the result of two proline carbonyl chromophores which are essentially non-interacting: in the cyclohexapeptide, because they are far apart, and in the diketopiperazine, because the angle between the two carbonyl groups is around 180°, giving a net dipole-dipole resultant near zero.

The UV spectrum of L-Pro-L-Pro diketopiperazine (FIG. 3) displays its λ_{max} at 193 mµ (ϵ = 8100), in the same region as previously observed values for other diketopiperazines[18].

Additional support for the supposition that the CPK models of L-Pro-L-Pro diketopiperazine and cyclo(tri-L-pro-lyl) are

TABLE 1. Nuclear Magnetic Resonance Spectra of Cyclic Proline Peptides

	Ring H's	N-C Ring H's	C_α H's
L-Pro-L-Pro diketo-piperazine	2.10 (m)	3.55 (t)	4.25 (t)
Cyclo(tri-L-Prolyl)	2.15 (m)	3.50 (m)	5.10 (m)
Ratios in both cmpds:	4H :	2H :	1H

Solvent: $CDCl_3$. Values given in ppm downfield from tetramethylsilane. m= multiplet, t=triplet.

in fact satisfactory representations of the conformations of these materials, can be obtained from the nmr data shown in Table 1.

The models indicate that the two C_α-protons in the diketopiperazine lie in a plane practically perpendicular to the plane of the peptide bonds, while the three C_α-protons in cyclo(tri-L-prolyl) are practically in the plane of the peptide bonds. On this basis, one would expect the latter three α-H's to undergo greater deshielding due to the electrons which impart partial double-bond character to the C-N peptide linkage, and hence be shifted to lower field in the nmr spectrum. Thàt this is the case can be seen from the Table, where all ring protons in the two compounds occur at comparable positions, but a downfield shift of nearly one ppm is observed for the α-H's of the cyclo(tri-L-prolyl), from 4.25 to 5.10 ppm.

Further studies on the unique problems associated with the syntheses of other cyclic proline-containing peptides are required. When such compounds become available, the investigation of their optical properties should supplement our knowledge of the relationships of these properties to molecular structure.

Acknowledgment

We wish to acknowledge support of this work (in part) by U.S. Public Health Service Grants AM-07300 and AM-10794. One of us (CMD) was a recipient of a U.S. Public Health Service Postdoctoral Fellowship. One of us (A.S.) was a recipient of a National Research Council of Italy Postdoctoral Fellowship.

REFERENCES

1. For a review, see J. P. Carver and E. R. Blout in Treatise on Collagen (G. Ramachandran, ed.), Vol. 1, Academic Press, New York, 1967, pp. 441-526.

2. G. N. Ramachandran and V. Sasisekharan, Adv. Protein Chemistry, 23, 283 (1968).

3. A. Berger, J. Kurtz, and E. Katchalski, J. Am. Chem. Soc., 76, 5552 (1954).

4. J. Kurtz, A. Berger, and E. Katchalski, Nature, 178, 1066 (1956).

5. E. R. Blout and G. D. Fasman, in Recent Advances in Gelatin and Glue Research, Permagon Press, London, 1957, pp. 122-130.

6. W. F. Harrington and M. Sela, Biochim. et Biophys. Acta, 27, 24 (1958).

7. A. R. Downie and A. A. Randall, Trans. Faraday Soc., 55, 2132 (1959).

8. I. Z. Steinberg, W. F. Harrington, A. Berger, M. Sela, and E. Katchalski, J. Am. Chem. Soc., 82, 5263 (1960).

9. G. D. Fasman and E. R. Blout, Biopolymers, 1, 3 (1963).

10. F. A. Bovey and F. P. Hood, Biopolymers, 5, 325 (1967).

11. M. Rothe, K. D. Steffen, and I. Rother, Angew Chem. Int. Ed., 4, 356 (1965).

12. R. Schwyzer, J. P. Carrion, B. Gorup, H. Nolting, and Aung Tun-Kyi, Helv. Chim. Acta, 47, 441 (1964).

13. J. A. Reader and P. W. G. Smith, J. Chem. Soc., 3479 (1965).

14. W. B. Gratzer, W. Rhodes, and G. D. Fasman, Biopolymers, 1, 319 (1963).

15. C. M. Venkatachalam, Biochem. Biophys. Acta, 168, 397 (1968).

16. C. M. Venkatachalam and G. Ramachandran, Biopolymers, 6, 1255 (1968).

17. J. A. Schellman and E. B. Nielsen in Conformation of Biopolymers (G. Ramachandran, ed.), Vol.1, Academic Press, New York, 1967, pp. 109-122,

18. D. Balasubramanian and D. B. Wetlaufer, ibid., pp. 147-156.

173

STRUCTURE-TASTE RELATIONSHIPS
OF SOME SMALL PEPTIDES

R. H. Mazur, J. M. Schlatter, and A. H. Goldkamp
Chemical Research Department
G. D. Searle & Co., Skokie, Illinois

During the course of work on the preparation of Z-Trp-Met-Asp-Phe-NH_2, one of us (J. M. Schlatter) discovered that Asp-Phe-OMe[1] had a pronounced, sucrose-like sweet taste. The present report describes briefly the results of an intensive study of structure-taste relationships of peptides related to Asp-Phe-OMe. All amino acids have the L-configuration unless otherwise noted.

Test compounds were made up as 1% solutions, a cotton swab stick soaked in the test solution and the compound sucked off the swab. Successive ten-fold dilutions were made as required to determine relative potency. This procedure gave satisfactorily consistent results from subject to subject, but we do not claim the degree of statistical significance that could be obtained from a trained taste panel. The 1% concentration was chosen because it is the approximate threshold value for sucrose for untrained tasters. Sweetness potency was estimated as follows: + = sucrose, ++ = 10x sucrose,

+++=100x sucrose. In addition, 0 = tasteless, and - = bitter. No attempt was made to quantitate the latter taste. On this scale, Asp-Phe-OMe was +++.

The plan of our synthetic work was to vary independently the two amino acids and the C-terminal functional group and to use these results, if definite structural requirements for a sweet taste were discovered, in the design of additional compounds.

Dipeptides were obtained commercially in which aspartic acid was replaced by other amino acids. Methyl ester hydrochlorides were prepared by acid catalyzed esterification and the products tasted as the hydrochlorides and as the free esters. Table 1 lists the compounds. All these dipeptide esters had a pronounced bitter taste.

TABLE 1
Phenylalanine Dipeptides

Ala-Phe-OMe	Pro-Phe-OMe
His-Phe-OMe	Sar-Phe-OMe
Ile-Phe-OMe	Ser-Phe-OMe
Leu-Phe-OMe	Thr-Phe-OMe
Lys-Phe-OMe	Trp-Phe-OMe
Nle-Phe-OMe	Tyr-Phe-OMe
Nva-Phe-OMe	Val-Phe-OMe
Phe-Phe-OMe	

The results of replacement of phenylalanine were of more interest since several of the esters were sweet. Table 2 summarizes the results for these compounds.

TABLE 2

Taste of Phenylalanine Dipeptide Esters

Asp-Ala-OMe	-	Asp-Met-OMe	+++
Asp-Cys-OMe $\overset{\text{Me}}{\mid}$	+	Asp-Met-OMe $\overset{O_2}{\mid}$	++
Asp-Cys-OMe $\overset{Me(O_2)}{\mid}$	0	Asp-Ser-OMe	0
Asp-Gly-OMe	-	Asp-Thr-OMe	0
Asp-His-OMe	0	Asp-Trp-OMe	-
Asp-Ile-OMe	-	Asp-D-Trp-OMe	-
Asp-Leu-OMe	-	Asp-Tyr-OMe	+++
		Asp-Val-OMe	-

After the data of Table 2 were obtained, modifications were studied of both Asp-Phe-OMe and Asp-Tyr-OMe. Asp-Met-OMe was not stable enough to be of practical interest. Examples of position isomerism, homology, and optical configuration are shown in Table 3. All the compounds were bitter.

Considerable attention was given to the importance of the C-terminal functional group. The results are shown in Tables 4 and 5.

TABLE 3

Miscellaneous Dipeptide Esters

Asp⌐Phe-OMe	Glu-Tyr-OMe
Asp⌐Tyr-OMe	L-Asp-D-Phe-OMe
Glu-Phe-OMe	D-Asp-L-Phe-OMe
Glu⌐Phe-OMe	D-Asp-D-Phe-OMe

TABLE 4

Taste of Aspartyl-Phenylalanine Dipeptides

Asp-Phe	-	Asp-Phe-NH$_2$	0
Asp⌐Phe	-	Asp-Phe-NHMe	-
⌐Asp-Phe⌐	0	Asp-Phe-NMe$_2$	-
Asp-Phe (OMe)	-	Asp-Phe-NHCH$_2$CH$_2$OH	+
Asp-Phe-OEt	++	Asp⌐Phe-NH$_2$	0
Asp-Phe-OPr^n	+	Asp-Phe (NH$_2$)	0
Asp-Phe-OPr^i	+	Asp-Phe-NHNH$_2$	-
Asp-Phe-OBu^t	+	Asp-Phe-NHNMe$_2$	-
Me-Asp-Phe-OMe (Me)	-		

TABLE 5

Taste of Aspartyl-Tyrosine Dipeptides

Asp-Tyr	-	Asp-Tyr-NH$_2$	0
⌐Asp-Tyr⌐	0	Asp-Tyr-NHMe	-
Asp-Tyr-OEt	++	Asp-Tyr-NMe$_2$	-
Me Asp-Tyr-OMe	+	Asp-Tyr-NHNH$_2$	0
Et Asp-Tyr-OMe	+	Asp-Tyr-NHNMe$_2$	0

Our work shows that the structure specificity for a sweet taste in this series of compounds is rather rigid as might be expected of a biochemical reaction. However, certain changes are permitted and a definite pattern can be discerned here.

The presence of both the free, unsubstituted amino and one carboxyl group of aspartic acid as well as the distance between them and the absolute configuration of the asymmetric carbon are completely critical. This is strikingly shown by

Me   OMe   ⌐Phe-OMe
Me-Asp-Phe-OMe, Asp-Phe, Asp   , Glu-Asp-OMe, D-Asp-L-Phe-OMe. These ionic groups must bind directly to the active receptor site of the taste-triggering enzyme in the taste buds.

In addition, another site on the enzyme is involved, which is slightly less critical, although obviously still very important. The requirement of absolute L-configuration still holds (L-Asp-D-Phe-OMe). An electron-rich side chain seems to be required (Asp-Met-OMe, Asp-Tyr-OMe) although size and/or polarity must be just right (Asp-His-OMe and Asp-Trp-OMe are not sweet;

Me   Et
Asp-Tyr-OMe and Asp-Tyr-OMe are less sweet).
Binding also takes place to the relatively non polar ester group (Asp-Phe, Asp-Phe-NH$_2$, Asp-Phe-NHNH$_2$ are not sweet). There seems to be a definite size requirement since sweetness falls off rapidly with increasing bulk (Asp-Phe-OEt, Asp-Phe, OPr, Asp-Phe-OBu^t).

In summary, it would seem that if retention of sweetness is desired, changes in the aspartic acid part cannot be tolerated but there is room for substantial manipulation of the phenylalanine portion. Work in progress is directed along these lines.

REFERENCES

1.   J. M. Davey, A. H. Laird, and J. S. Morley, J. Chem. Soc., 555 (1966).

RECENT ADVANCES IN THE SYNTHESIS OF GASTROINTESTINAL HORMONES

Miguel A. Ondetti, John T. Sheehan, and Josip Pluščec

The Squibb Institute for Medical Research
New Brunswick, New Jersey

SYNTHESIS OF 3-β -ASPARTIC ACID SECRETIN

The occurrence of unexpected rearrangements during the

synthesis of fairly large peptide chains is often very difficult

to detect by the direct examination of these large molecular

weight products. This task can be somewhat simplified by

dissecting the molecule so that the rearranged portion can be

isolated as a low molecular weight fragment that permits

better characterization. Enzymes are among the most

efficient tools to achieve this dissection. The problems

encountered during the synthesis of secretin[1,2] can serve

as a good example in this connection. Retracing the steps

of the structural work[3], synthetic secretin was digested with

trypsin (FIG. 1) and the peptide mixture was fractionated

by preparative paper electrophoresis and chromatography.

Peptide b was further digested with chymotrypsin. These

techniques allowed the isolation of the N-terminal hexapeptide

(S_{1-6}) and the tetrapeptide a (S_{15-18}), containing the two

aspartyl residues present in the sequence. When this

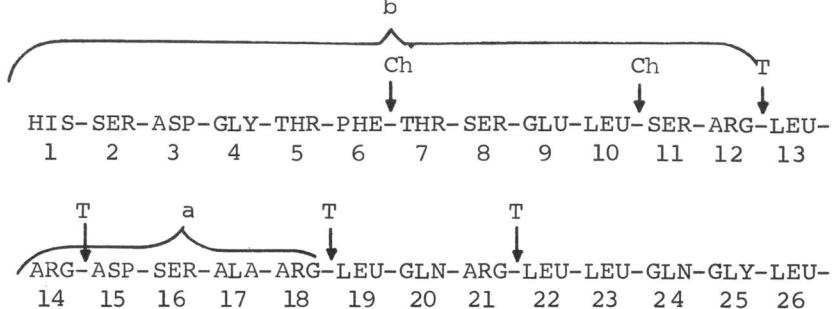

FIG. 1

procedure was applied to samples or synthetic secretin of low biological potency, and the peptides S_{1-6} and S_{15-18} thus isolated were characterized by quantitative amino acid analyses after acid and enzymatic degradation, only peptide S_{15-18} gave the expected results. The N-terminal hexapeptide S_{1-6} showed the correct amino acid composition after acid hydrolysis, but it was incompletely degraded with leucine aminopeptidase. Paper chromatographic examination of this hexapeptide revealed it to be a mixture of two components, which, on the basis of their electrophoretic behavior, were assumed to be the α - and β -aspartyl hexapeptides (FIG. 2). This identification was confirmed by comparison with samples of authentic α - and β -aspartyl hexapeptides synthesized by unequivocal routes[4].

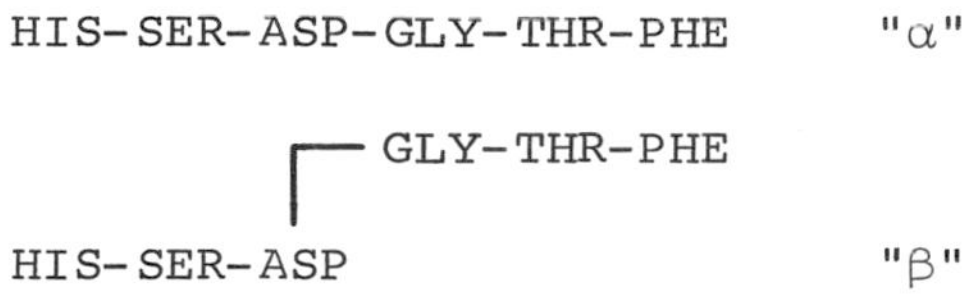

HIS-SER-ASP-GLY-THR-PHE
"α"
GLY-THR-PHE
HIS-SER-ASP
"β"

FIG. 2

Unfortunately, this evidence was not sufficient to permit the conclusion that the contaminant present in the low potency samples of synthetic secretin was the 3-β -aspartic acid analog, because the 3-β -aspartimidyl derivative would have also led to the same results. We have shown that under the conditions of tryptic or chymotryptic digestion the cyclic derivative will open to give a mixture of α - and β -aspartyl peptides.

In order to clarify this point, the 3-β -aspartic acid analog of secretin was synthesized by the unequivocal procedure schematically described in FIG. 3.

GLY-N3
BOC-HIS-SER-ASP
THR- ......-VAL-NH2
1 2 3 4 5 27
TFA
GLY-THR- ......-VAL-NH2
HIS-SER-ASP
1 2 3 4 5 27

FIG. 3

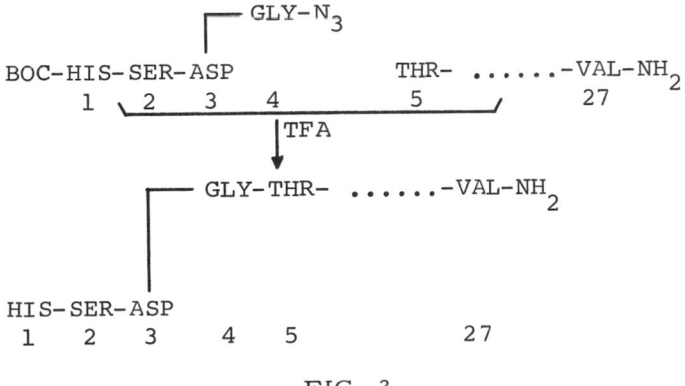

The syntheses of the protected tetrapeptide azide and of the fully free tricosapeptide amide fragments have been described[4,5]. Azide coupling was carried out utilizing the technique described by Medzihradszky[6]. After removal of protecting groups, the free heptacosapeptide amide was isolated by countercurrent distribution in the system n-butanol: 0.1 N phosphate buffer pH 7 (1:1), in which this material showed the same K value (0.5) as the contaminant present in the samples of synthetic secretin of low biological potency. The 3-β -aspartic acid analog of secretion showed only 0.6% of the potency of pure synthetic secretin in stimulating flow and bicarbonate secretion from the dog pancreas.

SYNTHESIS OF THE C-TERMINAL OCTAPEPTIDE OF CHOLECYSTOKININ-PANCREOZYMIN

Cholecystokinin-pancreozymin (CCK-PZ) is a straight chain polypeptide of thirty-three residues[7]. Fractionation of the tryptic digest of pure CCK-PZ permitted the isolation of the C-terminal fragment, an octapeptide amide with the amino acid sequence depicted in FIG. 4[8].

$$\overset{\displaystyle SO_3H}{\overset{|}{\text{ASP-TYR-MET-GLY-TRP-MET-ASP-PHE-NH}_2}}$$

FIG. 4

The similarity to the C-terminal portions of gastrin II[9,10] and of caerulein[11] is most remarkable, particularly when the widely different origin of these three peptides is taken into consideration.

A convenient approach to the synthesis of an O-sulfated tyrosyl peptide would be the use of a two-stage procedure:

    a) synthesis of the corresponding tyrosyl sequence, and

    b) introduction of the sulfate ester moiety.

The alternative procedure of introducing the tyrosyl moiety with its hydroxyl group already esterified with sulfuric acid is also an interesting possibility, although a severe limitation in the selection of protecting groups is inherent in this approach, due to the acid lability of the tyrosine-O-sulfate.

In the synthesis of the octapeptide of FIG. 4, we have followed the first approach. The preparation of the corresponding tyrosyl octapeptide was achieved by two different procedures described in FIGS. 5 and 6.

Any procedure for the introduction of the sulfate moiety on the tyrosine residue of the fully free octapeptide has to contend with several difficulties arising from the very nature of this starting material, namely: the free alpha amino group which could form sulphamic acid derivatives, and the presence of aspartic acid and tryptophan residues with their known lability under acidic conditions.

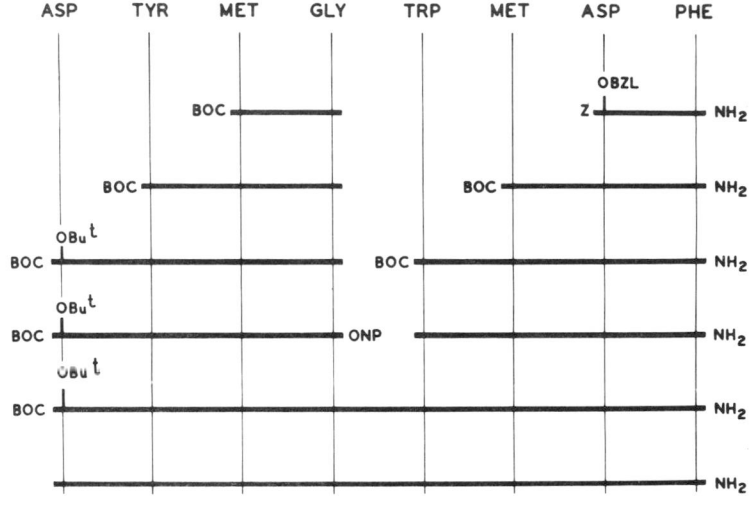

FIG. 5

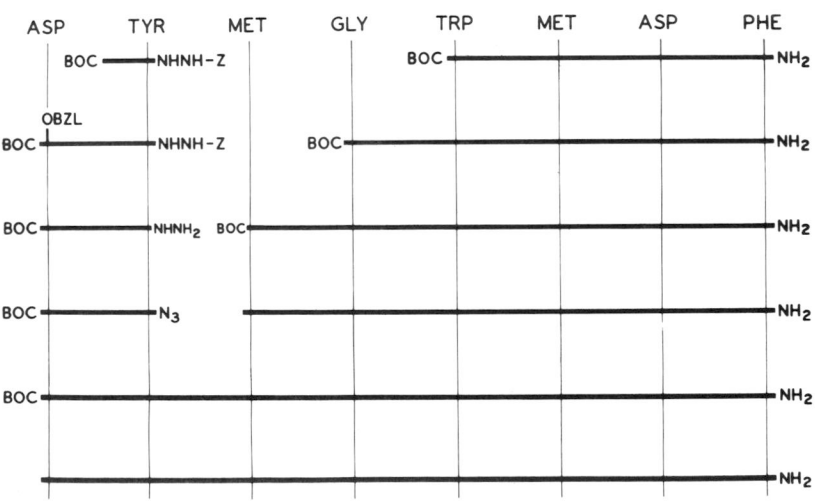

FIG. 6

Sulfation of tyrosine-containing peptides with concentrated sulfuric acid[12, 13] has to cope not only with some of the disadvantages mentioned before, but also with the possible formation of sulfonyl derivatives of tyrosine. From preliminary experiments on the sulfation of tyrosine itself, it was evident that a low reaction temperature was a very important factor in securing large yields of the O-sulfated derivative. In the case of the octapeptide, low temperature also proved to be of importance, not only to avoid significant amounts of C-sulfation, but also because of the presence of labile aspartyl and tryptophyl moieties.

It was learned, however, that temperature is not the only parameter to be controlled. Reactions at -15° for several hours led to the almost exclusive formation of sulfonic acid derivatives. Here, time of reaction was shown to be of utmost importance. O-sulfation was predominant during the first minutes after the dissolution of the octapeptide in concentrated sulfuric acid.

In dealing with these highly competitive reactions, it was of considerable practical importance to have available analytical techniques that could distinguish between the starting octapeptide and its O-sulfated and C-sulfated derivatives. Paper chromatography and paper electrophoresis can easily separate the former from the other two products. However, these techniques are of no particular value for the

187

separation of the O-sulfate and the sulfonic acid derivatives. Degradation with aminopeptidase M or leucine aminopeptidase, followed by two-dimensional paper electrophoresis and chromatography of the amino acid mixture, gives a very clear separation of tyrosine-O-sulfate and 3'-sulfonyl tyrosine, and the relative amounts of the two indicates the proportion of O- and C-sulfated products present in the original mixture. A much simpler analytical technique was found in infrared spectroscopy. Sulfonyl tyrosine-containing peptides show a very strong and broad band at 1225 cm^{-1} and two sharp bands of medium intensity of 1020 and 1080 cm^{-1}. On the other hand, O-sulfate tyrosyl peptides show a strong and broad band at 1250 cm^{-1} and a very sharp and strong band at 1050 cm^{-1}.

The O-sulfated tyrosyl octapeptide was shown to be indistinguishable from the C-terminal tryptic fragment of CCK-PZ when compared by paper chromatography and electrophoresis. Both compounds gave the same products when degraded with chymotrypsin and cyanogen bromide.

In assays involving the gall bladder of the guinea pig, both in situ and in vitro, the O-sulfated tyrosyl octapeptide showed a potency of approximately 30,000 Ivy dog units per milligram. In the same assays the corresponding tyrosyl octapeptide had a potency of about 50 Ivy dog units per milligram.

ACKNOWLEDGMENTS

The authors wish to express their gratitude to Dr. Bernard Rubin and Dr. Stanford Engel (Squibb) for the assays with the guinea pig gall bladder, to Dozent Dr. Viktor Mutt (Karolinska Institutet) for the comparison between natural and synthetic materials, and to Dr. Morton I. Grossman (Veterans Administration - Los Angeles) for the pancreatic flow bioassays.

REFERENCES

1. M. Bodanszky, M. A. Ondetti, S. D. Levine and N. J. Williams; J. Am. Chem. Soc., 89, 6753 (1967).

2. M. A. Ondetti, J. T. Sheehan, and M. Bodanszky, in Pharmacology of Hormonal Polypeptides and Proteins, Plenum Press, New York, 1968, p. 18.

3. V. Mutt, S. Magnusson, J. E. Jorpes and E. Dahl, Biochemistry, 4, 2358, (1965).

4. M. A. Ondetti, A. Deer, J. T. Sheehan, J. Pluscec, and O. Kocy, Biochemistry, in press.

5. M. A. Ondetti, V. L. Narayanan, M. Von Saltza, J. T. Sheehan, E. F. Sabo, and M. Bodanszky, J. Am. Chem. Soc., 90, 4711 (1968).

6. K. Medzihradszky, Communication at the 3rd European Peptide Symposium, Basle, 1960; cf. also M. Zaoral, Collection. Czech. Chem. Commun., 30, 1853 (1965).

7. V. Mutt, and J. E. Jorpes, Europ. J. Biochemistry, in press.

8. Personal Communication from Dozent V. Mutt and Professor J. E. Jorpes.

9. H. J. Tracy and R. A. Gregory, Nature, 204, 935 (1964).

10. H. Gregory, P. A. Hardy, D. S. Jones, G. W. Kenner, and R. C. Sheppard, Nature, 204, 935 (1964).

11. A. Anastasi, V. Erspamer, and R. Endean, Experimentia, 23, 699 (1967).

12. H. C. Reitz, R. E. Ferrel, H. Fraenkel-Conrat, and H. S. Olcott, J. Am. Chem. Soc., 68, 1024, (1946).

13. K. S. Dodgson, F. A. Rose, and N. Tudball, Biochem. J., 71, 10 (1959).

THE STRUCTURAL REQUIREMENTS
FOR
THE ACTIONS OF PEPTIDE AND AMINE
HORMONES ON ADIPOSE TISSUE

Daniel Rudman

Departments of Medicine and Biochemistry
Emory University School of Medicine
Atlanta, Georgia

1. PHYSIOLOGY OF THE FAT CELL(1).

We now recognize that the mammalian fat cell performs

certain metabolic functions at a rapid rate, and that these

functions are controlled by various peptide and amine hor-

mones. The metabolism and regulation of the young rat's

fat cell are illustrated in FIG. 1. Stored triglyceride is

continuously being hydrolyzed by a (hormone-sensitive)

triglyceridase-diglyceridase system to 3 free fatty acids

(FFA) and glycerol. The latter is not reutilized by the cell.

A major portion of the FFA may be secreted from the cell

into the extra-cellular fluid; the remainder is reesterified

with α -glycerolphosphate (derived from the continuing

metabolism of glucose). Glucose enters the fat cell by way

of several different hexose-transport mechanisms. Once

intracellular, glucose is metabolized via the embden-

meyerhof and pentose shunts to CO_2, α -glycerol PO_4 and

fatty acids as the major metabolic end-products. Still

191

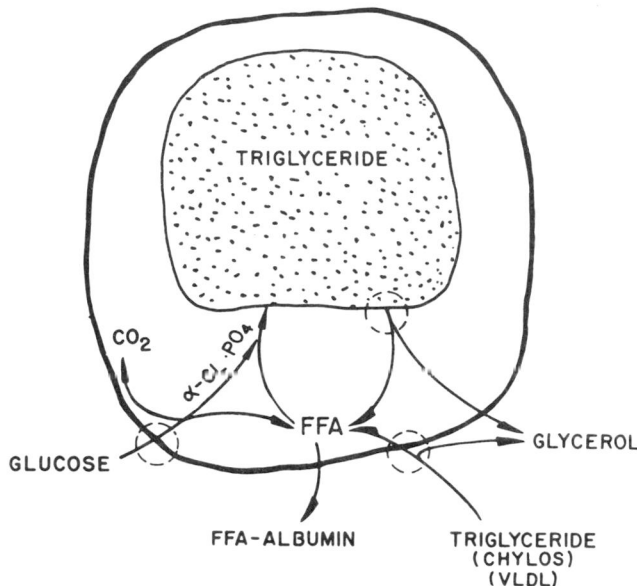

FIG. 1

Major pathways in the young rat's fat cell for uptake of
extracellular triglyceride, for uptake and metabolism of
glucose, and for mobilization of stored triglyceride.
Circles indicate major points of hormonal control:
Transport of glucose across the cell membrane, activity
of the hormone-sensitive lipase which hydrolyzes intracellular stored triglyceride, and activity of the lipoprotein
lipase which hydrolyzes extracellular triglyceride.
'Chylos" and 'Vldl" signify chylomicra and low density
lipoproteins of plasma.

another pathway by which fatty acids arise within the fat

cells (besides lipolysis of stored triglyceride and lipogenesis

from glucose) is by the action of lipoprotein-lipase (in the

region of the cell membrane) upon the triglyceride moiety

of extracellular chylomicra and very low density lipopro-

teins: The resulting fatty acids, but not the glycerol, are

efficiently taken up by the fat cells. Fatty acids arising

by all 3 routes are esterified with a -glycerol PO_4 to

triglyceride. Thus, we can say that out of this network

of pathways, 4 metabolic functions emerge:

(1) Uptake of circulating glucose and conversion of the

hexose to fatty acids; (2) Uptake of the fatty acid moiety

of circulating triglyceride; (3) Esterification of fatty acids

arising by both pathways, and storage of these acids as

triglyceride; (4) Mobilization of the lipid moiety of stored

triglyceride as FFA.

Each function is controlled by hormones. Insulin activate

one of the several hexose-transport sites on the fat cell

membrane, thereby, leading to increased rate of uptake

and metabolism of the sugar (the "glucose-transport"action

of insulin). Insulin may also be concerned with maintaining

the activity of the lipoprotein lipase. The activity of

the hormone-sensitive triglyceridase is stimulated by

pituitary peptides, glucagon, and catechol amines

("Lypolytic" effect of peptide and amine hormones), appar-

ently through the mechanism of stimulating adenyl cyclase

with resultant formation of 3, 5 cyclic AMP which is

believed to be the actual activator of the triglyceridase[2]

This lipolytic action is opposed by insulin, evidently

through the latter hormone's suppressive effect on the

adenyl cyclase ("Antilipolytic" property of insulin)[3,4]

2. DOSE-RESPONSE CURVES FOR IN VITRO HORMONAL EFFECTS ON ADIPOSE TISSUE SLICES.

Three of the four effects mentioned, viz. the lipolytic effect, the glucose-transport effect, and the antilipolytic effect can be made to assume reproducible, sigmoid-shaped log dose-response curves under suitable assay conditions. These are illustrated in FIGS. 2-4. In the

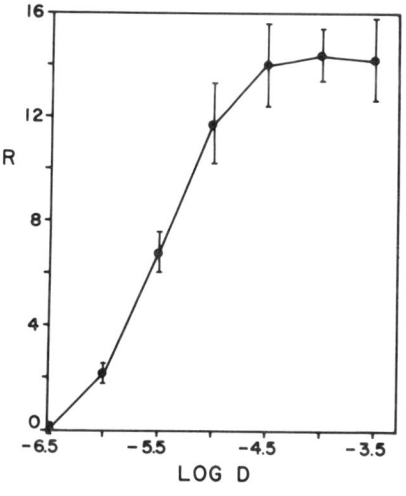

FIG. 2

Relationship between logarithm of the dose of norepine-phrine and the response of slices of hamster adipose tissue. Abscissa; logarithm of the molar concentration of norepinephrine in the medium at the beginning of incu-bation. Ordinate: Increase in concentration of FFA in the tissue slices at the end of two hours incubation over that in slices incubated in KRP medium not containing adipokinetic substance. Each point represents the average of four observations. Standard error of the mean is also shown. All the tissue slices were obtained from a single hamster.

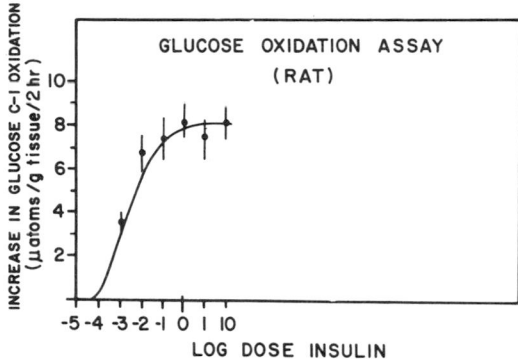

FIG. 3

Log dose vs. response curve for the effect of bovine insulin in stimulating slices of rat epididymal adipose tissue to convert extracellular glucose C-1 to CO_2. "Dose" of insulin refers to G/ML of the hormone in the incubation medium. Technique of the assay is detailed in reference (13).

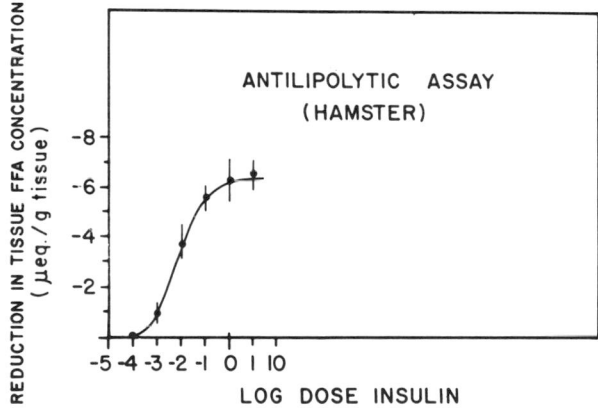

FIG. 4

Log dose vs. response curve for the effect of insulin in reducing the lipolytic response of hamster epididymal adipose tissue slices to 1 G/ML epinephrine. "Dose" of insulin refers to G/ML of hormone in the incubation medium. Technique of the assay is described in reference (13).

195

lipolytic assay, slices of epididymal or perirenal adipose
tissue are incubated for 1. 5 Hr. in Kress-Ringer phosphate
medium (KRP) containing various concentrations of the
test material. At the end of incubation, the concentration
of FFA in the tissue slice is measured; the increase in
this value represents the response to the test substance.
In the antilipolytic assay, the slices are incubated in KRP
containing (A) A standard concentration of a lipolytic
substance (usually 1 G/ML ACTH or epinephrine), and also
(B) Varying concentrations of the material being tested for
antilipolytic action. The reduction in tissue FFA concentration in slices exposed to lipolytic hormone test substance, compared to the FFA level in slices exposed only
to lipolytic hormone, represents the response in this assay.

In the glucose-transport assay, the tissue slices are
incubated in DRP containing 4 G/100 ML albumin,
50 MG/100 ML glucose which is labeled in the C-1 position,
and various concentrations of the test substance. At the
end of the two hour incubation, the quantity of extracellular
glucose C-1 which had been taken up by the tissue and oxidized to CO_2 is measured; increase in this value serves
as the response in this assay. (Uniformly labeled or C-6
labeled glucose can also be used, and the increase in conversion to tissue triglyceride-fatty acids can then be
utilized as the biologic response).

As illustrated in FIGS. 2, 3, and 4, the log dose vs. response curve in each assay exhibits a sigmoid shape. Clark[5] and Stetten[6] have pointed out that curves of this form can be explained by the following model: The hormone interacts in reversible manner with a set of cell receptors, and the magnitude of the biological response is linearly related to the abundance of the cell-receptor complexes. A consequence of this interpretation is that the maximal response elicited by the hormone is determined by the number of receptors available to it while the minimal effective dose (MED) is determined by the affinity of these receptors for the hormone. While this model must remain hypothetical until the postulated receptors can be isolated and chemically defined, this interpretation is presented here as a possible explanation for the characteristic differences in maximal response and minimal effective dose which will become evident in the sections to follow.

3. STRUCTURAL BASIS FOR THE LIPOLYTIC EFFECT

As shown in Table 1, the endocrine system contains several substances which stimulate lipolysis in the fat cells, but only one agent (insulin), with antilipolytic and glucose-transport properties. Our approach to the structure-activity question has been: In the case of the sizeable group of natural lipolytic agents, to examine the structures of the members of this group in search of a common structural

TABLE 1

NATURALLY OCCURRING SUBSTANCES WHICH CAUSE
ACUTE ALTERATIONS IN ADIPOSE TISSUE METABOLISM

	LIPOLYTIC	ANTILIPOLYTIC	GLUCOSE TRANSPORT
PITUITARY	ACTH		
	α MSH		
	β MSH		
	PEPTIDE I		
	PEPTIDE II		
	FRACTION L'		
	β LPH		
	γ LPH		
	TSH		
	ARGININE VASOPRESSIN		
PANCREAS	GLUCAGON	INSULIN	INSULIN
SYMPATHETIC NERVOUS SYSTEM	EPINEPHRINE NOREPINEPHRINE		

feature; and in the case of the antilipolytic and glucose-transport actions of insulin, to test the activities of fragments of the insulin molecule.

The several natural lipolytic agents are not all active on the adipose tissue of the same species, but in each species certain members of the lipolytic family can be compared. Such comparison shows parallel dose-response curves with identical maximal responses, differing only in MED[7]. This parallelism, together with recent evidence that the different lipolytic agents all operate through the adenyl cyclase mechanism to activate lipolysis[2], leads one to

examine the structures of the lipolytic substances in
search of a common feature which might be the basis of
the lipolytic property, as shown in Table 2. The α and
β -MSH molecules have in common with ACTH the sequence,
TYR. X. MET GLU HIS PHE ARG TRY. GLY. The
lipolytic activity of these 3 peptides must therefore reside
within this sequence, a conclusion confirmed by the assays
of Tanaka, et al.[8], on synthetic fragments corresponding
to this region of the ACTH molecule.

Further information comes from inspection of the
structures of arginine vasopressin and lysine vasopressin,
Table 2. The inactivity of the latter indicates the essential role of arginine. But arginine and most arginyl peptides arc inactive, so that additional residues are required.
Comparison of arginine vasopressin with ACTH, α MSH and
β MSH suggests that the common feature may be TYR. A.
B. GLU C. D. ARG (2). This at any rate seems to be the
only point of similarity between arginine vasopressin,
α MSH, β MSH and ACTH. Furthermore, glucagon contains
a sequence . . . TYR SER LYS TYR LEU ASP SER ARG
ARG . . . in which the relationships between TYR, ASP,
and ARG are similar (though not identical) to those of the
lipolytic hypophyseal peptides.

The structure-activity relationships in the aromatic
amine series may conceivably be analogous. Here the

199

TABLE 2

STRUCTURES OF CERTAIN PEPTIDES DISCUSSED IN THE TEXT

ACTH(PIG)

SER-TYR-SER-MET-GLU-HIS-PHE-ARG-TRY-GLY-LYS-
PRO-VAL-GLY-LYS-LYS-ARG-ARG-PRO-VAL-LYS-VAL-
TYR-PRO-ASP-GLY-ALA-GLU-ASP-GLU(NH$_2$)-LEU-ALA-
GLU-ALA-PHE-PRO-LEU-GLU-PHE

α-MSH (PIG, CATTLE, HORSE, MONKEY)

ACETYL-SER-TYR-SER-MET-GLU-HIS-PHE-ARG-TRY-
GLY-LYS-PRO-VAL-NH$_2$

β-MSH (CATTLE)

ASP-SER-GLY-PRO-TYR-LYS-MET-GLU-HIS-PHE-ARG-
TRY-GLY-SER-PRO-PRO-LYS-ASP

ARGININE VASOPRESSIN (MAN, SHEEP, HORSE, COW)

CYS-TYR-PHE-GLU(NH$_2$)-ASP(NH$_2$)-CYS-PRO-ARG-
⌐S————S⌐
GLY-NH$_2$

LYSINE VASOPRESSIN (PIG, HIPPOPOTAMUS)

CYS-TYR-PHE-GLU(NH$_2$)-ASP(NH$_2$)-CYS-PRO-LYS-
⌐S————S⌐
GLY-NH$_2$

GLUCAGON (CATTLE)

HIS-SER-GLU(NH$_2$)-GLY-THR-PHE-THR-SER-ASP-
TYR-SER-LYS-THR-LEU-ASP-SER-ARG-ARG-ALA-
GLU(NH$_2$)-ASP-PHE-VAL-GLU(NH$_2$)-TRY-LEU-MET-
ASP(NH$_2$)-THR

requirement is for a primary or secondary amine group, separated by either a 2 or 3 carbon atom bridge from a hydroxylated benzene ring; the presence of an oxygen function on the β -carbon enhances activity[10]. Is it possible, as suggested in FIG. 5, that the functions of the catechol ring, β -carbon oxygen function, and positively charged amine group (which 3 functional groups must be separated from each other by fixed distances) may be analogous to these of the (aromatic) tyrosyl, (carboxyl-containing) glutamyl(or aspartyl) and (positively charged) arginyl side chains, which must also

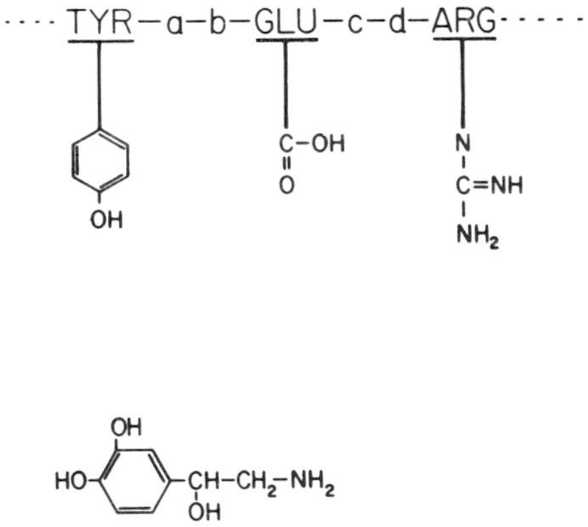

$$\cdots\cdots \text{TYR} - a - b - \text{GLU} - c - d - \text{ARG} \cdots\cdots$$

FIG. 5

Postulated analogy between (1) the aromatic side chain of tyrosine, the carboxyl-bearing side chain of glutamyl, and the guanidinated side chain of arginine, separated at fixed distances in the lipolytic peptides, and (2) the catechol ring, the β -carbon hydroxyl group, and the amine group, which characterize the lipolytic aromatic amines.

be separated at fixed distances? Does the coiling of the
peptide chain allow the functional groups of these 3
residues to align themselves in the same spatial configuration as the (possibly) corresponding 3 functional
groups of the catechol amine?

4. STRUCTURAL BASES FOR THE ANTILIPOLYTIC AND GLUCOSE-TRANSPORT EFFECTS.

Our interest in this subject developed as a result of
investigations on an insulin-cleaving enzyme system
present in the adipose tissue of the myomorph rodents
rat, mouse and hamster, but absent from that of the
caviamorph rodent guinea pig and from that of the lago-
morph rabbit[11]. Since the former three tissues are highly
responsive either to the glucose-transport or antilipolytic
action of insulin or to both, while the latter two tissues
are insensitive to the hormone, it seemed possible that
the insulin-cleaving enzyme system might be a determinant
of insulin responsiveness. Therefore, we investigated the
chemistry of the cleavage process and the possible biologic
activity of the cleavage products.

The "insulinase" system of myomorph adipose tissue is
located in the aqueous-insoluble fraction of the tissue,
from which all soluble nitrogenous material can be removed
by repeated washing. When insulin is incubated with this
preparation at pH 7.0 in ammonium acetate buffer, the

hormone is rapidly cleaved into 20-30 cleavage products
of which 5-8 represent free amino acids and the remainder
peptides. Disulfide groups remain intact. The insoluble
enzyme preparation is readily removed by centrifugation
and the mixture of cleavage products isolated in salt-free
form by lyophilization. When this mixture was resolved
by ion-exchange chromatography, high voltage electrophoresis and paper chromatography into its components,
we found that the molar composition of the mixture of free
(non-basic) amino acids was: TYR 27%, LEU 25%, PHE 17%,
ALA 7%, ASN GLU 8%. In two experiments a total of 28
peptide fragments of insulin were isolated and their structures deduced from the quantitative amino acid composition.
These peptides could be arranged into 5 groups on the
basis of the region of the insulin molecule from which they
were derived, as shown in Table 3. All this information
[12-14] on the nature of the amino acid and peptide cleavage
products, on the number of free amino acids released,
and on the number of internal bonds split per insulin
molecule, were compatible with the following hypothesis
(FIG. 6): The initial step in the cleavage process is
hydrolysis of bonds A 13-14 (LEU TYR), A 18-19 (ASN TYR),
B 11-12 (LEU VAL), B-15-16 (LEU TYR), B 24-25(PHE PHE),
and B 25-26 (PHE TYR) (All of which join nonpolar
residues). The resulting 5 fragments then come under

TABLE 3

PEPTIDES ISOLATED FROM MIXTURE OF CLEAVAGE
PRODUCTS FORMED BY ACTION OF INSOLUBLE FRACTION
OF RAT ADIPOSE TISSUE UPON BOVINE INSULIN

GROUP 1	A3-7-12	A4-7-12	A3-7-12
	S	S	S
	S	S	S
	B2-7-9	B1-7-14	B7-8
	A3-7-11	A5-7-12	A-7-11
	S	S	S
	S	S	S
	B2-7-8	B2-7-11	B2-7-11
	A3-7-12		
	S		
	S		
	B2-7-11		
GROUP 2	B12-14		
GROUP 3	A15-18		
	A16-17		
	A15-18		
GROUP 4	A20-21	A20-21	A20-21
	S	S	S
	S	S	S
	B19	B17-19-21	B17-19-23
A20-21	A20-21	A20-21	A20
S	S	S	S
S	S	S	S
B18-19	B19-21	B18-19-21	B17-19-23
A20	A20		
S	S		
S	S		
B18-19-21	B17-19-22		
GROUP 5	B28-30		
	B29-30		
	B26-30		
	B26-28		
	B26-27		

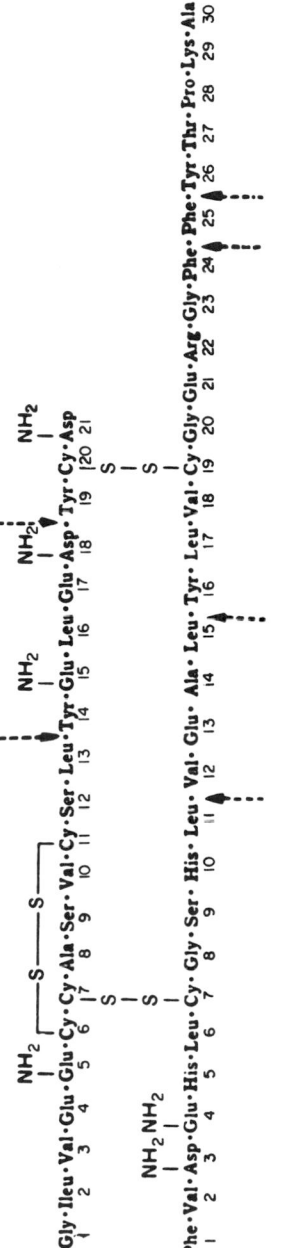

FIG. 6

Postulated sites of initial cleavage of bovine insulin molecule by the insulin-degrading enzyme system of rat adipose tissue.

the influence of an amino - and a carboxypeptidase with
stepwise removal of terminal residues from both termini,
leading to the formation of 5 groups of peptides of related
structure. Experiments with model peptidase substrates
indicated the presence in the tissue enzyme preparation of
a non-specific amino and carboxypeptidase which could
account for the release of the free amino acids, but suggested that the endopeptidase responsible for the initial
internal cleavages is specific for the insulin molecule[12].

After the chemical mode of cleavage had been clarified,
we returned to the subfractions of the cleavage product
mixture to examine the possible antilipolytic and glucose-
transport potencies[13]. No activity had been generated for
the insulin-sensitive guinea pig and rabbit tissues, suggesting that inability of these adipose tissues to cleave
insulin in this manner (as the insulin-sensitive myomorph
adipose tissues can) is not the cause of the former two
adipose tissues' lack of insulin-responsiveness. Antilipolytic activity (as assayed on the hamster tissue, which
is highly responsive to this action of insulin) was totally
absent from the mixture of cleavage products. Weak but
detectable glucose-transport activity (characterized by a
maximal response only 1/2 to 1/4 that produced by
insulin) was exhibited by fractions from the ion-exchange
column containing peptides of Groups I and IV (FIG. 7)[14]

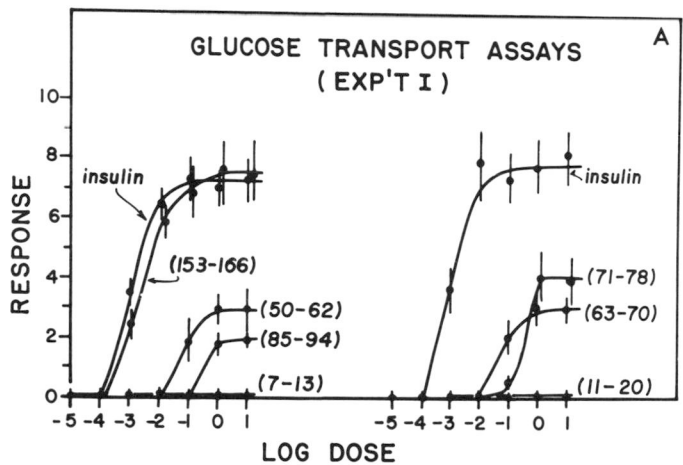

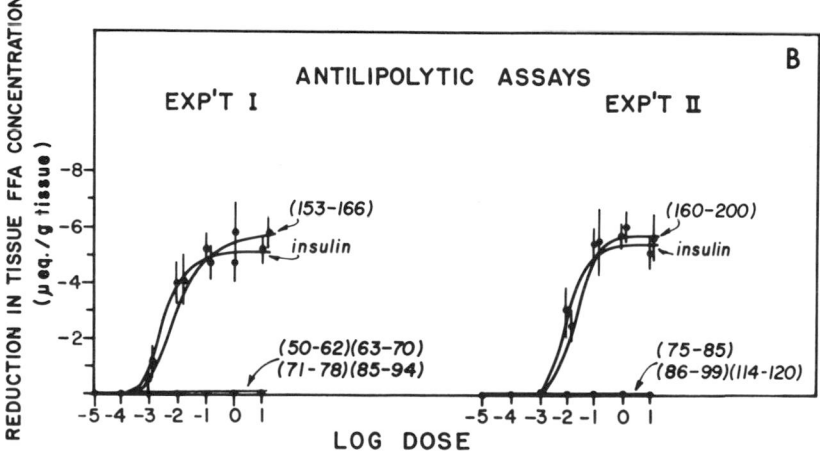

FIG. 7

Assays of fractions of mixture of cleavage products
produced by incubating insulin with insulin-degrading
enzyme system of rat adipose tissue (13). Panel A shows
results of glucose-transport assay, Panel B those of
antilipolytic assay. Fraction (153-166) contained largely
uncleaved insulin; fractions (7-13) and (11-20) free amino
acids and peptides of groups II, III and V; fractions (50-62),
(63-70), (71-78) and (85-94), mixtures of Group I and IV
peptides.

Isolation of the active peptide(s) in these fractions has not yet been accomplished. The data nevertheless suggested that the glucose-transport and antilipolytic properties of insulin reside in different regions of the hormone molecule.

This question was now further pursued with derivatives of insulin generously made available by Dr. F. H. Carpenter (University of California)[14]. These preparations were assayed for both glucose-transport and antilipolytic properties: desalanine-insulin; desasparagine-desalanine insulin; desoctapeptide insulin; and the heptapeptide B 23-29. The assay results are summarized in FIG. 8. Desalanine insulin is equipotent with insulin in both assays; the heptapeptide is inactive in both respects. Desoctapeptide- and desalanine-desasparagine derivatives are markedly (1000 x and 100 x) attenuated in the glucose-transport potency, with a 50% reduction in maximal response; the loss of antipolytic activity is less marked.

These results indicated that both properties reside within the desoctopeptide-desasparagine structure but are markedly enhanced by the presence of B 23-30 and A 21. What features within the desoctapeptide-desasparagine structure are responsible for the attenuated but still detectable glucose-transport and antilipolytic activities?

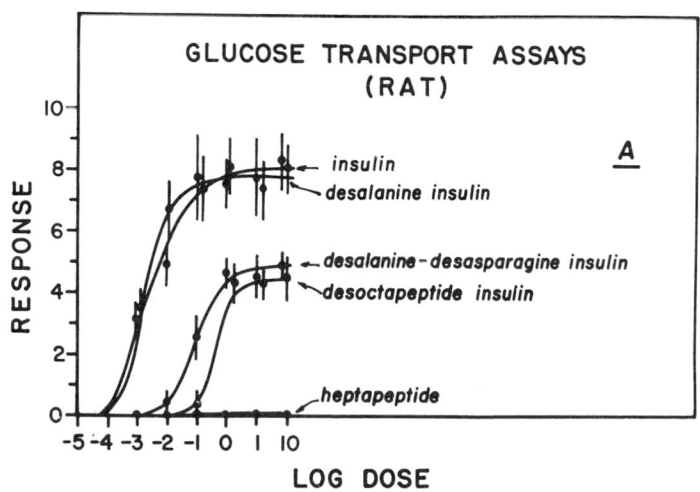

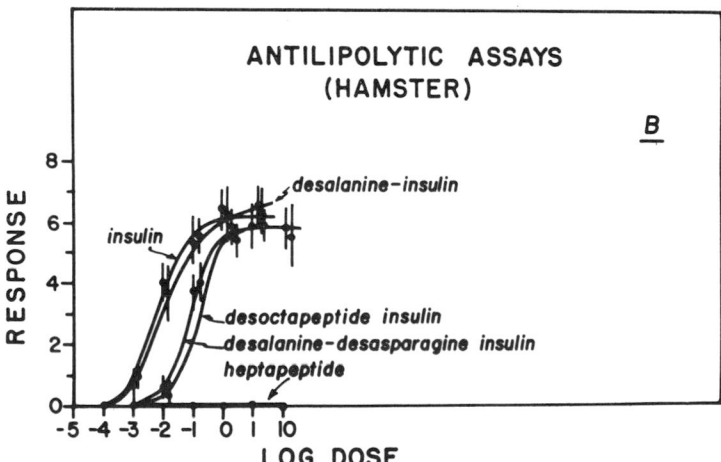

FIG. 8

Glucose transport (Panel A) and antilipolytic (Panel B)
assays of derivatives of bovine insulin from laboratory of
Dr. F. H. Carpenter (14).

We believed we had a clue in our earlier finding (see above) that cleavage of the desoctapeptide-desasparagine ring structure at LEU TYR, ASN TYR and LEU VAL bonds abolished antilipolytic activity but did not further reduce glucose-transport activity below that possessed by the desoctapeptide-desasparagine structure. Therefore, we examined the possible activity of synthetic Di- and Tri-peptides containing LEU, TYR, ASN, VAL and other residues. As shown in Table 4 and FIG. 9, blocked peptides containing LEU TYR or (to a lesser extent) GLY TYR exhibited antilipolytic activity about 1/1000 as great as insulin; these compounds were inactive in the glucose-transport assay. Inspection of Table 4 shows that the

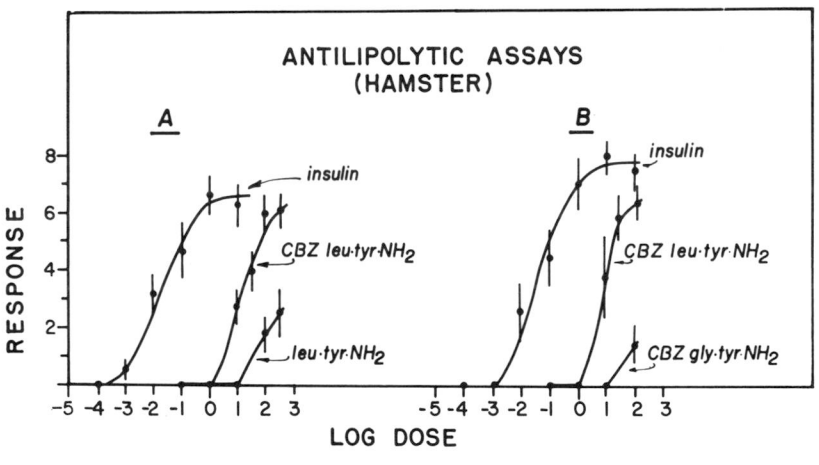

FIG. 9

Antilipolytic assays of bovine insulin and certain synthetic dipeptides.

TABLE 4

Synthetic Peptides Tested For Capacity to Reduce the In Vitro Lipolytic Response
of Hamster Adipose Tissue to 1 μG/ML of ACTH,[a]

ANTILIPOLYTIC

N-CBZ-LEU-TYR-NH$_2$(MED 10 μG/ML)

LEU-TYR-NH$_2$(MED 100 μG/ML)

N-CBZ-GLY-TYR-NH$_2$(MED 100 μG/ML)

GLY-TYR-NH$_2$(MED 300 μG/ML)

NO ANTILIPOLYTIC EFFECT AT 500 μG/ML

TYROSYL PEPTIDES	GLYCYL PEPTIDES	OTHER PEPTIDES
N-CBZ-SER-TYR-NH$_2$	N-CBZ-GLY-PHE	N-BENZOYL-PHE-NH$_2$
LEU-TYR	N-CBZ-GLY-TYR	N-BENZOYL-PHE
N-CBZ-LEU-TYR	N-CBZ-GLY-TRP	N-CBZ-PHE-PHE-NH$_2$
TYR-GLY	N-CBZ-GLY-NH$_2$	N-CBZ-GLU-PHE
N-BENZOYL-TYR-GLY-NH$_2$	N-BENZOYL-GLY-GYL-NH$_2$	N-CBZ-ALA-ASN-NH$_2$
N-ACETYL-TYR-NH$_2$	N-CBZ-ALA-GLY-NH$_2$	N-CBZ-S-BENZOYL-CYS-ALA
TYR	N-CBZ-GLY-SER-NH$_2$	N-BENZOYL-GLY-LYS
	N-CBZ-GLY-PHE-NH$_2$	N-BENZOYL-GLY-ARG
LEUCYL PEPTIDES	N-CBZ-S-BENZOYL-CYS-GLY-NH$_2$	N-BENZOYL-ARG-ETHYL ESTER
N-CBZ-LEU-VAL-NH$_2$	N-CBZ-GLY-ALA-NH$_2$	N-BENZOYL-ARG-NH$_2$
N-CBZ-LEU-GLY-NH$_2$	N-BENZOYL-GLY-GLY	
N-CBZ-ALA-LEU-NH$_2$	N-CBZ-GLY-GLU	
N-CBZ-GLY-GLY-LEU-NH$_2$	N-LYS-GLY-NH$_2$	
N-CBZ-PHE-LEU-NH$_2$	GLY-NH$_2$	
N-CBZ-GLY-LEU	GLY-SER	
LEU-GLY	GLY-HIS	
N-CBZ-LEU-NH$_2$	LYS-GLY	
N-BENZOYL-GLY-LEU-NH$_2$	GLY-PHE	
N-CBZ-SER-LEU-NH$_2$	LYS-GLY-NH$_2$	
N-CBZ-HIS-LEU-NHNH$_2$		

---

[a]OPTICALLY ACTIVE AMINO ACIDS WERE OF THE L CONFIGURATION IN ALL
CASES. MED = MINIMAL EFFECTIVE DOSE.

antilipolytic activity is specific for the LEU TYR or
GLY TYR sequence among those studied, that a blocked
COOH-terminus is essential, and that a blocked NH_2-
terminus enhances activity.

These data to date are compatible with the motion that
the antilipolytic activity of insulin stems from the LEU TYR
sequences A 13-14 and B 15-16 while the glucose-transport
activity arises from regions of the desoctapeptide-desasparagine structure including disulfide bridges not yet
identified.

SUMMARY

The metabolic functions of the fat cell in assimilating,
synthesizing, storing and mobilizing fatty acids are controlled by peptide and amine hormones. ACTH, TSH,
α and β MSH, other novel pituitary peptides related in
structure to MSH, arginine vasopressin, glucagon, and
the catechol amines all share the property of accelerating
mobilization of FFA ("lipolytic property"). Evidence is
presented to support the idea that the structural basis for
the lipolytic property is TYR A B GLU C D ARG and that
the function of each member of this triplet, furthermore,
may be analogous to that of the hydroxylated benzene ring,
β -carbon oxygen function, and amino group, in the catechol
amine series.

Insulin exerts the dual effects of accelerating glucose-transport and suppressing lipolysis. Evidence is presented that (A) both glucose-transport and antilipolytic properties reside within the desoctapeptide-desasparagine structure but are markedly enhanced by the presence of B 23-29 and A 21; (B) the antilipolytic property arises from the two LEU TYR sequences A 13-14 and B 15-16; (C) the glucose-transport property arises from a different region of the desoctapeptide-desasparagine structure, which involves disulfide bridges not yet identified.

FOOTNOTES

(1)   The reader is referred to reference [1] for a comprehensive review of this subject.

(2)   With the proviso that ASP, ASPN or GLN may replace GLU. Amidation of GLU in this position is known not to impair the lipolytic activity of synthetic α MSH[9].

ACKNOWLEDGMENTS

This work was supported by U. S. Public Health Service Grants AM-13129, AM-13122, and FR-39.

REFERENCES

1.   Handbook of Physiology, Section V, Adipose Tissue, (A. E. Renold and G. F. Cahill, Jr., eds.) Am. Physiol. Soc., New York, 1965.

2.   R. W. Butcher, R. J. Ho, C. H. Meng, and E. W. Sutherland, J. Biol. Chem., 240, 4515 (1965).

3.   R. L. Jungas, E. G. Ball, Biochemistry, 2, 383, (1963).

4. R. W. Butcher, J. G. T. Sneyd, C. R. Park, and E. W. Sutherland, Jr., <u>J. Biol. Chem.</u>, 241, 1652, (1966).

5. A. J. Clark, in A. Hefter's <u>Handbuch Der Experimentellen Pharmacologie</u>, Vol. 4, (A. Hefter, ed.), Julius Springer, Berlin, 1937.

6. D. Stetten, Jr., <u>Science,</u> 124, 365 (1956).

7. D. Rudman, S. J. Brown, and M. F. Malkin, <u>Endocrinology,</u> 72, 528, (1963).

8. A. Tanaka, B. T. Pickering, and C. H. Li, <u>Arch. Biochem.</u>, 99, 294, (1962).

9. M. S. Raben, R. Landolt, F. A. Smith, K. Hormann, and H. Yajima, <u>Nature,</u> 189, 681 (1961).

10. D. Rudman, L. A. Garcia, S. J. Brown, M. F. Malkin, and W. Perl, <u>J. Lipid Res.</u>, 5, 28, (1964).

11. D. Rudman, and M. DiGirolamo, <u>Adv. Lipid Res.</u>, 5, 35, (1967).

12. D. Rudman, L. A. Garcia, M. DiGirolamo, and P. W. Shank, <u>Endocrinology,</u> 78, 169, (1966).

13. D. Rudman, L. A. Garcia, A. Del Rio, and S. Akgun, <u>Biochem.</u>, 7, 1864 (1968).

14. D. Rudman, L. A. Garcia, and A. Del Ria, <u>Biochem.</u>, 7, 1875 (1968).

STRUCTURAL STUDIES ON PORCINE THYROCALCITONIN USING EDMAN DEGRADATION

H. D. Niall and J. T. Potts, Jr.

National Heart Institute
National Institutes of Health
Bethesda, Maryland
and
Endrocrine Unit
Massachusetts General Hospital
Boston, Massachusetts

The hypocalcemic peptide hormone, thyrocalcitonin, was isolated in pure form in our laboratory in 1967 and was shown to consist of a single chain of 32 amino acids[1,2].

We have determined the complete sequence[3] of the molecule by sequential Edman degradation of the intact hormone and three peptide subfragments. The results were in complete agreement with those provided by another quite independent method. Our second approach involved cleavage of the molecule by a number of different enzymatic and chemical means, with separation and analysis of 61 different peptide subfragments. The covalent structure of the hormone that we proposed[3] based on this dual approach (FIG. 1) has since been confirmed by subsequent reports of completely independent structural analyses[4,5] and by synthesis of fully active material[6,7].

215

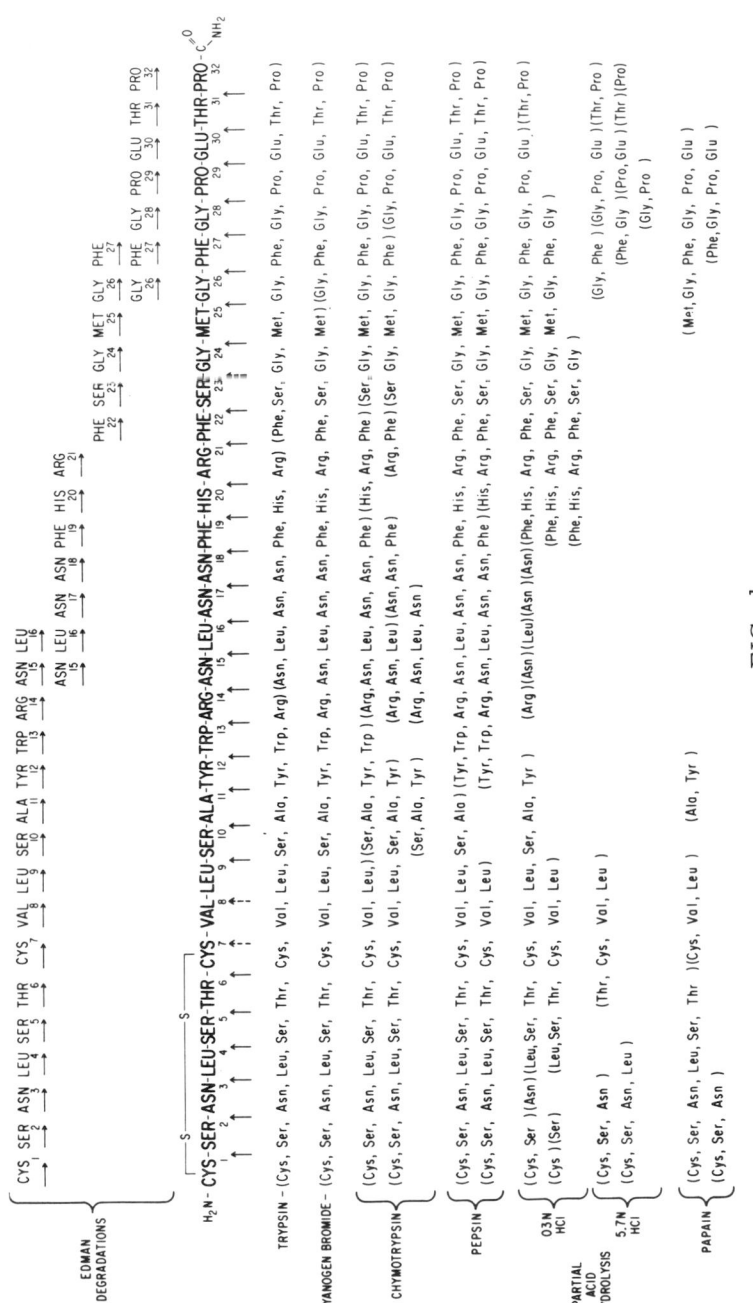

FIG. 1

Approaches used in defining the amino acid sequence of porcine thyrocalcitonin.

The main structural features of the molecule are illustrated in FIG. 2. There is a 1-7 intrachain disulfide bridge, constituting a 23 membered ring at the amino terminus. The carboxyl terminal residue is prolinamide. No significant biological activity is associated with the cyanogen bromide[8] or tryptic fragments of the molecule[9] nor with the hormone itself after modification of the half-cystine[10], tyrosine, or tryptophan residues.[11] On the other hand, the methionine residue may be oxidized or alkylated without loss of activity[10].

The principal purpose of this paper will be to discuss the methods used and the problems encountered in establishing the complete sequence of the 32 amino acid polypeptide by use of the phenylisothiocyanate method of Edman[12].

EXPERIMENTAL

I. Materials

The peptides used were (1) intact thyrocalcitonin, (2) tryptic peptide T2 (residues 15-21), (3) tryptic peptide T3 (residues 22-32), and (4) smaller cyanogen bromide fragment CNBr 2 (residues 26-32).

The techniques used to prepare and isolate these fragments as well as the procedures used to modify the half cystine residues have been previously described[1,2].

Solvents and reagents for Edman degradation were purified before use. Phenylisothiocyanate, trifluoroacetic acid, benzene and ethyl acetate were purified according to previously described procedures[13]. The trifluoroacetic acid was re-

fluxed with solid chromium trioxide and redistilled prior to

use. Ethylene dichloride was purified as described pre-

viously for 1-chlorobutane[13]. Pyridine was refluxed with

potassium hydroxide pellets, distilled, refluxed with phthalic

anhydride and redistilled (114-116°C). Dimethylallylamine

was distilled, refluxed with phthalic anhydride and redis-

tilled (59-60°C).

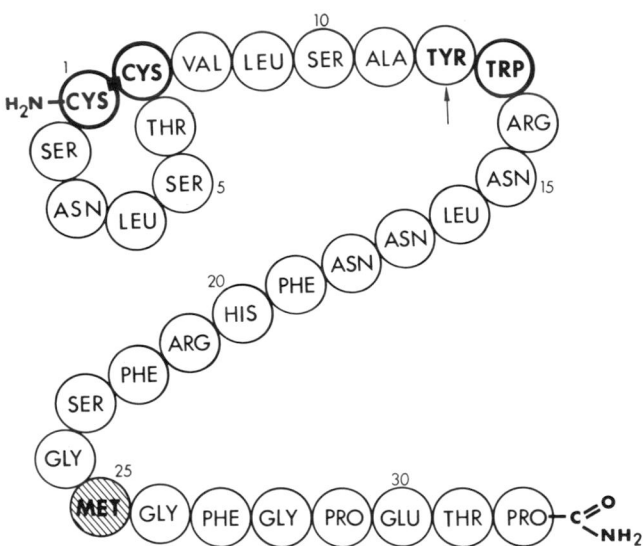

FIG. 2

Schematic representation of the covalent structure of porcine
thyrocalcitonin. Residues important for biological activity
are indicated in boldface and heavy circles. Methionine
(shaded) residue 25 is not essential for biological activity.

II. Methods

A modified three-stage manual Edman degradation[14]
was used throughout. The basic procedure may be summarized
as follows. Reaction with phenylisothiocyanate is performed
in 0.1 - 0.5 ml of a pyridine-water mixture (3:2, v/v) containing
0.4 M dimethylallylamine and adjusted to pH 9.5 with trifluoroacetic acid. After coupling (stage 1), the solution is
extracted 3 times with 2 volumes of benzene. The aqueous
phase is then freeze-dried. The dry residue is washed 3
times with 1 volume of ethyl acetate. After further drying,
cleavage of the thiazolinone (stage 2) is performed in anhydrous trifluoroacetic acid (50-100 μl). The shortened peptide
is precipitated by addition of ethylene dichloride and washed
with the same solvent. The separated thiazolinone solution
is dried in a nitrogen stream and converted (stage 3) to
the more stable thiohydantoin by heating in 1 N HCl at 80°C
for 10 minutes[15]. The residual peptide, after drying, is
ready for the next degradation cycle.

Since the native molecule and its peptide subfragments
were hydrophobic in character (FIG. 2), severe losses of
material during extraction steps would have been encountered
if the usual procedure had been followed. Alterations included omission of the ethyl acetate extraction after coupling,
reduction in the extent of benzene extraction, or, at times,
its replacement by a sublimation step. Separation of the

219

thiazolinone from the residual peptide after cleavage was performed after removal of the trifluoroacetic acid by drying in a nitrogen stream. This minimizes solubility of the peptide in the ethylene dichloride used for extractions.

For the degradation on T2, a different procedure was used to separate the cleaved amino acid derivative from the residual peptide. After cleavage, the trifluoroacetic acid was evaporated. The residue was dissolved in 150 µl water and extracted 3 times with 1 ml n-butyl acetate. It was found that derivatives of amino acids without charged side chains could be extracted by this maneuver. A similar extraction is used in the "dansyl" method[16] with a different purpose (purification of residual peptide).

The exact choice of extraction schedules used with each peptide is outlined below.

In the course of many of the degradations, measured aliquots of the residual peptide were taken after certain cycles, acid hydrolyzed and subjected to quantitative amino acid analysis. This provided two sorts of information. Mechanical and extractive losses of material could be calculated from the yields of amino acids obtained. In addition, the analysis by revealing the persistence of amino acid residues which should have been removed by the degradation indicated the extent of incomplete reaction due, for example, to N-terminal blocking mechanisms.

Several methods were used to identify the phenyl thio-hydantoin derivatives obtained. Thin-layer chromatography and mass spectrometry as well as gas-liquid chromatography were applied; further confirmation of the identification of the phenyl thiohydantoin of PTH S-carboxymethyl cysteine (PTH SCMC) was obtained by the use of ^{14}C labelled iodoacetic acid for alkylation.

The gas chromatographic detection system is based upon an earlier method[17]. It is capable of detecting and quanti-tating all the PTH derivatives (except arginine) at high sensitivity. The details of this procedure[18] will not be dis-cussed here. However, all of the individual techniques used have been previously described. These include the use of commercially available liquid silicone phases such as DC 560[26], the use of "mixed phase" columns[27] and the technique of silylation[26] for preparing chromatographically suitable PTH derivatives of aspartic acid, glutamic acid, serine and threonine. Some of the results obtained during the work on thyrocalcitonin, using the DC 560 column, are shown in FIGS. 4-7. PTH-arginine has not so far been successfully chromatographed, and was identified by the Sakaguchi reac-tion in this work. However a variety of methods[19, 20] for derivatization of the highly polar guanidino group are now available; it seems likely that one of these could be used to produce an arginine derivative suitable for gas chromato-graphy.

221

RESULTS

Degradation on Intact Thyrocalcitonin

This region of the sequence was actually completed last, but will be discussed first here for convenience. Despite earlier reports that the N-terminus of the molecule was blocked, we found by Edman degradation of native, reduced and alkylated, and performic acid-oxidized material that a half cystine residue was N-terminal. Autoradiography of a thin-layer chromatograph demonstrated that the produce obtained from step 1 of the degradation of alkylated hormone was radioactive and migrated with the same Rf as an authentic PTH-SCMC standard. Initial degradations (4 cycles) with subtractive analysis were performed on reduced and alkylated and native hormone. This was done to examine the theoretical possibility of a cyclization reaction involving the alpha-amino group and the S-carboxymethyl side chain of the terminal alkylated cysteine residue. This reaction, analogous to the well-known cyclization of N-terminal glutamine, has been reported[21]. However, subtractive analysis after 4 steps showed that the first four residues had been quantitatively removed in both degradations. For the longer degradation, reduced and alkylated hormone was preferred to native material since the PTH cysteine or cystine derivatives which would be formed during degradation on the latter are quite unstable. PTH S-carboxymethyl cysteine on the other hand is sufficiently stable both during the degradation conditions and during gas chromatography to allow identification though with some losses during both procedures. Performic acid-oxidized material was not suitable since the tryptophan residue could not have been identified.

It was hoped that an overlap into tryptic peptide T2 (see FIG. 1) could be achieved, since this would very markedly reduce the amount of work necessary to establish the sequence. This was accomplished, the first 16 residues being identified. The extraction regime used was essentially that outlined in the "Methods" section for the three-stage procedure, except that the ethyl acetate extractions were omitted.

Repetitive yields are shown in FIG. 3. The yields of PTH amino acids known to be stable during degradation (shown by closed circles) fall close to a straight line. The linear plot shows that the fall in yield at each step was approximately constant and amounted to 5% per step of the material initially present. By hydrolysis and amino acid analysis of an aliquot of the residual peptide after completion of several cycles, it was shown that the 5% repetitive loss reflected mechanical and extractive losses of thyrocalcitonin during degradation rather than incomplete coupling or cleavage of successive amino-terminal residues. The PTH amino acids (serine, S-carboxymethyl cysteine, thyrosine, tryptophan) shown by open circles are those known to be subject to partial destruction during degradation, con-

223

version or GLC identification procedures. The yields of
serine and S-carboxymethyl cysteine are consistent with their
known tendency to undergo β elimination reactions. Threonine, calculated as the sum of PTH (threonine plus dehydro-
threonine) is recovered in good overall yield because the
dehydrated product does not undergo further decomposition.
Tyrosine apparently reacts with phenylisothiocyanate[22] via
its phenolic hydroxyl group during the degradation; this may
account for its low yield. Tryptophan decomposes in anhydrous acid[13]. Its yield (6%) after 13 cycles is consistent
with findings[23] with other tryptophan containing proteins and
peptides. Some destruction of tryptophan also occurs during

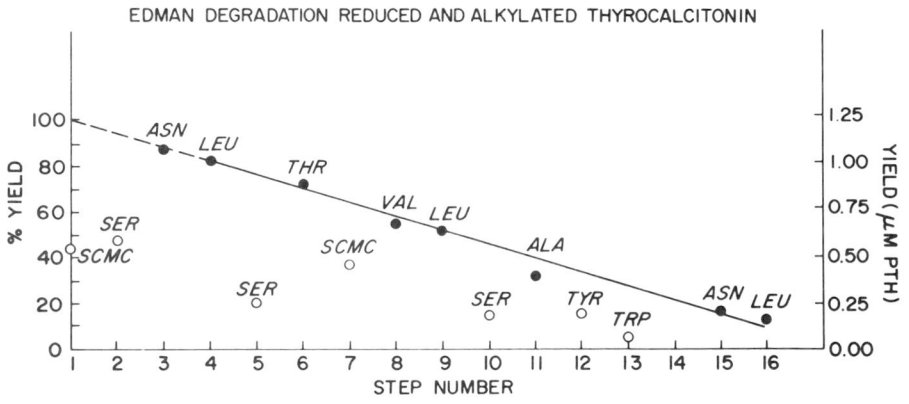

FIG. 3

Yield data from Edman degradation on reduced and alkylated
thyrocalcitonin. Closed circles: "Stable" PTH amino acids.
Open circles: "Labile" PTH amino acids. Since the first
PTH amino acid is labile, the "theoretical" yield at step 1 has
been obtained by extrapolation as shown, and taken to be 100%
as a point of reference.

the conversion reaction. Despite the low yields of tyrosine
and tryptophan, the identification of these residues in positions 12 and 13 was unequivocal; the products were clearly
identified by GLC, and no other PTH amino acid was seen at
either step. PTH arginine (step 14) was identified by the
Sakaguchi reaction. The aqueous phases from steps 13 and
15 were used as controls. Steps 15 and 16 provided an overlap
into T2.

FIGS. 4 and 5 show the tracings obtained at step 8
(valine) and step 16 (leucine) of this degradation. The
absence of significant quantities of other PTH amino acids
and of contaminants can be seen.

Apart from omission of the ethyl acetate extractions,
no attempt was made to modify the extent of extraction
during this degradation. The amount of material remaining
after 16 cycles (0.16 μm) and its purity (as evidenced by the
result of the 16th cycle) would have been adequate for at least
several more steps if the reduced extraction schedules used
for T2, T3, and CNBr 2 had been applied at that point.
However, since the sequence of T2 had already been established, the degradation was stopped.

Degradation of T2

The known composition of T2 was Asn (3), Leu (1),
Phe (1), His (1), Arg (1). Since the amount of material was
small (0.06 μm), it was important to reduce extractive

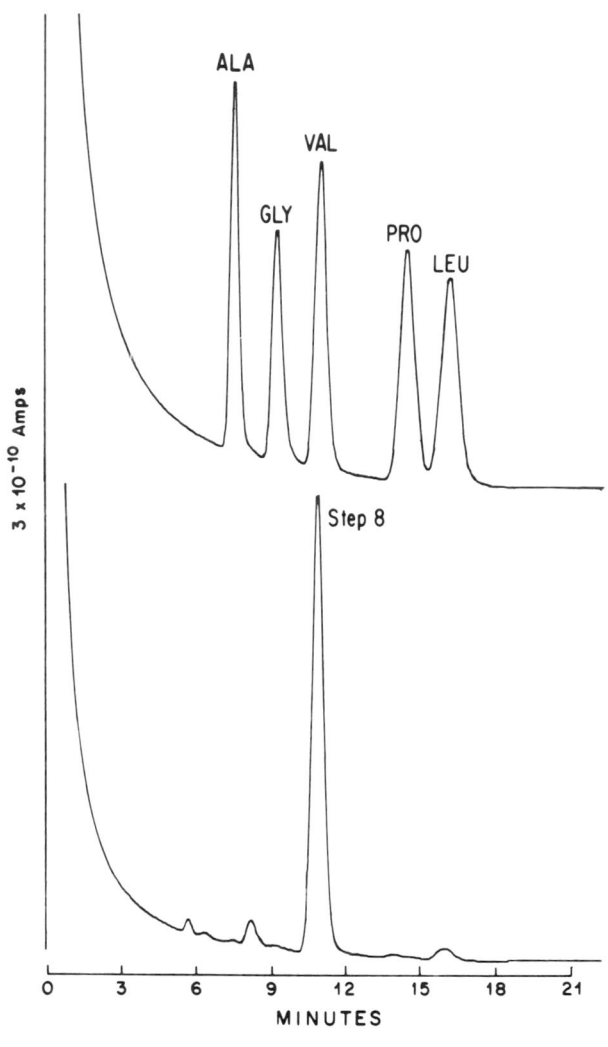

FIG. 4

DC 560 column. Upper tracing: Mixture of standard PTH amino acids. Lower tracing: Sample from step 8 of degradation on intact thyrocalcitonin (valine).

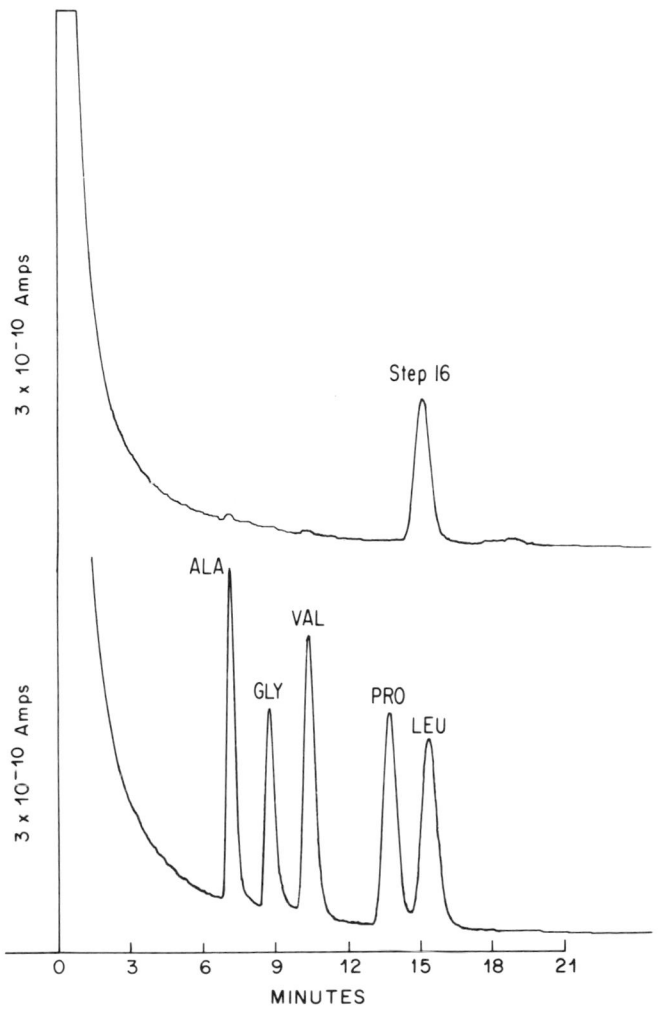

FIG. 5

DC 560 column. Upper tracing: Sample from step 16 of
degradation on intact thyrocalcitonin (leucine). Lower
tracing: Mixture of standard PTH amino acids.

losses if the whole sequence was to be determined. The
arginine could be tentatively placed at the C terminus on the
basis of trypsin specificity, so that at least two charged
groups (the guanidino-group and the alpha-carboxyl group)
would persist throughout the degradation. The other potentially charged sites were the alpha amino group and the
imidazole group of the histidine residue. It seemed likely
that the overall polarity of this peptide would be adequate
to minimize losses if both sets of extractions were made
from an aqueous phase. The coupling mixture was therefore
extracted 3 times with 0.5 ml of benzene. After lyophilization of the residual aqueous phase, cleavage, and evaporation
of the trifluoroacetic acid, the residue was dissolved in
water and extracted with n-butyl acetate as described above.

Of the N-terminal 6 residues of T2, only the histidine
derivative would not be obtained. If no product was found at
any particular step, it was planned to assign that position
tentatively to histidine and continue the degradation. In a
repeat experiment, a different extraction procedure could
then be used at that step alone. However, the first five
steps gave the sequence Asn (0.05 μM), Leu (0.044 μ M),
Asn (0.034 μM), Asn (0.027 μ M), Phe (0.032μ M). This
allowed the last two residues to be designated as His-Arg,
on the basis of composition and assumed site of tryptic
cleavage. However, to obtain direct evidence, a 6th cycle

of coupling and cleavage was performed. The trifluoroacetic acid was evaporated off, but no attempt was made to extract out the histidine derivative. Instead, the residue was subjected to the conditions of "conversion."

The conversion solution then was found to contain PTH histidine (0.014 μM), derived from the penultimate amino acid and identified by gas chromatography, and free arginine, the last amino acid, identified by amino acid analysis (0.013 μM). Subtractive analysis indicated the efficiency of the preceding degradation cycles; after acid hydrolysis only arginine was found, with a trace of histidine which probably derived from partial regeneration of the free amino acid from the thiohydantoin.

Degradation of T3

The first 6 amino acids were established as Phe (0.07 μM)-ser (0.015 μM)-gly (0.05 μM)-met (0.02 μM)-gly (0.0 < 6 μM) -phe (0.016μ M). Since the peptide was hydrophobic, extractions were considerably reduced. After coupling, the aqueous phase was extracted twice with 0.3 ml benzene. After cleavage the thiazolinone was extracted with a total of 0.5 ml ethylene dichloride. Finding the position of the methionine in the sequence was very useful since it established continuity with CNBr 2. Since CNBr 2 was available in quite large quantities, it seemed to offer a better possibility of reaching the carboxyl end of the molecule

than the longer T3, available only in limited amounts. (This
was important since there was reason to believe on other
grounds that the alpha-carboxyl group of the C-terminal
might be amidated.) Accordingly, degradation of T3 was
stopped after 6 cycles.

Degradation on CNBr 2

The complete sequence of this peptide was established
on 1.22 μm material. For the first 3 cycles two benzene
extractions, each of 0.5 ml, were used; the thiazolinones
were extracted with 0.5 ml of ethylene dichloride. Yields
were gly (1.0 μM), phe (0.78 μM), and gly (0.45 μM).
(Fig. 6) Extrapolation of these yields suggested that the
degradation could not be continued beyond the fourth or fifth
step. Accordingly, for the fourth and subsequent cycles,
the benzene extraction was omitted completely and the coupling
mixture taken to dryness in vacuo. This was followed by
sublimation at 60°C, also under high vacuum (80 microns).
After cleavage and evaporation of the trifluoroacetic acid,
the thiazolinones were separated by a single extraction with
0.3 ml of ethylene dichloride. Yields for the next two steps
were pro(0.43 μM) and glu (0.38 μM). In the sixth cycle,
after coupling, sublimation and cleavage, no extraction was
performed. One-fifth of the sample, in trifluoroacetic acid,
was dried and subjected to the conditions for "conversion."
The produce was identified by GLC as PTH threonine (0.22
μM), corrected for the entire sample.

An aliquot of the remaining four-fifths of the unextracted reaction mixture was run on the acid/neutral column of the amino acid analyzer. If the carboxyl terminal residue had been unsubstituted proline, it should have been detected in high yield. However, only a trace of proline, and no other amino acid, could be seen on this column. On the basic column, however, a peak was seen at 41 minutes with a unique ratio of absorbance at 570 to 440 mμ (1.14). Authentic prolinamide eluted at the same position and had the same distinctive absorbance ratio. Total yield (based on prolinamide found) was 0.21 μm.

Another aliquot was subjected to a seventh cycle of Edman degradation, which gave PTH proline, the amide

EDMAN DEGRADATION THYROCALCITONIN CYANOGEN BROMIDE HEPTAPEPTIDE

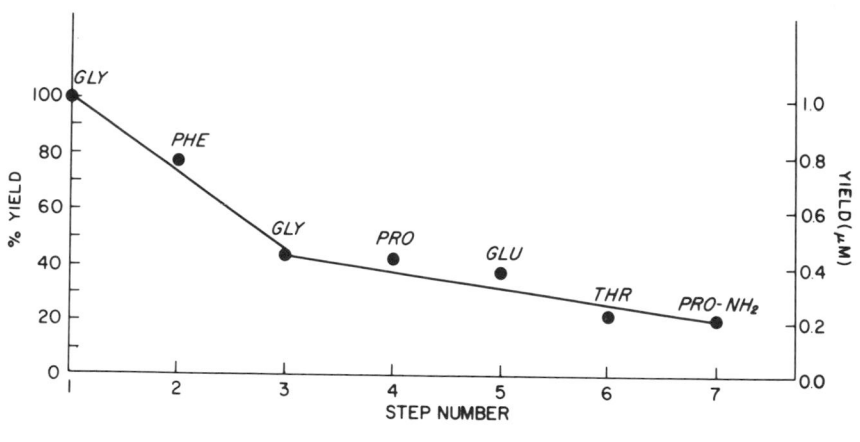

FIG. 6

Yield data from degradation on CNBr 2. The extent of extraction was greatly reduced after the third cycle.

group being split off during the cyclization reaction. In
this situation reliance only on identification of the PTH derivative of the C-terminal residue would obviously have led to
error, since the amide group would not have been found.

Other Applications: Quantitative Edman Degradation of

Peptide Mixtures

The four repetitive degradations reviewed above provided
sufficient information to propose the complete amino acid
sequence of thyrocalcitonin. During the parallel studies
which involved preparation and isolation of many peptide
fragments, another extremely valuable application of the
Edman procedure was demonstrated.

As reported earlier[3] and currently being examined in
greater detail[9], anomalous results were noted during tryptic
digestion; more than the expected number of three peptides
(based on the presence of only two tryptic-sensitive sites--
two arginines) were detected. It proved possible to analyze
and interpret the results of 6 cycles of Edman degradation
of the unfractionated tryptic digest. Obviously several PTH
amino acids were obtained at each step. FIG. 7 shows one
of the GLC tracings using the DC 560 column obtained in
this study.

Almost all the PTH derivatives illustrated are among
those to be expected from the three orthodox tryptic peptides.
However, at step 1 serine was detected by the silylation
technique. (In FIG. 7 it coelutes with the S-carboxymethyl

cysteine PTH).   The presence of alanine at step 2, and

tyrosine and tryptophan at steps 3 and 4 (seen on other

GLC columns) demonstrates clearly that the bond between leu_9

and ser_{10} had been cleaved by trypsin.   From the quantitative

yields the extent of cleavage was found to be 42%.   The bond

between tyr_{12} and trp_{13} was also found to be cleaved by

trypsin to the extent of 17%.   This study will be reported

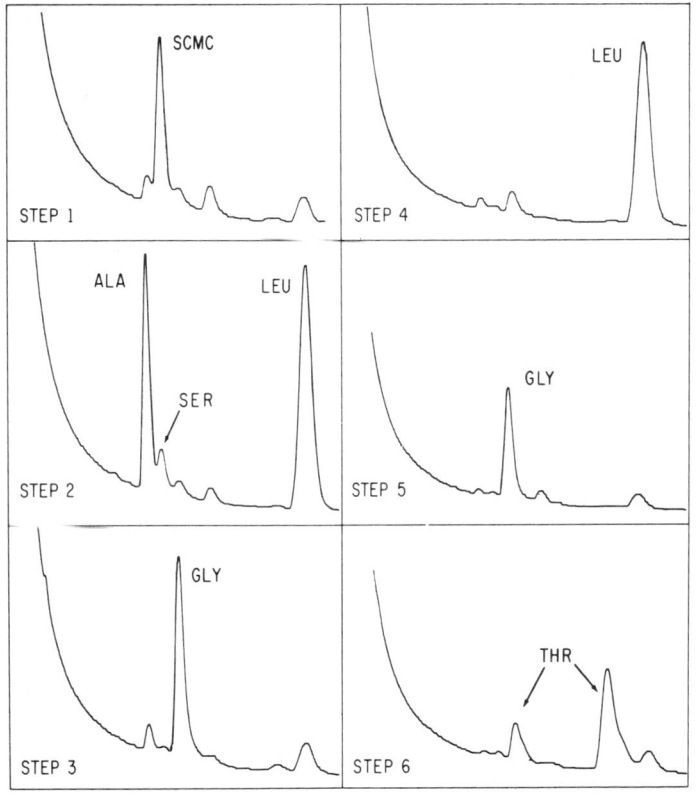

FIG. 7

DC 560 column. Samples, as indicated, derive from steps
1-6 of degradation on unfractionated tryptic digest of
thyrocalcitonin. See text.

fully later[24]. Incidentally, a large part of the sequence of the thyrocalcitonin molecule could be deduced from the results of the Edman degradation on the unfractionated tryptic digest, assuming a knowledge only of the composition of each of the three orthodox tryptic peptides previously isolated in trace amounts by elution from thin-layer chromatograms. This ancillary approach towards protein and peptide sequencing--i.e., degrading mixtures containing several peptide chains--is currently under study in our laboratory.

DISCUSSION

In determining the covalent structure of a protein or peptide, the fewer subfragments needed the greater the saving in time, effort, and material. In the present study the complete amino acid sequence of porcine thyrocalcitonin, a 32-residue peptide hormone, was established by Edman degradation alone on the native molecule and three daughter peptides. This was made possible by the use of a new approach to the three-stage Edman method which allows complete sequencing of short peptides by close regulation of solvent extractions, with quantitative identification of the PTH derivatives by gas-liquid chromatography. Quantitative evidence is provided for the proposed sequence and the worker may follow the progress of the degradation from step to step. Modifications in the extraction scheme can then be made on the basis of continual monitoring both of peptide losses and of the appearance of contaminants, as the C-terminus of the peptide being degraded is approached. Short peptides (e.g., T2) and hydrophobic peptides (e.g., CNBr 2) may be completely sequenced provided the solvent extractions are sufficiently reduced. Interference from contaminants can be made minimal for two reasons. Firstly, careful purification of solvents and reagents according to the procedures outlined in the "Methods" section greatly reduces the accumulation of contaminants during the degradation. Secondly, the GLC procedure has sufficient resolving power to separate the PTH amino acids from the usual contaminants. This is an advantage over thin-layer chromatographic systems for identification in which phenylthiourea and diphenylthiourea, for example, may be confused with PTH derivatives.

In the present work, it was found possible to omit completely the usual extraction of the PTC peptide with ethyl acetate. Some accumulation of diphenylthiourea occurs, but for reasons outlined above, this is minimal and does not interfere with identification. Further steps which may be taken to reduce peptide losses are, in order, reduction of extent of benzene extraction, omission of one of the two ethylene dichloride extractions, and complete omission of benzene extraction with substitution of high vacuum sublimation. The procedure used in the degradation of T2 took advantage of the unusual charge distribution of this peptide and is probably not widely applicable. However, it may have some value with other tryptic peptides C-terminal

H.D. NIALL AND J.T. POTTS, JR.

in arginine but otherwise consisting of relatively nonpolar residues.

The technique of subtractive amino acid analysis, though not used routinely at every cycle, is often most valuable when combined with the present approach. It is particularly useful in establishing the cause of a sudden fall in yield of PTH amino acid. Mechanical or extractive losses of peptide material may be distinguished from chemical "losses" due to N-terminal blocking reactions from aldehyde impurities in the reagents by analysis of a measured aliquot of the residual peptide. For example, the fall in yield from step-to-step during the degradations on thyrocalcitonin was shown by subtractive analysis to be due to losses during extractions. Subtractive analysis is also useful in another context. If the length of the peptide is known, the degradation may be stopped after cleavage of the penultimate residue, as illustrated with T2 and CNBr 2. This permits the second last residue to be identified by GLC as its PTH derivative, while the last residue is easily identified on the amino acid analyzer as the free amino acid. Acid hydrolysis of another aliquot followed by amino acid analysis will reveal the presence of undegraded peptide. As discussed above, this approach was particularly useful with the direct detection of prolinamide at the C-terminus of the molecule.

A quantitative Edman degradation obviously lends itself to the study of heterogeneous protein and peptide mixtures. In the study of the tryptic digestion of thyrocalcitonin the

exact sites and frequency of abnormal chromotryptic-like
cleavages were determined by repetitive Edman degradation
on the unfractionated tryptic digest. Automated Edman
degradation[25] of a mixture of normal human immunoglobulin
light chains (kappa subclass) has already been used to establish qualitatively which amino acids occupy the constant and
the variable positions of the first 18 residues. Repetition
of this kind of work with accurate quantitation is an obvious
extension which is now possible.

In summary, a new approach to Edman degradation of
short peptides has been described. It depends upon the use
of a modified three-stage degradation procedure, the PTH
amino acids being identified mainly by gas chromatography.
This identification method, combined with the usual form of
the Edman procedure, would not greatly change its scope.
The sensitivity and resolution of GLC are only useful if the
degradation itself is carried out cleanly and without undue
loss of material. Quantitation is already possible in forms
of degradation based solely on subtractive amino acid analysis
at each step. However, the flexible approach to solvent
extractions during the manual Edman method, illustrated
in the structural study on thyrocalcitonin, permits
successful degradation of a variety of peptides differing in
charge and chain length if proper attention is directed to a
number of details. Solvent and reagent purity is carefully

controlled to minimize interference from contaminants. The
initial extraction regime is chosen specifically with regard to
the amount available, chain length, composition and polarity
of the individual peptide being degraded. Further modifications in the extractions are employed during the actual degradation as the pattern of PTH amino acid yield from step to
step becomes evident. Subtractive amino acid analysis at
selected stages of the degradation is used to monitor extractive losses by a method independent both of the GLC procedure
itself and of losses of PTH amino acid prior to analysis.
This flexible chemical approach with quantitative detection
of the PTH amino acids by GLC provides an overall system
capable of completely sequencing even hydrophobic peptides
present in small amounts.

Further work by our laboratory in collaboration with
another group[28] has recently led to the development of an
automated instrument[29] capable of carrying out Edman
degradation on peptides[30] as well as on proteins. Unlike
the original sequenator[13], this instrument may be operated
with volatile reagents. Since prolonged solvent extractions
are, therefore, unnecessary, losses of peptide are minimized.
One would expect that the flexible approach to degradation of
peptides described in this paper could also be applied in an
automated mode. Preliminary work has confirmed this, and
extensive automated degradations have been carried out with

varied extraction regimes on calcitonins from several

species as well as on other peptides[30,31]

REFERENCES

1. J. T. Potts, Jr., H. B. Brewer, Jr., R. A. Reisfeld, P. F. Hirsch, R. Schlueter, and P. L. Munson, in Parathyroid Hormone and Thyrocalcitonin (Calcitonin), (. R. V. Talmage, L. F. Belanger, and I. Clark, eds.), Excerpta Medical Foundation, 1968, p. 54.

2. H. B. Brewer, H. T. Keutmann, J. T. Potts, Jr., R. A. Reisfeld, R. Schlueter, and P. L. Munson, J. Biol. Chem., 243, 5739 (1968).

3. J. T. Potts, Jr., H. D. Niall, H. T. Keutmann, II. B. Brewer, Jr., and L. J. Deftos, Proc. Nat. Acad. Sci., 59, 1321 (1968).

4. P. H. Bell, W. F. Barg, Jr., D. F. Colucci, M. C. Davies, C. Dziobkowski, M. E. Englert, E. Heyder, R. Paul, and E. H. Snedeker, J. Amer. Chem. Soc., 90, 2704 (1968).

5. R. Neher, B. Riniker, H. Zuber, W. Rittel, and F. W. Kahnt, Helv. Chim. Act., 51, 917 (1968).

6. W. Rittel, M. Brugger, B. Kamber, B. Riniker, and P. Sieber, Helv. Chim. Act., 51, 924 (1968).

7. St. Guttman, J. Pless, E. Sandrin, J. A. Jaquenoud, H. Bossert, and H. Willems, Helv. Chim. Act., 51, 1155 (1968).

8. H. D. Niall, P. L. Munson, and J. T. Potts, Jr., in preparation.

9. H. T. Keutmann, P. L. Munson, and J. T. Potts, Jr., in preparation.

10. H. B. Brewer, Jr., H. T, Keutmann, R. A. Reisfeld, P. Munson, R. Schlueter, and J. T. Potts, Jr., Fed. Proc., 27, 690 (1968).

11. H. B. Brewer, Jr., P. L. Munson, and J. T. Potts, Jr., unpublished work.

12. P. Edman, Acta Chem. Scand., 4, 283 (1950).

13. P. Edman, and G. Begg, Europe J. Biochem., 1, 80 (1967).

14. B. Blomback, M. Blomback, P. Edman, and B. Hessel, Biochim. Biophys. Acta 115, 371 (1966).

15. D. Ilse, and P. Edman, Austral. J. Chem., 16, 411 (1963).

16. W. R. Gray, in Methods in Enzymology, (C. H. W. Hirs, Ed.) New York, Academic Press, (1967), p. 469.

17. J. J. Pisano, W. Vanden Heuvel, and E. Horning, Biochem. Biophys. Res. Commun., 7, 82 (1962).

18. J. J. Pisano and H. D. Niall, unpublished work.

19. K. Toi, E. Bynum, E. Norris, and H. A. Itano, J. Biol. Chem., 240, 3455 (1965).

20. J. A. Yankeelo, Jr. in Symposium on Recent Developments in Research Methods and Instrumentation, National Institutes of Health, Abstracts, (1968), p. 3.

21. D. S. Smyth and S. Utsumi, Nature, 216, 332 (1967).

22. W. Konigsberg, in Methods in Enzymology (C. H. W. Hirs, ed.), New York, Academic Press, (1967), p. 461.

23. H. D. Niall, unpublished work.

24. H. D. Niall, H. T. Keutmann, and J. T. Potts, Jr., in preparation.

25. H. D. Niall, and P. Edman, Nature, 216, 262 (1967).

26. J. J. Pisano, in Theory and Application of Gas Chromatography in Industry and Medicine, (H. S. Kroman and S. R. Bender, Grove and Stratton, New York, 1968, p. 147.

27. J. J. Pisano, and T. J. Bronzert, Fed. Proc., 28, 661 (1969).

28. Work carried out in collaboration with members of the Research Department, Spinco Division, Beckman Instruments, Inc., Palo Alto, California.

29. This instrument, the "Protein/ Peptide Sequencer," is commercially available from Beckman Instruments, Spinco Division, Palo Alto, California.

30. H. D. Niall, H. Penhasi, P. Gilbert, R. C. Myers, F. G. Williams, and J. T. Potts, Jr., Fed. Proc., 28, 661 (1969).

31. H. D. Niall, H. T. Keutmann, and J. T. Potts, Jr., in preparation.

SYNTHESIS OF PORCINE THYROCALCITONIN (TCT)

St. Guttmann, J. Pless, E. Sandrin,
P.-A. Jaquenoud, H. Bossert and H. Willems

Research Laboratories, SANDOZ Ltd.,
Basle, Switzerland

Thyrocalcitonin discovered in 1962 by Copp[1] has aroused great interest because of its potential therapeutical value. This hormone was found in the thyroids of all mammals investigated and its administration to rats and other small mammals gives rise to a decrease of serum calcium and phosphate[2]. The urinary elimination of Ca, PO_4^{--} and hydroxyproline which is characteristic of bone resorption is decreased under the influence of TCT[3]. In addition TCT was shown to inhibit bone resorption in vitro[4].

Investigations were carried out in several laboratories[5-8] simultaneously in order to isolate this hormone, to characterize it and to establish its structure. Very recently three research groups [9-11] succeeded in determining its amino acid sequence and subsequently three others[12-14] reported its synthesis.

Thyrocalcitonin is a linear dotriacontapeptide containing a disulfide bridge between both cysteine residues in positions

1 and 7. On its N-terminal end it has a free amino group whereas on the C-terminal end a prolinamide group.

H-Cys-Ser-Asn-Leu-Ser-Thr-Cys-Val-Leu-Ser-Ala-Tyr-

-Trp-Arg-Asn-Leu-Asn-Asn-Phe-His-Arg-Phe-Ser-Gly-

-Met-Gly-Phe-Gly-Pro-Glu-Thr-Pro-NH_2

Its molecular weight is 3604 and its isoelectric point is over pH 10. This high basicity is due to its two arginine residues. The single carboxyl group present in the molecule neutralises only the α-amino group. Its optical rotation is $[\alpha]_D^{20} = -45^0$ (c = 1.0 in 1-n acetic acid).

Our synthesis was initiated on the basis of our own preliminary structural work[7] and completed with the help of the full structural results of Potts et al.[9].

The synthetic scheme (FIG. 1) followed a combination of sequential and step-wise techniques. In most syntheses of cysteine containing peptides, the SH-groups are protected by the benzyl group which is cleaved by sodium in liquid ammonia at the end of the synthesis. This treatment however is known often to cause fragmentation in the peptide chain. It was found that in the case of TCT treatment with Na/NH_3 was also associated with a loss in biological activity[15]. We therefore decided to cleave this protecting group at an early stage of the synthesis and to introduce the sequence containing the disulfide bridge at the last step only.

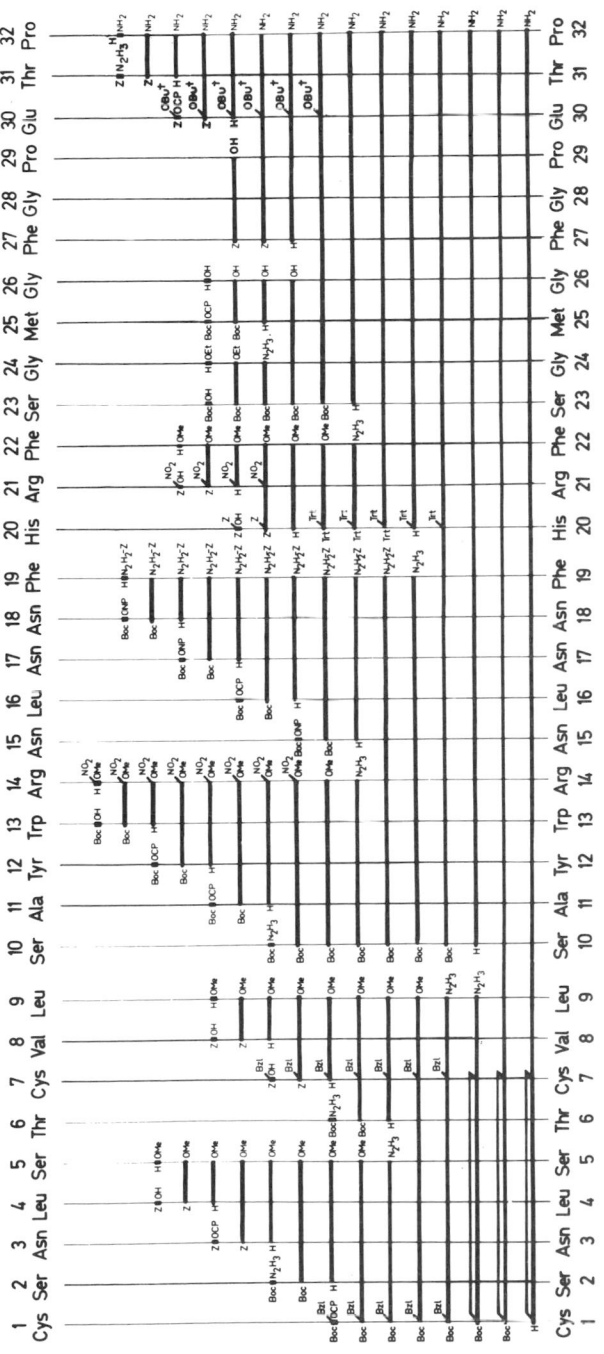

FIG. 1

Synthesis of porcine thyrocalcitonin.

First the sequences 1-9, 10-19 and 20-32 were synthesized. The OH-groups of serine, threonine and tyrosine were not protected, only the guanido residues of arginine being temporarily protected by nitration.

The sequence 20-32 (FIG. 2) was synthesized in a classical manner. CBO-Glu (OTB)-OCP was coupled with H-Thr-Pro-NH$_2$ and after hydrogenation of the CBO-group it was reacted with the tripeptide CBO-Phe-Gly-Pro-OH by the DCCI method. After catalytic hydrogenation the tetrapeptide 23-26 was coupled with the hexapeptide 27-32, resulting in the protected decapeptide 23-32. Finally, the latter, after treatment with TFA, was combined with the tripeptide azide 20-22 to yield the tridecapeptide 20-32.

The synthesis of the sequence 10-19 (FIG. 3) was accomplished in a step-wise manner. In the C-terminal phenylalanine a protected hydrazide group was introduced right from the beginning, in order to avoid side reactions in the three asparagine residues due to hydrazinolysis. This later allowed performance of a racemization free coupling with the N-terminal part 20-32. Beside the azide coupling method activated esters were used to lengthen the chain.

Peptide 1-9 (FIG. 4) was also synthesized in a step-wise way. After having transformed the protected nonapeptide ester into its hydrazide derivative, the benzyl group was cleaved by Na/NH_3. Neither the peptide bond nor the hydrazide group was damaged by this treatment. The disulfide bridge was closed by selective oxidation.

In the next step (FIG. 5) the decapeptide azide 10-19 was coupled with the tridecapeptide 20-32 to obtain the protected tricosapeptide 10-32. After cleavage of the

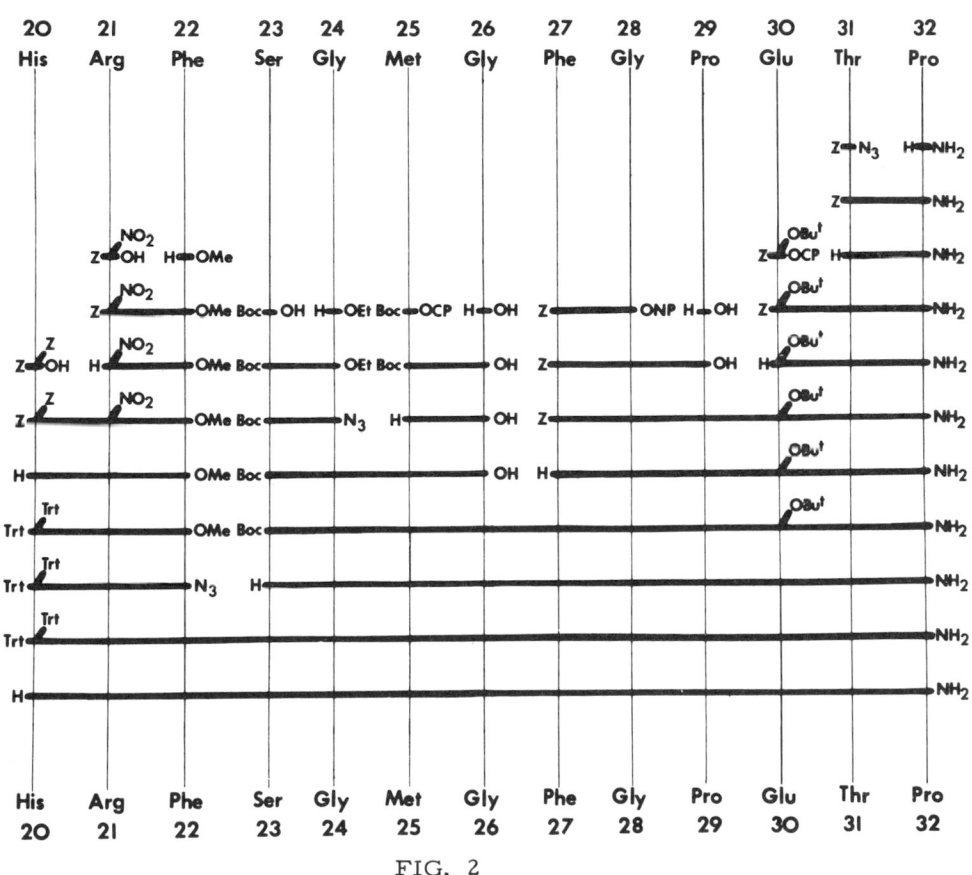

FIG. 2

Synthesis of the sequence 20-32 TCT.

protective group, the latter was reacted with the nonapeptide
azide 1-9. After treatment with TFA the resulting dotriacontapeptide already showed without further purification
50% of the expected biological activity. Finally the peptide
was purified by gel filtration and ion exchange chromatography.
The product was pure as indicated by both chromatography
and electrophoresis.

The synthetic product and the natural product behaved
in the same manner in gel filtration, which means they have
identical molecular weights. The optical rotatory values

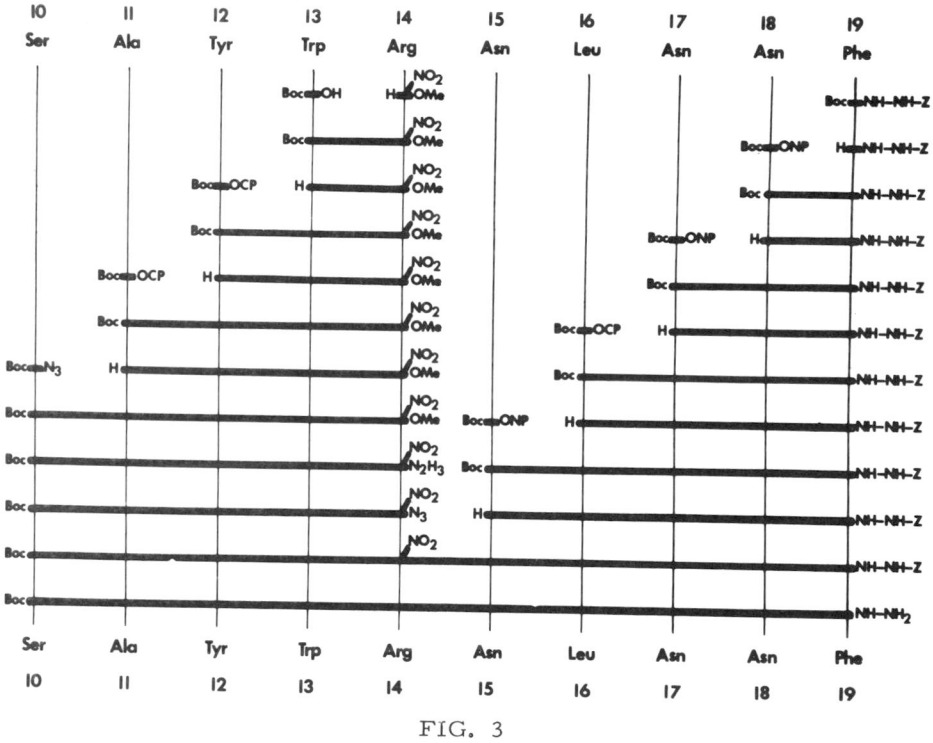

FIG. 3

Synthesis of the sequence 10-19 TCT.

and the quantitative amino acid composition are also the
same in the synthetic and natural products. Their biological
activities are practically identical. The synthetic product
seems to be somewhat more active than the natural one but
this difference is within the confidence limit of the biological
assay.

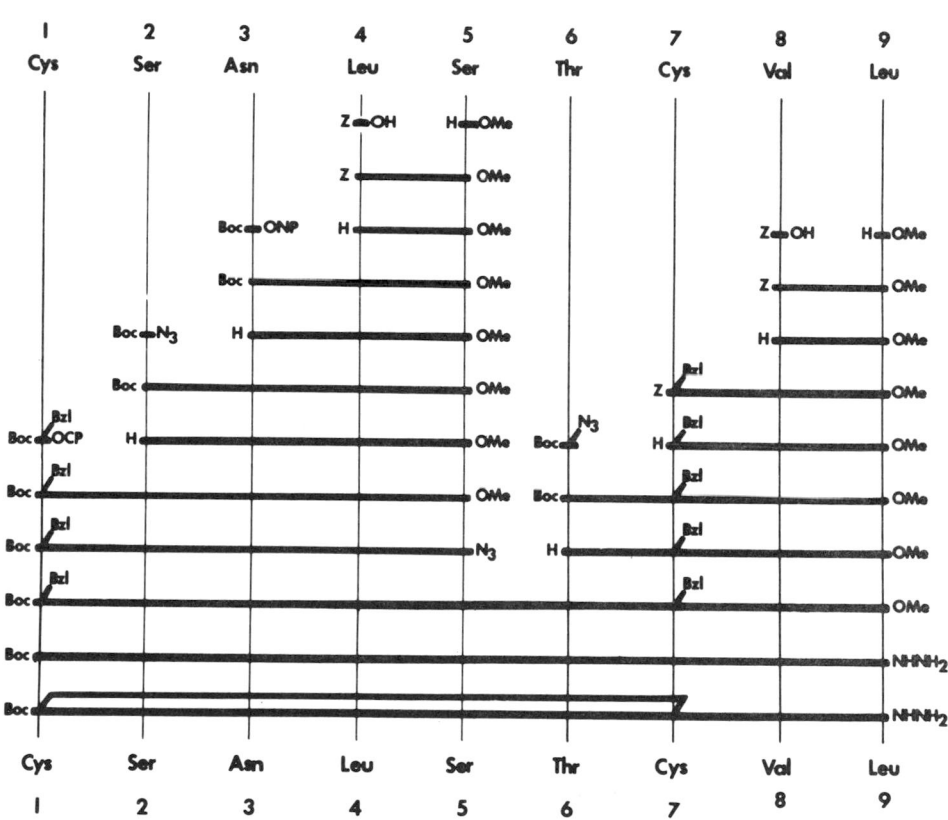

FIG. 4

Synthesis of the sequence 1-9 of TCT.

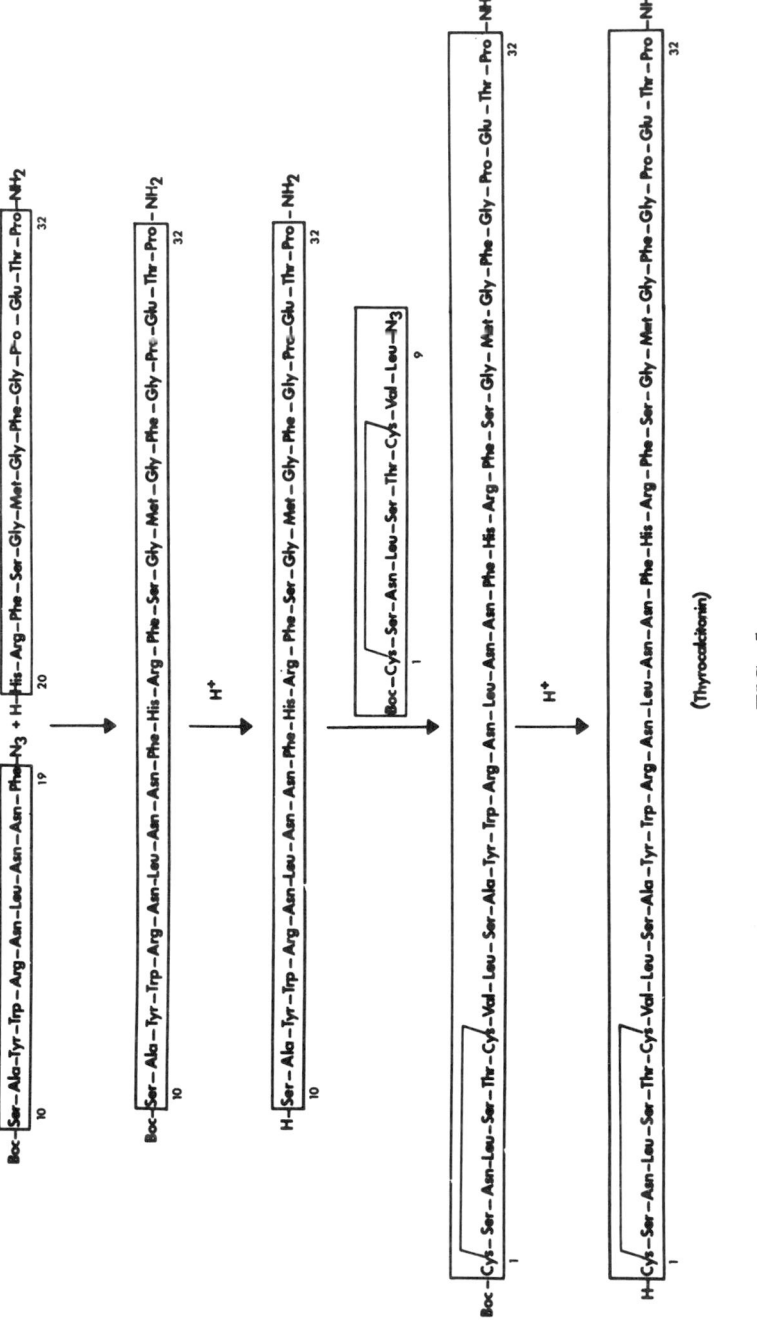

FIG. 5

Synthesis of TCT.

Table 1

	synthetic	natural
Molecular weight	3600	3600
$[\alpha]_D^{20}$ (c = 1 AcOH 1N)	-55°	-54°
$E_{1,9}$	0.9 Trp	0.9 Trp
$E_{5,8}$	1.0 Trp	1.0 Trp
Isoelectric point	> 10	> 10
Amino endgroup	Cys	Cys
Amino acid composition	identical	
Biological activity: a decrease of 1mg/100ml of the serum Ca-level in rat is caused by	ca. 0.03 µg	ca. 0.04 µg

If we compare in biological assay our synthetic material with the pure isolated natural product we can see that the dose-response curves are almost identical (FIG. 6). However the MRC-Standard - B which is rather impure and has a 20 times lower specific activity, gives a straight line with a different slope.

If we add a protein, e.g. bovine serum albumin, to either the pure natural material or to the pure synthetic material, as recommended by Kumar[16], and compare them with MRC-Standard - B to which the same protein has also been added, the dose response curves are completely parallel (FIG. 7).

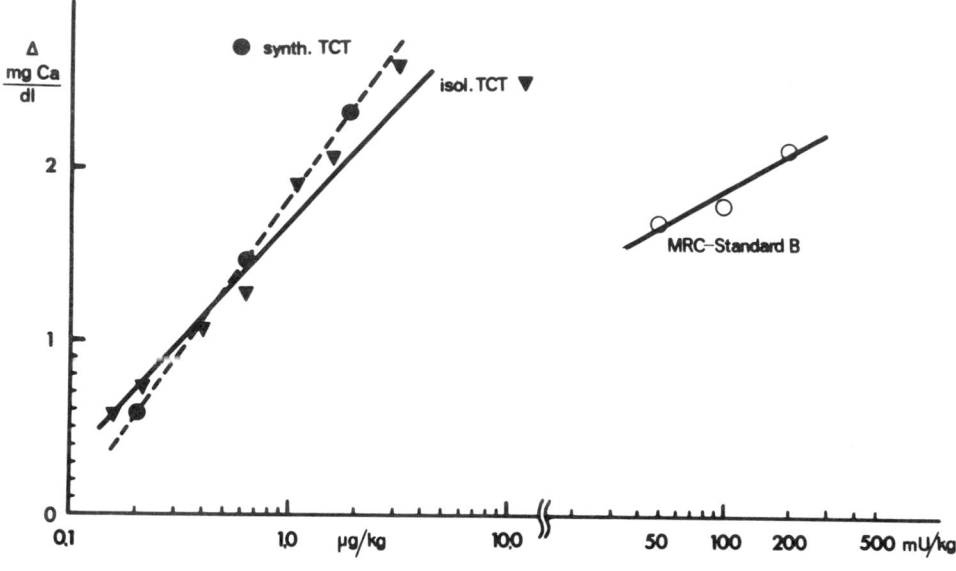

FIG. 6

Dose-response curve of natural and synthetic TCT in saline solution.

From the physical, chemical and biological properties, therefore, we consider that our synthetic product is identical to natural thyrocalcitonin and thus the structure proposed for TCT is confirmed.

ACKNOWLEDGMENTS

We wish to thank Dr. R. A. Boissonnas (Sandoz, Ltd.) for valuable discussions and advice, Dr. K. Zehnder (Sandoz, Ltd.) for carrying out the biological assays and Dr. J. T. Potts for having communicated us the content of his manuscript[9] before publication.

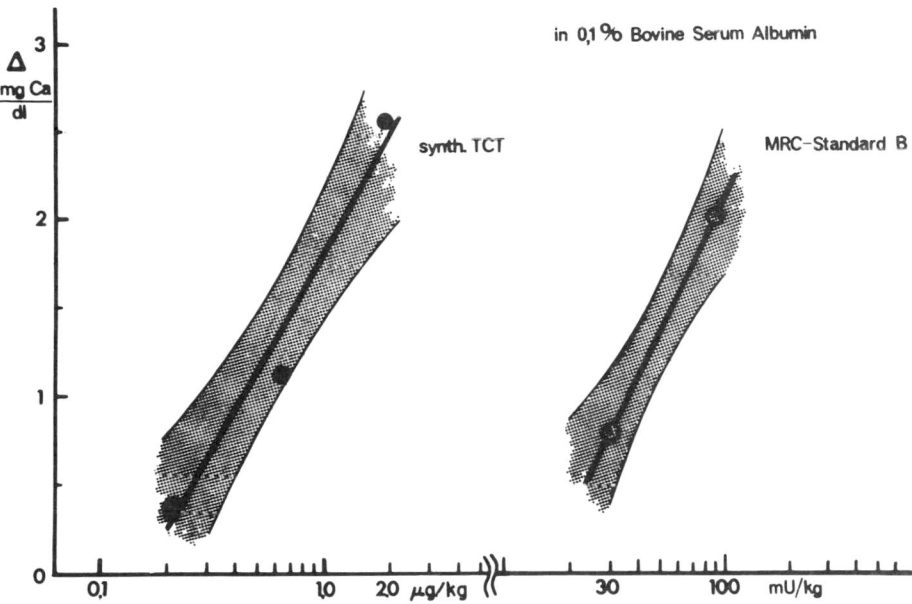

FIG. 7

Dose-response curve of synthetic TCT in 0.1 % BSA-solution

REFERENCES

1. D. H. Copp, E. C. Cameron, B. A. Cheney, A. G. T. Davidson, and K. G. Henze, Endocrinology, 70, 638 (1962).

2. P. H. F. Hirsch, Ed. F. Voelkel, and P. L. Munson, Science, 146, 412 (1964).

3. T. J. Martin, G. J. Robinson, and I. MacIntyre, Lancet, 1966, I, 900.

4. J. Friedman and L. G. Raisz, Science, 150, 1465 (1965).

5. J. T. Potts, R. A. Reisfeld, P. H. Hirsch, A. B. Wasthed, E. F. Voelkel, and P. L. Munson, Proc. Nat. Acad. Sci. U.S.58, 328 (1967).

6. I. Putter, E. A. Kaczka, R. E. Harman, E. L. Rickles, A. J. Kempf, L. Chaiet, J. W. Rothrock, A. W. Wase, and F. J. Wolf, J. Am. Chem. Soc., 89, 5301 (1967).

253

7. J. Franz, J. Rosenthaler, K. Zehnder, W. Doepfner, R. Huguenin, and St. Guttmann, Helv. Chim. Acta, 51, 218 (1968).

8. F. W. Kahnt, B. Riniker, I. MacIntyre, and R. Neher, Helv. Chim. Acta, 51, 214 (1968).

9. J. T. Potts, H. D. Niall, H. T. Keutmann, H. B. Brewer, and L. G. Deftos, Proc. Nat. Acad. Sci. U.S.,59, 1321 (1968).

10. P. H. Bell, W. F. Barg, D. F. Colucci, M. C. Davies, C. Dziobkowski, M. E. Englert, E. Heyder, R. Paul, and E. H. Snedeker, J. Am. Chem. Soc., 90, 2704 (1968).

11. R. Neher, B. Riniker, H. Zuber, W. Rittel, and F. W. Kahnt, Helv. Chim. Acta., 51, 917 (1968).

12. St. Guttmann, J. Pless, E. Sandrin, P. -A. Jaquenoud, H. Bossert, and H. Willems, Helv. Chim. Acta, 51, 1155 (1968).

13. W. Rittel, M. Brugger, B. Kamber, B. Riniker, and PL Sieber, Helv. Chim. Acta, 51, 924 (1968).

14. J. B. Anderson, F. M. Callahan, A. E. Lanzilotti, and J. E. Zimmerman, see ref. 10, footnote 14.

15. J. T. Potts, personal communication.

16. M. A. Kumar, E. Slack, A. Edwards, M. A. Soliman, A. Baghdianz, G. V. Forster and I. MacIntyre, J. Endocrinol., 33, 469 (1965).

RACEMIZATION CONTROL IN THE SYNTHESIS OF PEPTIDES BY THE MIXED CARBONIC ANHYDRIDE AND DICYCLOHEXYLCARBODIIMIDE METHODS

George W. Anderson

Lederle Laboratories, American Cyanamid Co.
Pearl River, New York

This paper will summarize studies recently reported by our group[1-3] with both methods and those of Weygand and associates[4,5] with dicyclohexylcarbodiimide which show that racemization can be controlled in test syntheses. In work in our laboratory on the synthesis of calcitonin peptides, the newer procedures are receiving practical application. Some of the results to date will be given. In the long run, it is only by such practical applications that improved procedures can be adequately evaluated.

THE MIXED ANHYDRIDE METHOD

In our work with the mixed anhydride method, we confirmed the report of Vaughan and Osato[6] that isobutyl chloroformate gave the best yields of several alkyl chloroformates, so this reagent was chosen as the standard. The racemization tests were the synthesis of Z•Gly-Phe-Gly•OEt which we developed[7], and the Bz•Leu-Gly•OEt synthesis of Williams and Young[8] which we modified for detection of small amounts of racemate[1].

The reactions may be written:

$$R_1CONH\overset{\overset{\displaystyle R_2}{|}}{C}HCOOH + CLCOOCH_2CH(CH_3)_2 + (R)_3N \longrightarrow$$

$$R_1CONH\overset{\overset{\displaystyle R_2}{|}}{C}HCOOCOCH_2CH(CH_3)_2 + (R)_3N\cdot HCl$$

$$(I)$$

$$(I) + NH_2CH_2COOCH_2CH_3 \longrightarrow$$

$$R_1CONH\overset{\overset{\displaystyle R_2}{|}}{C}HCONHCH_2COOCH_2CH_3 + CO_2 + HOCH_2CH(CH_3)_2$$

where $R_1CONH\overset{\overset{\displaystyle R_2}{|}}{C}HCOOH$ is

$CH_2OCONHCH_2CONH\overset{\overset{\displaystyle \text{⟨⟩}-CH_2}{|}}{C}HCOOH(L$

first test and $\text{⟨⟩}-CONH\overset{\overset{\displaystyle (CH_3)_2\,CHCH_2}{|}}{C}HCOOH(L)$ in the second.

In both cases, racemate in the final product is separated by fractional crystallization. Less than 1% racemate can be detected in both tests, although experience with the Bz-Leu-Gly-OEt test is not cumulative enough to be definite as far as precision is concerned.

Using the tripeptide test system, we discovered that the nature of the tertiary amine is the most critical factor in

racemization. An activation period (time for mixed anhydride formation) of 12 minutes was used in order to exag-
gerate racemization when it occured; further work indicated
that a minute or so was adequate for complete formation of
the mixed anhydride. Some results are given in Table 1.

TABLE 1. Tertiary Amine Effect on Z•Gly-Phe-Gly•OEt
Synthesis (Isobutylchloroformate, 12 min.
activation at -15°, THF solvent)

Amine, Equivalents		% Yield, DL	% Yield, L
Triethyl	1	8	82
"	2	16	59
Trimethyl	1	-	90
"	2	68	trace
Methyl diethyl	1	-	94
"	2	18	68
N-methylmorpholine	1	-	92
"	2	-	93

These and many other results indicated that both steric
factors and basicity are important in racemization. Racemization could be completely avoided only with amines containing at least one methyl group attached to the nitrogen.
The results with trimethylamine are instructive: lack
of racemization with one equivalent indicated that the amine
was completely utilized in forming the mixed anhydride, and

complete racemization with two equivalents showed that this amine is a good racemizer of the formed mixed anhydride. Other experiments with only a few percent excess of tri‑methylamine also gave complete racemization. A search for less basic tertiary amines containing methyl group disclosed N-methylmorpholine, which gave no racemization under the stringent conditions. Subsequent tests with this amine gave good yields (> 90%) when the activation time was a minute or less.

We concluded that the first step in mixed anhydride formation is complexing of the amine with the chloroformate, and the second is reaction with the carboxylic acid to form the anhydride. If conditions allowed racemization (presence of a strong tertiary base), this was an action of the base on the mixed anhydride before subsequent reaction with ethyl glycinate. The results with hindered bases such as triethylamine could be explained by incomplete complexing with one equivalent, and thus racemization of the formed mixed anhydride by the unreacted amine. Confirmation was provided by an experiment with two equivalents of a strongly hindered yet basic amine, ethyl diisopropylamine: only a 0.2% yield of DL and 3% yield of L tripeptide were obtained, indicating very little complexing with the chloroformate.

The ethyl benzoylleucylglycinate synthesis, which is a severe test, gave no racemization with one equivalent of trimethylamine and a 60 second activation time at -15°C. With N-methylmorpholine, no racemization up to 12 minutes activation time was found with one equivalent, two equivalents gave about 2% racemate at one minute and 16% at 12 minutes. These results indicate that normal peptide couplings are probably free from racemization with the less strenuous conditions.

We recommend a one or two minute activation time at -15° with one equivalent of N-methylmorpholine in a suitable solvent (tetrahydrofuran, ethyl acetate) as standard conditions for use of the mixed anhydride method. Dimethylacetamide is satisfactory where a better solvent is needed. N-Methylmorpholine is also a suitable base for neutralizing a hydrochloride or other acid salt of the amino acid ester or peptide ester to be reacted with the pre-formed mixed anhydride. However, triethylamine or other base can be used if not in excess.

Treatment of a solution of the mixed anhydride Z•Gly-Phe•OCOOCH$_2$CH(CH$_3$)$_2$ in tetrahydrofuran at -19° with trimethylamine liberated isobutyl alcohol (detected by gas chromatography) and oxazolone was formed (detected by infra-red absorption at 5.5μ). Other data obtained in various experiments also support the oxazolone mechanism of racemization when it occurs.

GEORGE W. ANDERSON

THE DICYLOHEXYLCARBODIIMIDE METHOD

We reported some years ago[7] that the Z•Gly-Phe-Gly•
OEt test gave some racemate under normal conditions of
use of dicyclohexylcarbodiimide (DCCD). The amount of
racemate was affected by temperature and solvent, but
conditions for no racemization were not found. Thus the
report by Wünsch and Drees[9] that addition of N-hydroxysuccinimide (HOSu) to a peptide coupling by DCCD improved
yields was of considerable interest to us. We had previously
found[10] that HOSu did not reduce racemization by the car-
bonyldiimidazole method, but decided to try it in a DCCD
racemization test. With one equivalent of added HOSu
(or 1.1 equivalents), no racemate was found in the Z•Gly-
Phe-Gly•OEt test, versus 8% racemate without it. More
dramatically, no racemate was found in the Bz•Leu-Gly•OEt
test with an equivalent of HOSu present and complete racemization without HOSu.[3]. Meanwhile, Weygand and associates[4,5] had also followed up the Wünsch observation and
found a favorable effect on racemization in other test systems.

To test whether or not the basicity of DCCD was involved
in the racemization without added HOSu, experiments with
an added equivalent of pivalic acid, which reacts only slowly
with DCCD because of steric hindrance, were done. In the
tripeptide test, no racemate was found, but complete racemization was found in the dipeptide test. We conclude that

neutralization of the basicity of DCCD is a minor factor. It seems likely that HOSu, which is a good nucleophile, reacts rapidly with the intermediate O-acylurea to form the OSu esters of the carboxylic acids involved. These in turn react with the amine component to form the test peptide without racemization.

ACTIVE ESTERS BY THE DCCD AND MIXED ANHYDRIDE METHODS

As with active esters of acylaminoacids, active esters of acylpeptides could have use in peptide synthesis if they could be readily prepared. In particular, better yields in coupling and more easily purified products would make their preparation worthwhile. We therefore used several active ester components in experiments with both the DCCD[3] and mixed anhydride[11] procedures. In the DCCD experiments (Table 2), the ester components were added to Z·Gly-Phe· OH plus H·Gly·OEt in tetrahydrofuran solvent before the DCCD. Results show that only derivatives of hydroxyl- amine prevented racemization, and the phenol and 8-hy- droxyquinoline additives actually increased racemization. With the mixed anhydride procedure, the active ester com- ponents were added after the mixed anhydride was formed, then the H·Gly·OEt was added (Table 3). Again, only the hydroxylamine derivatives (N-hydroxysuccinimide and

261

TABLE 2.   Z·Gly-Phe-Gly·OEt Synthesis at 25° in THF
by the DCCD Method

Additive	Equiv.	%DL	%L
		7.5	73
N-Hydroxysuccinimide	1.1	0	90
p-Nitrophenol	1.1	13	70
N-Hydroxypthalimide	1.1	0	81
2,4,5 Trichlorophenol	1	15	58
Pentachlorophenol	1	15	60
8-Hydroxyquinoline	1	9	70

TABLE 3.   Racemization Via Active Esters

Z·Gly-Phe·OH $\xrightarrow{\frac{M. A.}{HOR}}$ Z·Gly-Phe·OR→Z·Gly-Phe-Gly·OEt

R	%L	Tripeptide %DL
	94	0
	71	0
	40	32
	33	45

N-hydroxypiperidine) gave no racemization. In other

experiments, active esters of N-hydroxysuccinimide and

N-hydroxypiperidine were isolated as intermediates but

N-hydroxyphthalimide esters were not formed by the mixed

anhydride procedure; all three types were isolated by the

DCCD method. Since N-hydroxypiperidine esters are

relatively unreactive, and N-hydroxysuccinimide esters

have advantages over N-hydroxyphthalimide esters[12], we

conclude that N-hydroxysuccinimide is the compound of

choice for active ester formation from acylpeptides.

USE OF N-HYDROXYSUCCINIMIDE ESTERS IN SYNTHESIS
OF CALCITONIN FRAGMENTS

Recently our group at Lederle has been involved in the

synthesis of the new hormone calcitonin and related peptides.

This work is not yet ready for publication. However, it is

pertinent here to say that we have used the new conditions

for the mixed anhydride method, N-hydroxysuccinimide

esters of acylamino acids and peptides, and the dicyclo-

hexylcarbodiimide-N-hydroxysuccinimide method in this

work. What data we have, largely from enzymatic degrada-

tions, indicates no racemization has occurred. We have

indications that HOSu esters of small peptides (up to about

5 amino acids) are readily made, but reactions with larger

peptides are slower. Our favored approach at the moment is

the synthesis of small peptides by the mixed anhydride method

CHART 1

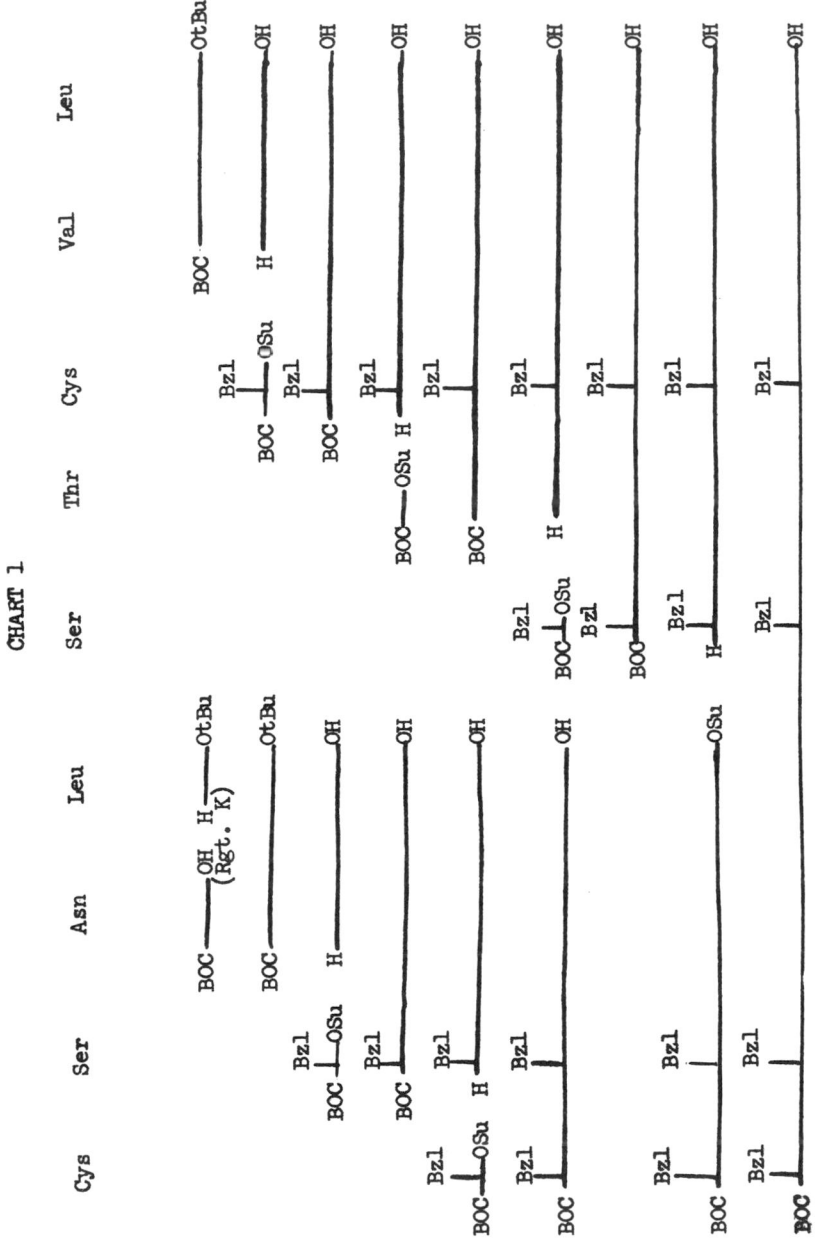

or by way of HOSu esters, and the condensation of larger peptides with DCCD plus an equivalent of HOSu.

Illustrative of fragment synthesis, we have synthesized the N-terminal nonapeptide (Derivatized) of calcitonin as shown in Chart 1. Yields were in the 80%-97% range. The process is one which can be scaled up readily. The last preparation of the nonapeptide derivative was on a 22 g. scale.

REFERENCES

1. G. W. Anderson, J. E. Zimmerman and F. M. Callahan, J. Am. Chem. Soc., 88, 1338 (1966).

2. G. W. Anderson, J. E. Zimmerman and F. M. Callahan, J. Am. Chem. Soc., 89, 5012 (1967).

3. J. E. Zimmerman and G. W. Anderson, J. Am. Chem. Soc., 89, 7151 (1967)

4. F. Weygand, D. Hoffmann and E. Wunsch, Z. Naturforsch., 21 b, 426 (1966).

5. F. Weygand and U. Ragnarsson, Z. Naturfursch., 21 b, 1141 (1966).

6. J. R. Vaghan, Jr. and R. L. Osato, J. Am. Chem. Soc., 74, 676 (1952).

7. G. W. Anderson and F. M. Callahan, J. Am. Chem. Soc., 80, 2902 (1958).

8. M. W. Williams and G. T. Young, J. Chem. Soc., 881 (1963).

9. E. Wunsch and F. Drees, Chem. Ber., 99, 110 (1966).

10. G. W. Anderson, F. M. Callahan and J. E. Zimmerman, Acta Chim. Hung., 44, 52 (1965).

11. G. W. Anderson, F. M. Callahan and J. E. Zimmerman, J. Am. Chem. Soc., 89, 178 (1967).

12. G. W. Anderson, J. E. Zimmerman and F. M. Callahan, J. Am. Chem. Soc., 86, 1839 (1964).

RACEMIZATION MECHANISMS IN PEPTIDE SYNTHESIS

M. Goodman and C. Glaser

Department of Chemistry
Polytechnic Institute of Brooklyn
Brooklyn, New York

INTRODUCTION

Racemization remains the single most important limitation on the synthesis of biologically active peptides. As a result, slow and tedious procedures are required to build peptide chains without racemization. A clear example can be seen in the non-political efforts used by the Chinese scientists to synthesize insulin. We believe that a fundamental under-standing of racemization is essential to improved facile methods of synthesis.

Peptide bond formation is a two-step process. The first step generally involves carboxyl activation of an N-blocked amino acid or peptide. This intermediate may be isolated, or it may be allowed to react in situ with an amino acid ester. The optical purity of the product may be lowered in either the activation or the subsequent coupling reaction.

In this paper, emphasis will be placed on the oxazolone intermediate as it is related to the racemization problem.

Other mechanisms for racemization will also be considered briefly. In addition, various approaches to the synthesis of optically pure peptides will be discussed.

Investigations, principally by Bergmann[1] and duVigneaud[2-4] have shown that amino acids racemize on treatment with acetic anhydride. They postulated that the mechanism may involve intermediates such as oxazolones (or azlactones):

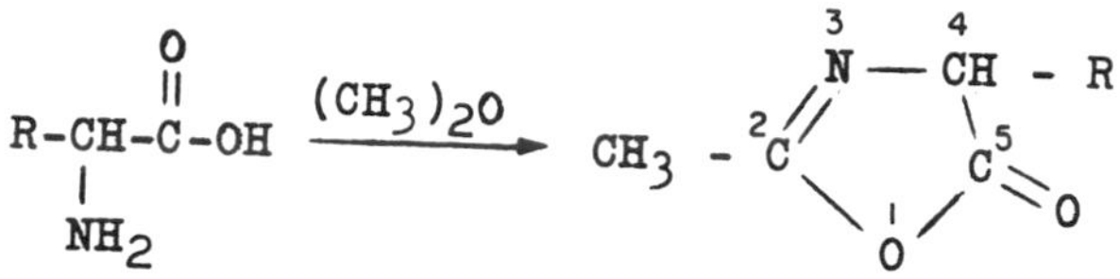

$$R-CH-C-OH \xrightarrow{(CH_3)_2O} CH_3 - C$$

FIG. 1

The oxazolone, once formed, racemizes readily by base cleavage of the asymmetric C-H bond. This is facilitated by resonance stabilization of the resultant anion.

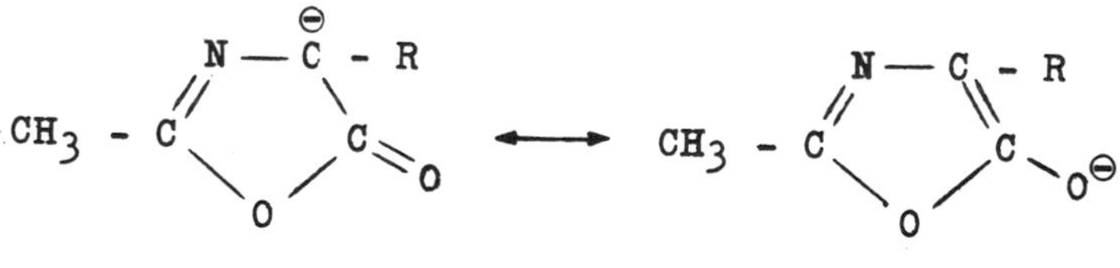

FIG. 2

Early attempts[5] to isolate optically active oxazolones were unsuccessful. Csonka and Nicolet[6] trapped and converted optically active oxazolone intermediates to optically active thiohydantoins by the addition of ammonium thiocyanate

to acetic anhydride solutions of amino acids.

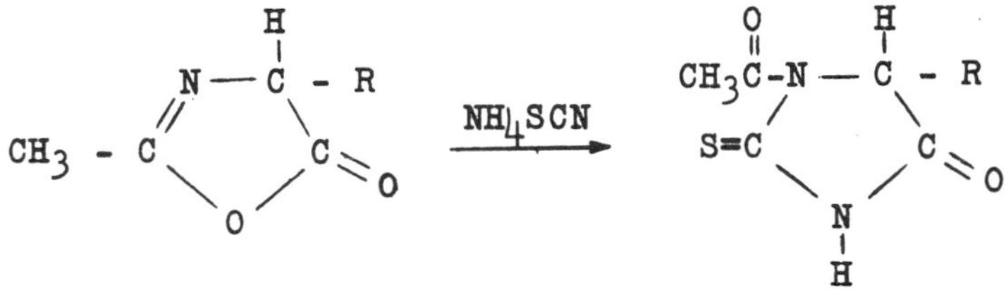

FIG. 3

In a review article in 1946, Carter[7] described the

racemization of oxazolones as an extremely facile process

such that no optically active modifications could be isolated.

THE OXAZOLONE AS AN INTERMEDIATE IN PEPTIDE RACEMIZATION

Goodman and Stueben[8] studied the alkaline hydrolysis

of benzyloxycarbonylglycyl-L-phenylalanine p-nitrophenyl

ester, and found that the rate of racemization is ten times

faster than the rate of hydrolysis to the free acid. They

were able to isolate D, L-p-nitrophenyl ester. By running

the hydrolysis in deuterium oxide, they demonstrated by the

presence of the characteristic 2195 cm^{-1} infrared band of

the C-D bond that the deuterium exchange for hydrogen had

taken place at the α -carbon atom. Product analysis showed

more than 80% deuterium incorporation. On the other hand,

benzyloxycarbonyl-glycyl-L-N-methylphenylalanine p-nitro-

phenyl ester does not racemize extensively under similar

conditions. This indicates that the peptide bond is intricately involved in the racemization process. Based on these results, a mechanism involving an oxazolone intermediate was proposed to explain the racemization and hydrolyses of benzyloxycarbonyl-glycyl-L-phenylalanine p-nitrophenyl ester.

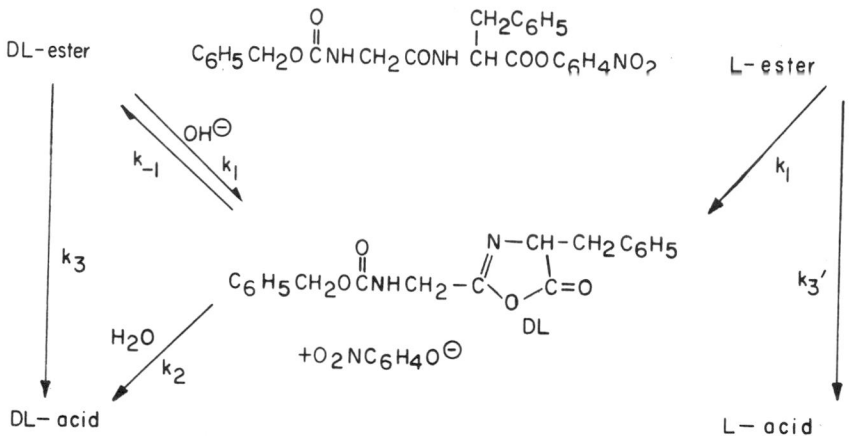

FIG. 4

Once formed, the oxazolone rapidly racemizes. It can then react with hydroxide ion (k_2) to give DL-acid or with p-nitrophenylate ion (k_{-1}) to give DL-ester.

In a related series of experiments, Williams and Young[9] allowed benzoyl-L-leucine p-nitrophenyl ester to react with triethylamine and observed the formation of oxazolone by the appearance of the characteristic 1832 cm^{-1} infrared band. They also found that the optical rotation of the p-nitrophenyl ester falls in a manner parallel to the loss of the ultraviolet absorption band at 270 mμ (the maximum for the p-nitrophenyl group). From the reaction of benzoyl-L-leucine p-nitrophenyl

ester with glycine ethyl ester in the presence of a tertiary

amine they were able to isolate partially racemized dipeptide

and inactive 4-isobutyl-2-phenyl-5-oxazolone. The following

equilibrium was proposed for the course of the reaction:

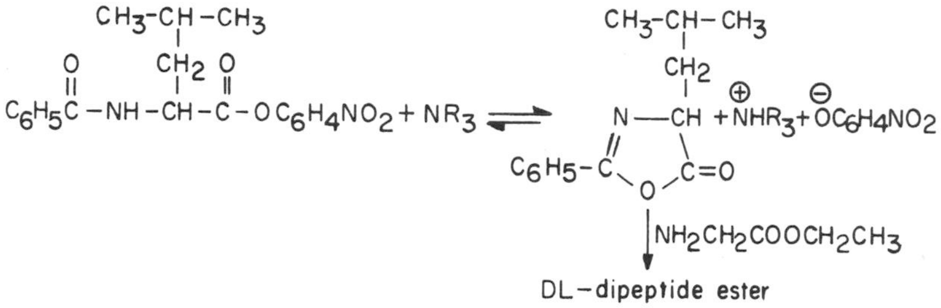

FIG. 5

Antonovics and Young[10] reported that the p-nitrophenyl

esters of benzoyl-L-phenylalanine and benzyloxycarbonylgly-

cyl-L-phenylalanine, which can form oxazolones, are race-

mized by triethylamine in dichloromethane much more

rapidly than the analogous esters of benzyloxycarbonyl-L-

phenylalanine or phthaloyl-L-phenylalanine, which cannot

form oxazolones. In the case of phthaloyl-L-phenylalanine,

the hydrogen at the asymmetric carbon should be more

acidic because of increased electrophilic inductive and

resonance effects (see FIG. 36 and accompanying discussion).

Compelling evidence in favor of the involvement of the

oxazolone intermediate in the racemization of acyl peptides

during coupling was provided by Antonovics and Young[10].

To a solution of benzoyl-glycyl-L-phenylalanine p-nitrophenyl
ester in methylene chloride was added one equivalent of triethylamine and ten equivalents of the oxazolone derived from
benzyloxycarbonylglycyl-DL-phenylalanine. When the rotation of the solution dropped to 51% of its initial value the
reaction was stopped and the mixed esters recovered. If
racemization proceeded by direct exchange of hydrogen at
the asymmetric carbon then recovered ester should be 49%
racemic. If, on the other hand, racemization proceeded via
oxazolone, the large excess of benzyloxycarbonyl-derived
oxazolone present acts as a scavenger for the p-nitrophenylate
ion and prevents the formation of benzoylglycyl-DL-phenyl-
alanine p-nitrophenyl ester by the reverse reaction (i.e.,
k_2 in FIG. 6). Analytically and optically pure benzoylglycyl-
L-phenyl-alanine p-nitrophenyl ester was recovered in 46%
yield and no racemic ester was found, giving strong evidence
for the oxazolone as the major racemization route in this
reaction.

EASE OF FORMATION OF OXAZOLONES

In general, oxazolone formation may result either during
the activation or during the subsequent coupling of an acyl
amino acid, or of an N-blocked peptide.

Base attack on the amide hydrogen to form the amide
anion can provide a driving force for cyclization; alternatively,
a concerted pathway involving base may be envisioned.

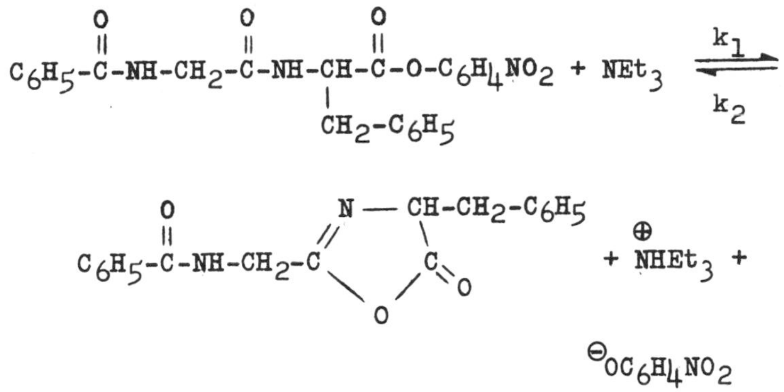

$$C_6H_5-\overset{\overset{\displaystyle O}{\|}}{C}-NH-CH_2-\overset{\overset{\displaystyle O}{\|}}{C}-NH-\underset{\underset{\displaystyle CH_2-C_6H_5}{|}}{CH}-\overset{\overset{\displaystyle O}{\|}}{C}-O-C_6H_4NO_2 \; + \; NEt_3 \; \underset{k_2}{\overset{k_1}{\rightleftharpoons}}$$

$$C_6H_5-\overset{\overset{\displaystyle O}{\|}}{C}-NH-CH_2-\overset{\displaystyle N \; - \; CH-CH_2-C_6H_5}{\underset{\displaystyle O}{C \diagup \diagdown \underset{\diagdown \diagup}{C} \diagdown O}} \; + \; \overset{\oplus}{NHEt_3} \; +$$

$$\overset{\ominus}{O}C_6H_4NO_2$$

FIG. 6

X = $-C_6H_4NO_2$, $-O\overset{\overset{\displaystyle O}{\|}}{C}-o$-isobutyl,

$-Cl$, $-OCH_2CN$,

$-O-\underset{\underset{\displaystyle NH-R_3}{|}}{C}=N-R_3$ etc.

$R_1 =$ H, CH_3, C_6H_5, $-\underset{\underset{\displaystyle R_4}{|}}{CH}-NH-$

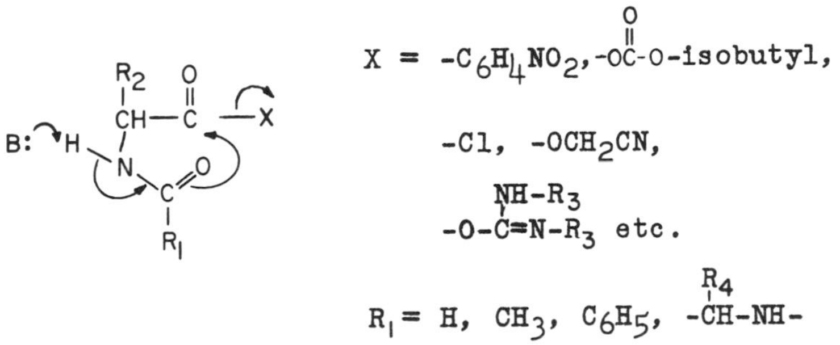

FIG. 7

Kemp and Chien[11] explored the nature of the dependence

of the base on the rate of oxazolone formation. They point

out that the amide involved in the cyclization can have a dual

nucleophilicity, depending on the relative concentrations of

neutral amide and amide anion present in the reaction media.

In studies on the triethylamine catalyzed racemization of

O-(benzyloxycarbonylglycyl-L-phenylalanyl)-N-ethylsalicyl-

amide in dimethylformamide containing triethylammonium

fluoroborate, the authors found a linear dependence of rate
on the amide:amide salt ratio, together with an insensitivity
of rate to the absolute amine concentration at constant amine:
amine salt ratios. The results are most easily interpreted
as requiring the intermediacy of a conjugate amide anion of
the neutral activated species.

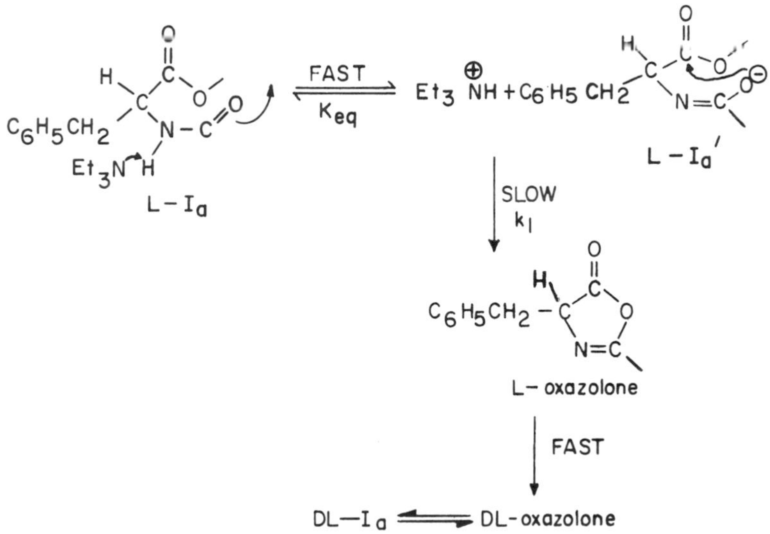

$$\frac{d(DL-I_a)}{dt} = k_I \left[L-I_a' \right] = k_I K_{eq} \left[L-I_a \right] \left[Et_3N / Et_3\overset{+}{N}H \right]$$

FIG. 8

The authors noted that for the case studied, the rate of
racemization could be slowed by as much as 50-fold by the
addition of the corresponding fluoroborate salt.

It must be pointed out that these results are in contrast
to other well-known salt effects on peptide racemization[9,12].

274

RACEMIZATION MECHANISMS IN PEPTIDE SYNTHESIS

There have been no extensive investigations on the ease
of formation of oxazolones. Young and coworkers[13-15] found
that the yields of L-peptide in the dicyclohexylcarbodiimide
coupling of benzoyl, acetyl, and formyl-leucine with glycine
ethyl ester in dichloromethane were 54%, 70%, and 94%,
respectively. These values must be related to the relative
ease of formation of the oxazolone intermediate.

Siemion and Konopinska[16a] suggested that oxazolone
formation is only possible in the case of the trans-conformation of the peptide. They studied the value of the optical
rotation and the optical rotatory dispersion curves of benzoyl,
acetyl, and formyl leucine ethyl esters in various solvents
and interpreted their results in terms of the cis-trans equilibrium of the amide function. They found that benzoyl-
leucine ethyl ester has a greater tendency to exist in the
trans conformation than either acetylleucine ethyl ester
or formylleucine ethyl ester. Blaha and coworkers[16b],
however, pointed out that this interpretation was largely
based on an incorrect assignment for the cis-amide II
band. Their re-examination of the infrared spectra
indicated that the benzoyl-leucine ethyl ester is entirely
in the trans-conformation in the solid state and in chloro-
inated hydrocarbon solvents. Acetyl-leucine ethyl ester
contains less than 5% of the cis conformer. In addition, we

know that a measure of cis-trans conformations need not be in any way related to the ease of formation of oxazolone since establishment of a cis-trans equilibrium for the amide bond is extremely rapid. This will always guarantee a substantial concentration of the reactive conformation.

The difference between the acyl and alkoxy-carbonyl residues as amine blocking groups was investigated by Determan[17]. He examined the infrared and nuclear magnetic resonance spectra of a number of blocking groups. The acyl groups (benzoyl, acetyl, formyl, aminoacyl) have a lower carbonyl frequency in the infrared (1680-1690 cm^{-1}) than the alkoxycarbonyl groups (ethoxycarbonyl, tert-butyl-oxycarbonyl, benzyloxycarbonyl) (1720-1725 cm^{-1}) indicating a lower double bond character for the amide carbonyl as compared to the urethane carbonyl. This provides evidence for the dipolar form 9-a for normal amides which results in a higher nucleophilicity for the oxygen atom leading to racemization via oxazolone formation. The fact that the urethane carbon atom is attached to three electronegative groups reduces the significance of the analogous structure 9-b. In this case, the diminished nucleophilicity of the carbonyl oxygen does not allow for ring closure to form oxazolone.

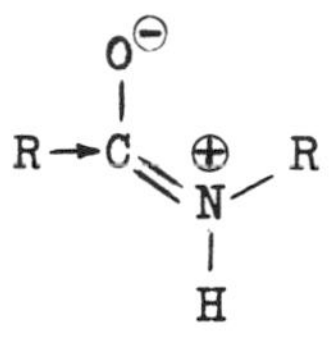

FIG. 9

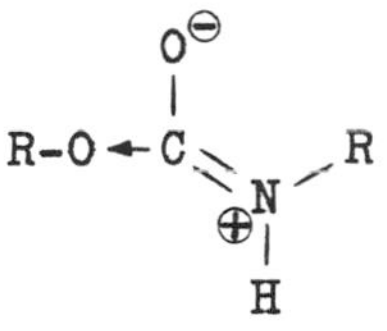

Such an interpretation is strengthened by the NMR results. Normal amides exhibit a clear N-H signal in trifluoroacetic acid, while the proton signal disappears for the urethane group. This indicates that in the latter case the nitrogen atom retains its basic character in contrast to that of ordinary amides.

OXAZOLONIUM SALTS

It is well known that N-substituted amino acids show a much smaller tendency to racemization than amino acids with primary amine functions. Acylated, N-substituted amino acids have no enolizable amide hydrogen and therefore the cyclization reaction must be much slower, since no base catalysis is possible. The resulting compounds would be charged oxazolonium salts.

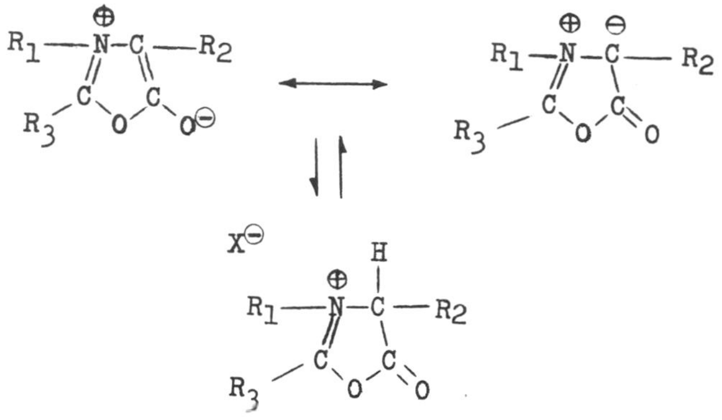

FIG. 10

As was noted earlier, amino acids can racemize when treated with acetic anhydride through oxazolone intermediates. Jackson and Cahill[18] showed that proline does not racemize under similar conditions. A few years later, however, Carter and Stevens[19] noted that certain acyl derivatives of L-proline and N-methyl-D-phenylalanine do racemize with acetic anhydride in glacial acetic acid. Charged oxazolonium ion intermediates were suggested by Cornforth and Elliot[20] to account for such observations. O'Brien and Niemann[21] determined the "i" factor for each of a series of acyl amino acid derivatives in concentrated sulfuric acid. Benzoyl sarcosine shows an "i" factor of 3.8 indicating that the equilibrium shown below lies far to the right:

Huisgen and coworkers[22] reported the formation of mesoionic or zwitterionic compounds when N-benzoyl-N-

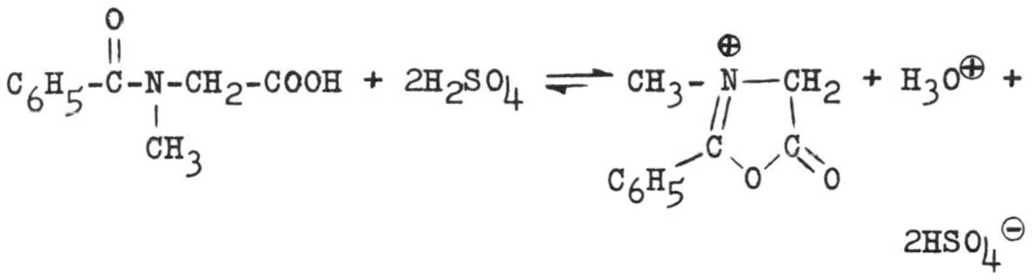

$$C_6H_5-\overset{\overset{\text{O}}{\|}}{C}-\underset{\overset{|}{CH_3}}{N}-CH_2-COOH \ + \ 2H_2SO_4 \ \rightleftharpoons \ CH_3-\overset{\oplus}{N}-CH_2 \ + \ H_3O^{\oplus} \ +$$

FIG. 11

methylphenylglycine is treated at 55° C with acetic anhydride

for a few minutes.

Goodman and Stueben found considerable racemization

in the preparation of the p-nitrophenyl esters of benzyloxy-

carbonylglycyl-L-phenylalanine and benzyloxycarbonylglycyl-

L-N-methylphenylalanine with tris (p-nitrophenyl) phosphite[23]

in dry pyridine[8]. However, benzyloxycarbonylglycyl-L-

proline p-nitrophenyl ester was prepared in high optical

purity by the same method. The authors proposed racemi-

zation via oxazolone and oxazolonium salt, respectively, in

the first two cases. For the proline derivative, they

proposed that the amide oxygen is prevented from intra-

molecular attack on the activated function because it is held

out of the plane of the ester carbonyl by the rigid five-

membered ring. The racemization found during the alkaline

hydrolysis (pH 8) of benzyloxycarbonylglycyl-L-proline

p-nitrophenyl ester was attributed to a diketopiperazine

intermediate. The diketopiperazine was isolated, and it was ascertained that these compounds can be racemized by alkaline conditions. Williams and Young[9] suggested that an intermediate oxazolonium salt can account for the small amount of racemization occurring in the conversion of p-nitrobenzoyl-L-proline into the p-nitrophenyl ester by the action of dicyclohexylcarbodiimide.

In conclusion, it is clear that N-substituted amino acid derivatives can racemize during coupling, although in general racemization is a less severe problem with these compounds than with comparable unsubstituted amino acid derivatives. The role of oxazolonium salts in peptide coupling remains questionable, although we do know that these salts can form under special non-coupling conditions.

ISOLATION AND REACTIONS OF OPTICALLY ACTIVE OXAZOLONES

A great impetus for many laboratories to study the chemistry of oxazolones was provided by the incorrect proposal of a thiazolidine-oxazolone structure for penicillin[24]. Optically active oxazolones were first isolated as a result of these efforts[24]. In 1964, Goodman and Levine[25], confirming the usefulness of the earlier techniques, synthesized the first optically active oxazolone in the crystalline state, 2-phenyl-L-4-benzyl-oxazolone. Benzoyl-L-phenylalanine was allowed to react with acetic anhydride in dioxane. The reaction was followed polarimetrically. The rotation changes from positive to negative as the product forms. At the point of maximum negative rotation the solvent is removed and the oxazolone purified. Rates of ring opening and racemization of this oxazolone using various nucleophiles were examined (Tables 1 and 2). In each case second-order rate constants for racemization were calculated from three pseudo first-order rate constants. For each of the nucleophiles studied racemization is a much faster process than ring opening. These investigations indicate that optically active acyl amino acid derivatives probably racemize via formation of an optically active oxazolone which rapidly reacts with base to give D, L-oxazolone. Ring opening follows, in a much slower reaction, to yield racemized product.

$$\text{L-oxazolone + AA ester} \xrightarrow{k_{ro}} \text{L-peptide}$$

$$\downarrow k_{rac}$$

$$\text{DL-oxazolone + AA ester} \xrightarrow{k_{ro}} \text{DL-peptide}$$

$$\frac{-d(\text{L-oxazolone})}{dt} = k_{ro}(\text{L-oxazolone})(\text{AA ester}) +$$

$$k_{rac}(\text{L-oxazolone})(\text{AA ester})$$

$$= (k_{ro} + k_{rac})(\text{L-oxazolone})(\text{AA ester}$$

$$= k'(\text{L-oxazolone})(\text{AA ester})$$

$$k' = k_o + k_{rac}$$

FIG. 12

281

TABLE 1

Rate Constants for the Racemization of 2-Phenyl-L-4-benzyl-oxazolone

Reagent causing racemization[a]	pK_a	Ratio reagent:oxazolone	$k_1 \times 10^2$ min.$^{-1}$	k_2 l./mole-min.	$t_{1/2}$ [b] min.
Pyridine	5.23	134:1 100:1 82:1	2.87 ± 0.09 1.87 ± .05 1.01 ± .05	0.03	3814
Phenylalanine methyl ester	7.06	2.4:1 1.8:1 1:1	7.46 ± .67 3.84 ± .23 1.85 ± .06	3.69	31
p-Nitrophenol and tri-n-butylamine	6.85[c]	0.25:1[d] 0.125:1[d] 0.065:1[d]	24.0 ± .7 13.1 ± .4 6.09 ± .19	115	0.99

[a] Solvent is dioxane in all cases. [b] Concentration of oxazolone is 8.74×10^{-3} M for all calculations. [c] Value obtained for aqueous media. [d] Ratio amine to oxazolone only; phenol:oxazolone = 3:1.

TABLE 2

Base-Catalyzed Ring-Opening Reactions of 2-Phenyl-L-4-benzyl-oxazolone

Ring-opening reagent	Ratio reagents:oxazolone	$k_1 \times 10^2$ min.$^{-1}$	$t_{1/2}$ min.	Products[a]
p-Nitrophenol and tri-n-butylamine	10:10:1	3.55 ± 0.12	19.5	Benzoyl-phe p-nitro-phenyl ester
Phenylalanine methyl ester	41:1	0.284 ± 0.11	244	Benzoyl-phe-phe methyl ester
Water	3.01×10^5:1	0.342 ± 0.20	203	Benzoyl-phe-OH
pH "8" buffer[b]	7560:1	2.89	24	Benzoyl-phe-OH
Pyridine	69:1	No reaction	---	DL-Oxazolone

[a] Phenylalanine is abbreviated pheOH.   [b] Buffer solution in presence of dioxane.

Siemion and Dzugaj[26] showed that the nitrogen atom of the oxazolone is sufficiently basic to form optically active oxazolone salts by reaction with dry hydrogen chloride in dioxane or trichloroacetic acid in chloroform. A much slower reaction is observed with a ten-fold excess of acetic acid in chloroform. The ability of the nitrogen atom in the oxazolone ring to behave as a basic proton acceptor provides a basis for the proposed mechanism of auto-racemization of oxazolones (FIG. 13). Autoracemization, however, is not a factor in normal peptide synthesis, where much more powerful bases are present.

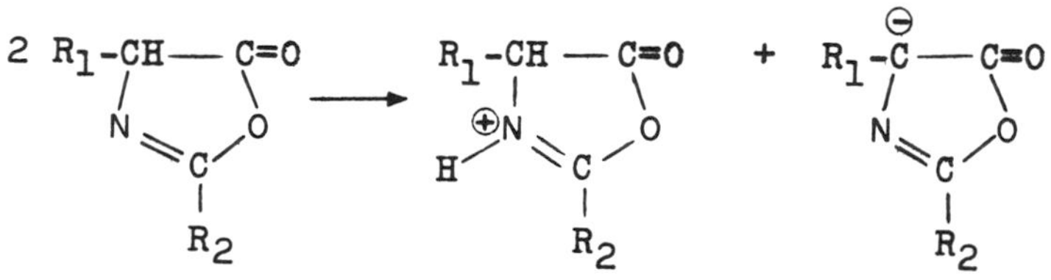

FIG. 13

Goodman and Levine[25] used infrared spectroscopy to study the equilibrium between 2-phenyl-L-4-benzyl-oxazolone and benzoylphenylalanine p-nitro-phenyl ester (FIG. 14). The equilibrium is in favor of p-nitrophenyl ester and the oxazolone can be present only in very small concentration. The authors conclude that steady state kinetics must be involved in the racemization process.

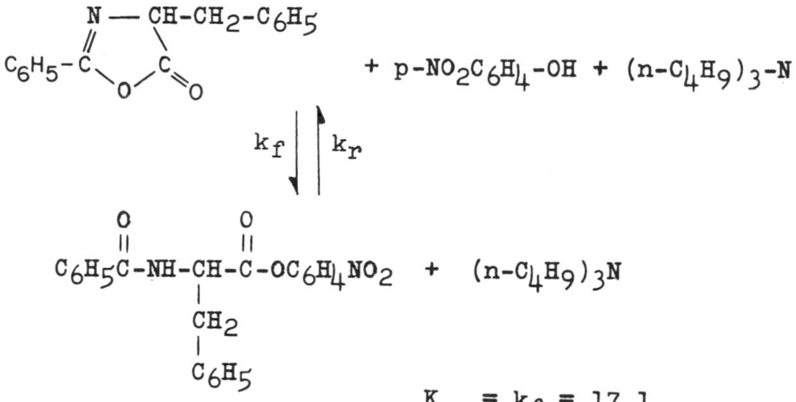

$$\text{C}_6\text{H}_5-\text{C}\underset{\text{O}}{\overset{\text{N}-\text{CH}-\text{CH}_2-\text{C}_6\text{H}_5}{\diagdown}}\text{C}{=}\text{O} \quad + \text{ p-NO}_2\text{C}_6\text{H}_4-\text{OH} + (\text{n-C}_4\text{H}_9)_3-\text{N}$$

$$k_f \Big\updownarrow k_r$$

$$\text{C}_6\text{H}_5\overset{\text{O}}{\overset{\|}{\text{C}}}-\text{NH}-\text{CH}-\overset{\text{O}}{\overset{\|}{\text{C}}}-\text{OC}_6\text{H}_4\text{NO}_2 \quad + \quad (\text{n-C}_4\text{H}_9)_3\text{N}$$
$$\text{CH}_2$$
$$\text{C}_6\text{H}_5$$

$$K_{eq} = \frac{k_f}{k_r} = 17.1$$

FIG. 14

Kenner and his associates[27] prepared the stable
inactive peptide oxazolone, 2-(1' -benzyloxycarbonyl-
amino-1' -methyl)ethyl-4, 4-dimethyl-oxazolone (15-A) by
heating benzyloxycarbonylaminoisobutyrlaminoisobutyric
acid with acetic anhydride. Recently, McGahren and
Goodman[28] reported the synthesis of two optically active
crystalline, peptide oxazolones, 2-(1' -benzyloxycarbonyl-
amino-1'-methyl)-ethyl-4-methyl-oxazolone (15-B) and
2-(1' -benzyloxycarbonyl-amino-1' -methyl)-ethyl-4-
benzyloxazolone (15-C). In addition to the preparation of
these compounds by the route employing acetic anhydride in
dioxane, treatment of the blocked dipeptides with dicyclo-

hexylcarbodiimide in ether yields rapid ring closure to form the desired product[29].

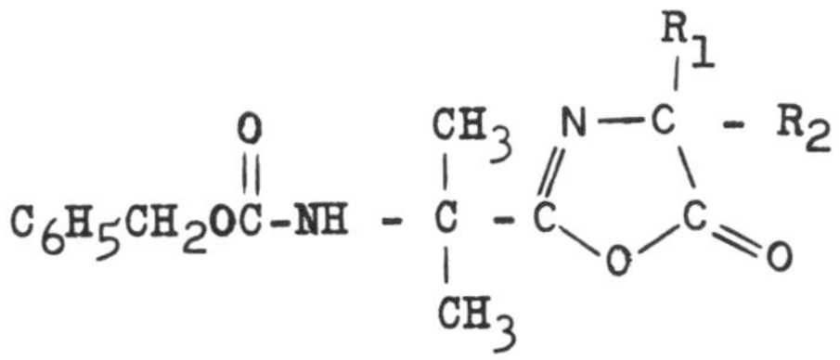

$$C_6H_5CH_2O\overset{\overset{\displaystyle O}{\|}}{C}-NH - \overset{\overset{\displaystyle CH_3}{|}}{\underset{\underset{\displaystyle CH_3}{|}}{C}} - \overset{N-\overset{\overset{\displaystyle R_1}{|}}{C} - R_2}{\underset{O}{\overset{\displaystyle //}{C}}\overset{C}{\diagdown}}{=}O$$

15-A (R_1 = CH$_3$, R_2 = CH$_3$)

15-B (R_1 = CH$_3$, R_2 = H)

15-C (R_1 = CH$_2$-C$_6$H$_5$, R_2 = H)

FIG. 15

The racemization and ring-opening reactions of oxazolone 15-C, derived from benzyloxycarbonylamino-isobutyl-L-phenylalanine, were studied in several commonly used peptide solvents[30]. In some cases, racemization and ring opening are found to proceed at comparable rates. For these reactions, observed rotations must be corrected for the optically active tri-peptide formed. This was accomplished by addition of n-butylamine at appropriate times to racemize instantly all remaining optically active oxazolone.

In this manner a correction curve of optical rotation of the tripeptide product vs. time is obtained. By amending

observed rotations measured during a racemization reaction
for the optically active product formed, the true oxazolone
optical rotation at any time is determined. When racemization
and ring-opening rates are comparable second order kinetics
for racemization are followed. When the rate of
racemization is much larger than the rate of ring opening,
our studies show that oxazolone racemization is a pseudo
first-order reaction. Ring-opening reactions are generally
followed by noting the disappearance of the carbonyl absorption for oxazolone at 1825 cm^{-1}. Where this approach
becomes impossible we employ thin layer chromatography to
give approximate results. The ring-opening reaction
proceeds via second-order kinetics.

Solvent, temperature and the nature of nucleophile are
fundamentally important in determining the relative rates of
racemization and ring-opening for oxazolones. Indirectly,
therefore, these variables are central to peptide coupling
reactions.

The ability of the solvent to accommodate separation of
charge appears to be a most important factor in determining
the extent of racemization in a given solvent. Dioxane, which
can accommodate charge separation by solvation of the depar-
ting proton, gives rise to much more racemization than
toluene, where such solvation is much less likely.

287

Young postulated a "chloride ion effect"[9,12] which is based on his observation of increased racemization when coupling reactions are carried out with an ester hydrochloride and an equivalent of tertiary amine rather than with the free amino acid ester. He attributes this to the basicity of the chloride ion in organic solvents. In our laboratory, it was found that oxazolones racemize very slowly at room temperature with triethylamine hydrochloride in chloroform. In the presence of DL-phenylglycine methyl ester this salt accelerates the rate of racemization and retards the rate of coupling. We attribute the effect noted by Young to the increased ionic strength of the system rather than to the basicity of the chloride ion.

Another important factor controlling the racemization of a given oxazolone is the nature of the incoming nucleophile (Tables 3-6). Attack by the reagent to produce a ring-opened product is a measure of the reagent's nucleophilicity. Alternately, attack by the reagent on the proton of the asymmetric carbon atom to racemize the oxazolone is indicative of the reagent's basicity. Of the amino acids studied by Goodman and McGahren[30], ethyl glycinate gives the greatest retention of optical activity. Methyl alaninate affords less favorable results. Methyl aminoisobutyrate, a highly hindered nucleophile, gives complete racemization

TABLE 3

Racemization and Ring Opening of L-Phenylalanine Peptide Oxazolone by Ethyl Glycinate

Solvent	k_{rac} 1 mole^{-1} min^{-1}	k_{ro} 1 mole^{-1} min^{-1}	% Retention of optical activity
Chloroform	2.1	5.0	66
Toluene	9.3[a]	13.3[a]	78
Dioxane	4.5	1.75	14
Ethyl acetate	3.2	3.6[b]	38

[a] Reactions in toluene were too fast for good kinetic studies.

[b] Rate constant calculated from an estimated half-time value obtained by TLC.

TABLE 4

Racemization and Ring Opening of L-Phenylalanine Peptide Oxazolone
by Methyl DL-Alaninate

Solvent	k_{rac}	k_{ro} 1 mole^{-1} min^{-1}	% Retention of optical activity
Chloroform	1.0 l. mole^{-1} min^{-1}	0.5	32
Toluene	2.2 l. mole^{-1} min^{-1}	2.4	52
Dioxane	10.34 ± 0.3 x 10^{-2} min^{-1}	0.14	0
Ethyl acetate	6.8 l. mole^{-1} min^{-1}	0.75[a]	11

[a] Rate constant calculated from estimated half-time value obtained using TLC.

TABLE 5

Racemization and Ring Opening of L-Phenylalanine Peptide Oxazolone
by Methyl DL-Phenylglycinate

Solvent	k_{rac} 1 mole^{-1} min^{-1}	k_{ro} 1 mole^{-1} min^{-1}	% Retention of optical activity
Chloroform	0.18	0.4	--
Toluene	0.7	2.1	74
Chloroform plus equimolar NEt$_3$·HCl[a]	0.35	0.25	--

[a] The same concentration, namely 0.03045 M, of oxazolone, methyl DL-phenylglycine and NEt$_3$·HCl used.

TABLE 6

Racemization and Ring Opening of L-Phenylalanine Peptide Oxazolone by Methyl α-Aminoisobutyrate

Solvent	$k_{rac} \times 10^2$ min^{-1}	$t_{1/2rac}$ min	k_{ro} $l\ mole^{-1}\ min^{-1}$	% Retention of optical activity
Chloroform	3.30 ± 0.08	21.0	0.0024	0
Toluene	3.03 ± 0.10	22.8	0.006	0
Dioxane	8.52 ± 0.04	8.1	0.008	0
Ethyl acetate	8.21 ± 0.05	8.4	---	0

in every case, undoubtedly because of the steric factor
involved. These results suggest that the use of ethyl
glycinate in the Anderson and Young tests for racemization
may give rise to a higher degree of retention of configuration than would be found with other amino acids. Methyl
aminoisobutyrate, on the other hand, offers a too stringent
test for racemization in coupling reactions.

Kovacs observed the rapid formation of oxazolone in
the reaction of benzyloxycarbonylglycyl-L-phenylalanine
with pentachlorophenol using dicyclohexylcarbodiimide[31].
The rate of ring opening of the isolated oxazolone from
benzyloxycarbonyglycyl-L-phenylalanine was followed for
reaction with pentachlorophenol (pK 5. 3), 2, 4-dinitrophenol
(pK 4. 1) and p-nitrophenol (pK 7. 2) and their respective
phenolate anions. The rate of ring opening of the phenols
is 2, 4-dinitrophenol $>$ pentachlorophenol $>$ p-nitrophenol.
In the presence of base, this order is reversed. However,
for 2, 4-dinitrophenol and pentachlorophenol, the ring opening
is faster in the absence of base than when base is present.
This result is indicative of another mechanism of oxazolone
ring opening for these two highly acidic phenols. In
addition, at -10° C, the 2, 4-dinitrophenyl and pentachlorophenyl
esters of benzyloxycarbonyglycyl-L-phenylalanine are formed
from the dicyclohexylcarbodiimide method with a high degree
of optical purity (Note: - DeTar and coworkers[32], in the

preparation of pentachlorophenyl esters using dicyclohexylcarbodiimide, observed the rapid formation of
oxazolone intermediate followed by appearance of extensively racemized active ester. These differences in
optical purity of product may be due to experimental conditions.) Kovacs proposed the following scheme to account
for the results found with highly acidic phenols.

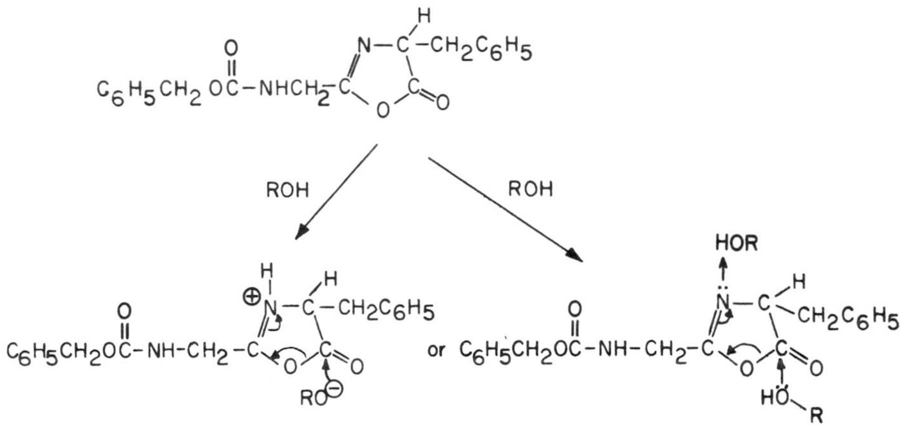

ROH = 2, 4-dinitrophenol, pentachlorophenol

FIG. 16

The intermediate L-oxazolone forms rapidly under the
reaction conditions. Protonation on the nitrogen atom of
the ring, followed by phenolate attack, leads to rapid ring
opening. Alternately, a concerted effect can be considered.

Kovacs also believes that complex formation occurs
between pentachlorophenol and dicyclohexylcarbodiimide.

Formation of the pentachlorophenyl ester by the use of the postulated complex gives ester with higher optical purity and at a faster rate than the usual dicyclohexylcarbodiimide procedure. The authors demonstrated that the complex dissociates in solution and postulate that the special behavior found is due to the large excess of pentachlorophenol present after dissociation.

COMPARISON OF AMINO ACID AND PEPTIDE OXAZOLONES

Investigations in our laboratory[25, 30, 33] allow certain comparisons to be made between the amino acid oxazolone, 2-phenyl-L-4-benzyl-oxazolone (17-A), and the peptide oxazolone, 2-(1'-benzyloxycarbonylamino-1'-methyl)-ethyl-4-benzyl-oxazolone (17-B). The second-order rate constants for ring opening and racemization in dioxane at 25°C were determined for reaction of each oxazolone with DL-phenylalanine methyl ester.

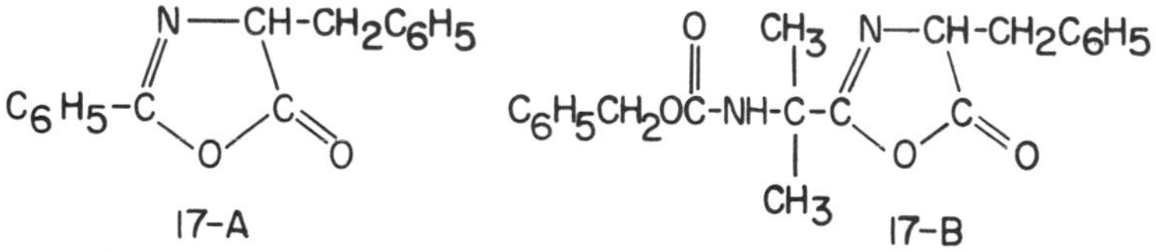

17-A

17-B

k_{ro} (l./mole-min)	*	0.065
k_{rac} (l./mole-min)	3.69	0.750

* Additional experiments are being conducted to obtain this result.

FIG. 17

Under our reaction conditions, the peptide oxazolone racemizes 11-12 times faster than it ring opens. Preliminary results indicate that racemization is also much faster than ring opening for the amino acid oxazolone. In both instances, ring-opening by DL-phenylalanine methyl ester results in an almost completely racemized peptide product. The amino acid oxazolone is racemized 5 times more readily than the peptide oxazolone because of the additional conjugation possible in the former case between the aromatic ring and the carbon-nitrogen double bond[18].

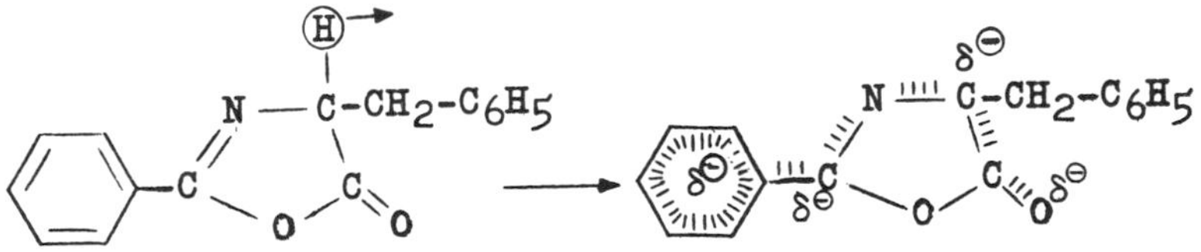

FIG. 18

Amino acid oxazolone formation appears to be a far more facile process than peptide oxazolone formation. Treatment of benzoyl-L-phenylalanine with acetic anhydride in dioxane gives the maximum negative polarimetric reading in 75 minutes, corresponding to the formation of L-oxazolone. Reaction of benzyloxycarbonylaminoisobutyryl-L-phenylalanine, under the same conditions, gives a maximum negative reading after 14 hours. These results may serve to explain why the Young test[15], involving the coupling of benzoyl-L-leucine with glycine ethyl ester, is a more severe test for racemization than the Anderson test[34] which involves the coupling of benzyloxycarbonylglycyl-L-phenylalanine with glycine ethyl ester.

α-NUCLEOPHILES AND BIPHILICITY

It has been possible to correlate reactivities of various nucleophiles by suitable examination of such parameters as polarizability and basicity. Edwards suggested an equation of the following form[35]:

$$\log k/k_o = \alpha P + \beta H$$

FIG. 19

The parameters a and b are reaction constants and P and H are functions of the polarizability and basicity of a nucleophile, respectively. The rate or equilibrium constant k_o, is for some reference standard nucleophile, usually water. Other, similar equations have been proposed[36-38]. One class of compounds does not appear to follow these correlations in its reaction with electrophilic centers. These nucleophiles are more reactive than would be predicted on the basis of polarizability and basic strength[39-41]. Their common structural feature is the presence of an unshared pair of electrons on the atom adjacent to the nucleophilic atom. Edwards and Pearson[42] noted that these nucleophiles exhibit an enhanced reactivity which they termed an alpha-effect (α-effect).

Hydrazine represents an example of this special group of vicinally bifunctional nucleophiles. We have shown that an excess of hydrazine hydrate reacts with the peptide oxazolone from benzyloxycarbonylaminoisobutyryl-L-phenylalanine, yielding optically pure hydrazide[30].

Siemion and Morawiec[43] reported similar results with the oxazolone from acetyl-L-leucine. In contrast, Siemion and Dzugaj[26] have reported that the ammonolysis of the oxazolone from acetyl-L-leucine gives completely racemic product.

Hydroxylamine and its derivatives are also α-nucleophiles and have been found to have enhanced reactivity[39-41]. Diethylhydroxylamine[44], N-hydroxy-piperidine[45-47], N-hydroxyphthalimide[48, 49], N-hydroxysuccinimide[50-53] and benzohydroxamic acid[54] have all been used in recent years as racemization-resistant activating agents in peptide coupling reactions. In our laboratory we are seeking a clear understanding of the nature of the α-effect to establish the mode of action of these hydroxylamine derivatives in peptide coupling. This, in turn, might provide new clues to improved reaction conditions in addition to suggesting other activating agents.

Bruice and coworkers[41] outlined various proposed explanations for the α-effect. They can be briefly summarized as follows:

a) Stabilization of the transition state owing to overlap

of the orbitals of the lone pair electrons in the α-position.

b) Diminished solvation, e.g., of HOO^- as compared to OH^-.

c) Ground state destabilization resulting from non-bonding electron pair repulsions.

d) Intramolecular general base catalysis.

e) Simultaneous push-pull mechanisms resulting from the "biphilic" nature of the reagent.

Most of the available evidence supports biphilic pathways for the α-effect:

1) α-Nucleophiles which cannot participate in push-pull transition states are found to have normal reactivity[39-41].

2) The α-effect is inoperative in amine general base catalyzed ionization of nitroethane[55].

3) The α-effect is inoperative for displacement on sp^3 carbon (CH_3I)[56].

4) Phenylhydroxylamine has a higher rate, lower E_a, and a high negative $\Delta S^{\ddagger}$ in relation to other nucleophiles in its attack on acetyl peroxide[57]. The high negative $\Delta S^{\ddagger}$ is indicative of a cyclic transition state.

We can view the biphilic nature of some α-nucleophiles in their reaction with activated carbonyl compounds (esters, acid halides, acylisoureas, anhydrides, oxazolones, etc.) as follows:

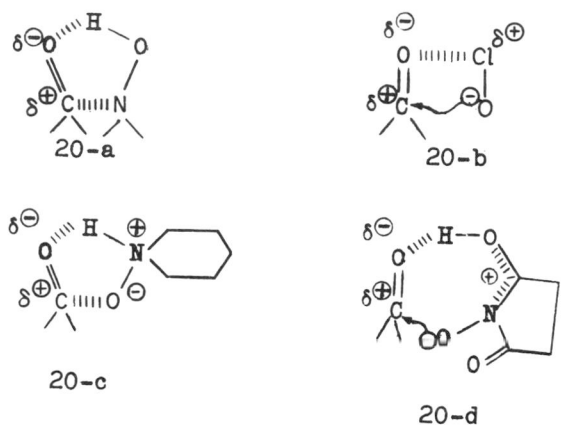

FIG. 20

Transition state 20-a illustrates the biphilic reaction of a neutral hydroxylamine involving H-bonding to the oxygen atom of the carbonyl. The high nucleophilicity of the hypochlorite anion has been attributed to the ability of chlorine to withdraw electrons in the transition state 20-b from the carbonyl oxygen via its empty d-orbital[39]. Analogous d-p orbital interaction seems to exist in the 1:1 adduct between acetone and bromine[58]. In the reaction of N-hydroxypiperidine no biphilic mechanism is possible for the neutral species. However, in the zwitterionic form, reaction may proceed via attack by the oxygen anion and simultaneous hydrogen bonding (transition state 20-c). In the case of N-hydroxysuccinimide, a simple zwitterion (analogous to 20-c) is not likely. However, in the zwitterionic structure illustrated (transition state 20-d), the delocalization of positive charge about three atoms makes possible an enhanced rate of reaction via a biphilic mechanism.

On the other hand, α -nucleophiles such as N, N-dimethyl-

hydrazine and N, O-dimethylhydroxylamine cannot yield

products via biphilic mechanisms. For N, N-dimethylhydra-

zine, attack by the primary amine function does not allow

for hydrogen bonding. Hydrogen bonding is possible for

attack by the dimethyl nitrogen atom. This cannot lead to

product, however, because the dimethyl nitrogen has no

proton to expel and cannot eliminate the positive charge

acquired during nucleophilic attack. The high basic

strength of the primary nitrogen atom rules out a zwitter-

ionic intermediate. For N, O-dimethylhydroxylamine,

neither a biphilic transition state nor a zwitterionic inter-

mediate is possible.

Our studies[33] on 2-phenyl-L-4-benzyl-oxazolone con-

firm these conclusions (Tables 7 and 8). Those α -nucleo-

philes which can participate in biphilic attack react much

more rapidly, and give products with a considerably higher

degree of optical purity, than those where this route is

impossible. Hydroxylamine, N-hydroxypiperidine, and

N-hydroxysuccinimide give products of high optical purity

(90-100%). The substantial racemization found for

N, N-diethylhydroxylamine as compared to N-hydroxypiperidine

can be explained by steric considerations which would retard

the ring-opening reaction. Racemization by direct proton

abstraction should be much less sterically dependent. The alkyl substituents on the nitrogen atom of N-hydroxypiperidine are restrained by being in a ring system. These restrictions on rotation do not apply to N,N-diethylhydroxylamine. Hydrazine compounds give substantial racemization showing that basicity may still compete in this series. The high degree of order necessary to form the cyclic transition state in biphilic attack is more easily attained at low temperatures. This may account for the increased optical purity found at lower temperatures. More racemization is found when an excess of nucleophilic reagent is used. This is expected because of the increased polarity of the solution.

The results of Siemion[59] are consistent with our biphilic interpretation of α-nucleophilic effects involving hydrogen bonding to the carbonyl oxygen of the oxazolone ring (see FIG. 20 and accompanying discussion). However, he proposed on alternate biphilic mechanism based on the influence of the weakly basic nitrogen atom in the oxazolone ring (see FIG. 13 and accompanying discussion on auto-racemization). Siemion suggests that as the oxazolone ring opens, the basicity of the ring nitrogen is strongly enhanced leading to racemization by abstraction of hydrogen from the adjacent carbon atom (transition state 21-a). According to this explanation, attack by hydrazine involves hydrogen bonding to the nitrogen atom of the ring (transition

state 21-b). This facilitates transfer of the proton from

hydrazine to the nitrogen atom of the ring and accounts for

the lack of racemization found.

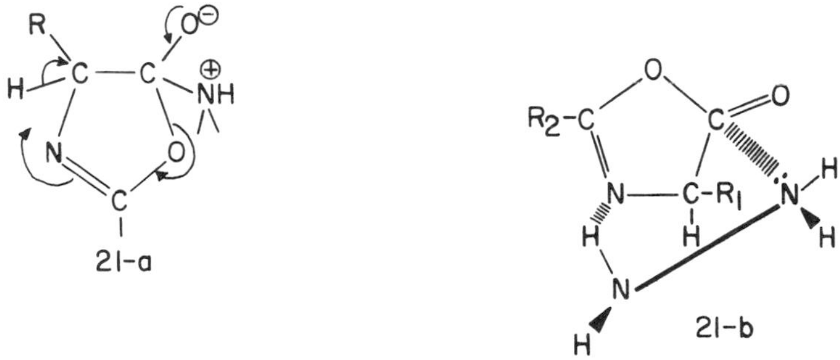

FIG. 21

We believe that the transition state 21-b is based on an

incorrect mechanism of racemization for oxazolones (21-a)

during peptide coupling. According to our view, racemiza-

tion involves the removal of the hydrogen atom on the asym-

metric carbon atom by a basic species. In autoracemization,

the nitrogen atom of a second oxazolone ring can furnish

the most basic species available for proton abstraction and

racemization proceeds slowly. During peptide coupling

conditions, oxazolone racemization is a facile process

because of the stronger bases present in the media. Ring

opening and racemization can thus be seen as two distinct,

and competing processes (as in FIG. 12). The experimental

facts clearly point to our explanation of oxazolone racemiza-

tion:

303

a. The wide variance in k_{ro}/k_{rac} found for different amino acid esters in reaction with peptide oxazolone 15-C[30] implies two separate processes for ring opening and racemization. It follows from Siemion's proposal that each of these reactions should have similar k_{ro}/k_{rac} ratios.

b. For highly hindered nucleophiles such as methyl aminoisobutyrate $k_{rac} \gg k_{ro}$, and in general $k_{rac} > k_{ro}$[30]. Siemion's proposal leads to a prediction that $k_{rac} \leqslant k_{ro}$ in all cases.

c. Tertiary amines[30], and even the much less basic dicyclohexylcarbodiimide[33], lead to rapid racemization of the oxazolone, even though ring opening is impossible for these compounds.

21-b is still a possible biphilic transition state. However, a structure involving hydrogen bonding to the carbonyl function of the oxazolone ring is more consistent with the general effect found for reactions of α -nucleophiles with activated carbonyl functions. In addition, the steric requirements of 21-b appear to be severe.

It appears likely that the biphilic mechanism of the hydroxylamine-derived activating groups makes possible the preparation of the active ester in a higher degree of optical purity than would be otherwise found. For example, we can illustrate the preparation of an N-hydroxypiperidine

active ester from a benzoyl amino acid using dicyclohexylcarbodiimide. (An analogous argument could be used
employing the mixed anhydride route.)

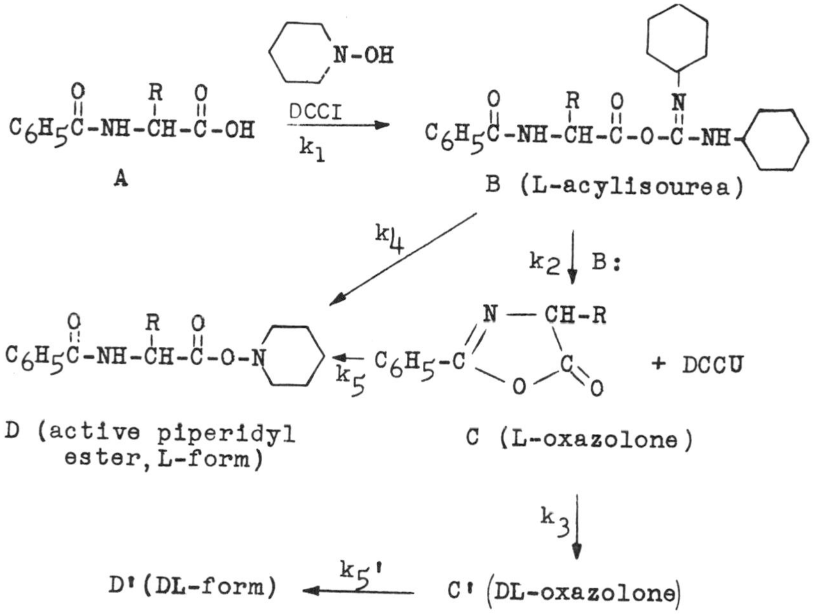

FIG. 22

Analysis of the reaction after formation of the initial
species (22-B) leads us to the following predictions:

1) k_4/k_2 will be substantially higher for N-hydroxy-
piperidines where a biphilic mechanism is operative, than
for p-nitrophenol, where it is not. Little oxazolone (22-C)
formation is expected in the first case, whereas substantial
oxazolone may be formed in the second.

2) Even were L-oxazolone (22-C) to form extensively, biphilic attack of N-hydroxypiperidine will lead to optically active 22-D. Thus k_5/k_3 will be much higher than for p-nitrophenol where no biphilic route is possible.

It cannot be stated at this time which of these factors is most important, but the net effect is clear. Intermediates which are obtained via biphilic reactions will have a high degree of optical purity.

As part of a comprehensive study on the chemistry of carbodiimides[32, 60, 61], DeTar and his associates studied the reactions of peptide acids with carbodiimides[32]. They found that the rate of reaction of benzoylphenylalanine with dicyclohexylcarbodiimide in the presence of p-nitrophenol is the same as with p-nitrophenol absent. Oxazolone is the first identifiable intermediate, confirming earlier results[62]. Under the reaction conditions the rate of reaction to form oxazolone from benzoylphenylalanine is one thousand times faster than the reaction of oxazolone with p-nitrophenol. As we noted earlier, Goodman and Levine[25] found that the reaction of isolated oxazolone from benzoyl-L-phenylalanine and p-nitrophenol is reversible, and racemization proceeds much more rapidly than ring opening for attack by p-nitro-phenylate anion. There have been several reports of race-mization during the preparation of p-nitrophenyl esters of

TABLE 7

Reactions of 2-Phenyl-L-4-benzyl-oxazolone with Hydrazine and its Derivatives

Nucleophile	Solvent	Temp. °C	% Racemization	Nucleophile/Oxazolone
NH_2NH_2	THF:MeOH (1:1)	0	0	large excess
	THF:MeOH (1:1)	25	14	large excess
	THF:MeOH (1:1)	44	32	large excess
$NH_2NH_2 \cdot HOAc$	THF	0	33	2.6:1
	THF	25	35	2.6:1
⬡—NH-NH$_2$	Et$_2$O	0	35	1.1:1
	Et$_2$O	0	75	5:1
	Et$_2$O	25	70	1.1:1
	THF	0	100	5:1
	CHCl$_3$	0	33	1.1:1
	CHCl$_3$	25	59	1.1:1
NO$_2$—⬡—NHNH$_2$	THF	25	100	1.1:1
OCH$_3$ ⬡—NHNH$_2$	Et$_2$O	25	40	1.1:1
t-BuOC—NHNH$_2$	Et$_2$O	25	75	1.2:1
$(CH_3)_2$-N-NH$_2$	Et$_2$O	25	100	1.1:1
	CHCl$_3$	0	100	1.1:1
	CHCl$_3$	25	100	1.1:1
	CHCl$_3$	25	100	8:1

TABLE 8

Reactions of 2-Phenyl-L-4-benzyl-oxazolone with Hydroxylamine and its Derivatives

Nucleophile	Solvent	Temp. °C	% Racemization	Nucleophile/Oxazolone
NH_2OH	MeOH	25	0	2.5:1
(piperidine) N-OH	Et_2O	0	<5	1.1:1
	Et_2O	25	<10	1.1:1
	THF	25	<10	1.1:1
(cyclopentanedione) N-OH	THF	0	0	1.1:1
	THF	25	0	1.1:1
	THF	0	0	4:1
$CH_3NH-OCH_3$	Et_2O	25	55	1.1:1
$(CH_3CH_2)_2N-OH$	Et_2O	0	42	1.1:1
	Et_2O	25	56	1.1:1
	THF	0	42	1.1:1

acylated derivatives from both the dicyclohexylcarbodiimide[25],
[31, 32, 63] and tris(p-nitrophenyl)phosphite[8] methods.

HYDROGEN BONDING IN ATTACK ON ACTIVATED SPECIES

Thus far our concern has been on the formation of active esters. Now we must turn our attention to the second stage, i.e., the attack of the nucleophile on the activated species. Young and coworkers[45, 47, 64-66], in their studies on the uncatalyzed reaction of piperidine esters with amines, proposed the following hydrogen-bonded transition state to explain a) the lack of racemization during aminolysis and b) the unexpectedly rapid rate of reaction for esters of such weakly acidic hydroxy compounds.

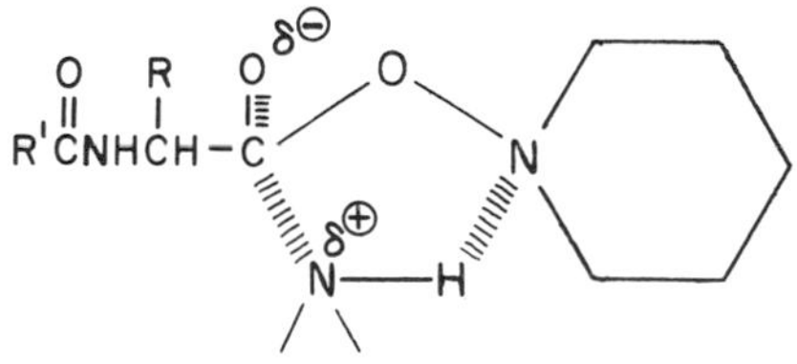

FIG. 23

Subsequent transfer of the proton in the complex to the heterocyclic nitrogen atom would then lead to product. The leaving group is the tautomer of N-hydroxypiperidine, rather than the unstable anion. The competing process, oxazolone formation, takes place through internal oxygen attack where no anchimeric assistance through hydrogen bonding is possible (FIG. 24). For this reason, oxazolone formation (and subsequent racemization) is suppressed and optically pure products can be obtained. Unfortunately, piperdyl esters exhibit marked steric hindrance, which leads to a low reactivity in many cases.

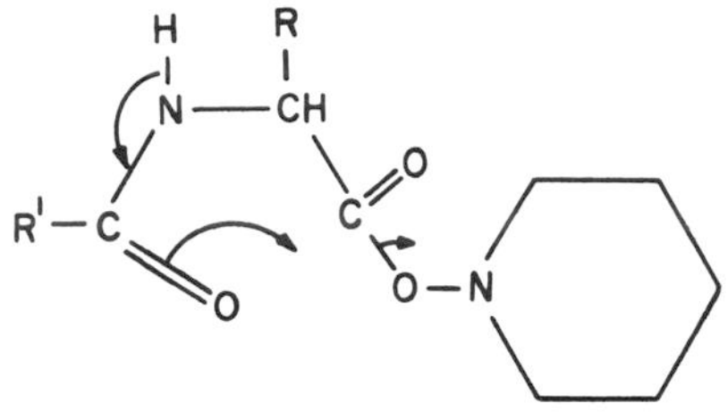

FIG. 24

N-Hydroxysuccinimide esters react much more readily but racemize much more easily than the corresponding piperidyl esters. In the absence of a suitable nucleophile for reaction, oxazolone formation appears likely. Anderson found benzoyl-L-leucine succinimide ester to be easily racemized in the workup[53]. Our results[33] show similar racemization with benzoyl-L-phenylalanine succinimide ester. We found, however, that optically pure benzoyl-L-phenylalanine succinimide ester can be prepared from the

reaction of 2-phenyl-L-4-benzyl-oxazolone with N-hydroxysuccinimide under various conditions. A solution of succinimide active ester in tetrahydrofuran at $0^{o}C$ reacts instantly
with a methanolic solution of hydrazine hydrate to give
optically pure hydrazide. DL-Phenylalanine methyl ester
also reacts without racemization. However, boiling of the
active ester in methanol for 25 minutes gives completely
racemized unreacted ester. Benzyloxycarbonyl-L-phenyl-
alanine succinimide ester shows only a 10% drop in optical
activity after the same treatment in methanol. It appears
that benzoyl-L-phenylalanine succinimide ester which can
form oxazolone racemizes primarily via this route. For
the benzyloxycarbonyl derivative, where oxazolone formation
is unlikely, direct proton abstraction by solvent probably
accounts for the racemization found.

In the presence of a nucleophile, a biphilic mechanism
involving hydrogen bonding to the carbonyl oxygen group in
the transition state seems plausible. Charge delocalization
favors this proposal, and the partial positive charge on the
nitrogen atom activates the leaving group.

This explanation might also account for the fact that
N-hydroxyphthalimide esters react more sluggishly than

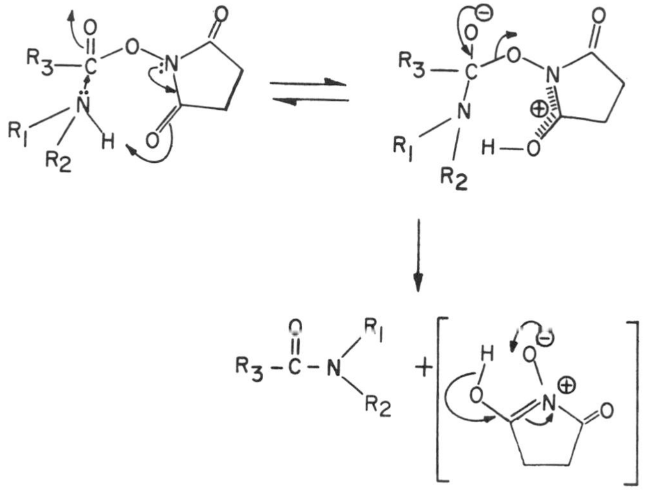

FIG. 25

succinimide esters. A similar transition state can be constructed with an even more facile hydrogen transfer to the
carbonyl oxygen because of further dispersal of positive
charge into the ring. This dispersal of charge, however,
causes the heterocyclic nitrogen atom to become less
electropositive. Thus the driving force for cleavage of the
ester bond is lowered.

Other hydrogen-bonded transition states have been
proposed to explain enhanced rates of reaction and reduced
racemization during aminolysis[67-70]. Jakubke and coworkers[67-68] proposed an analogous mechanism to Young
for the aminolysis of esters of 8-hydroxyquinoline (27-a).
In a related paper, a series of esters derived from 3, 6 and
8-hydroxyquinolines were synthesized and the rate of

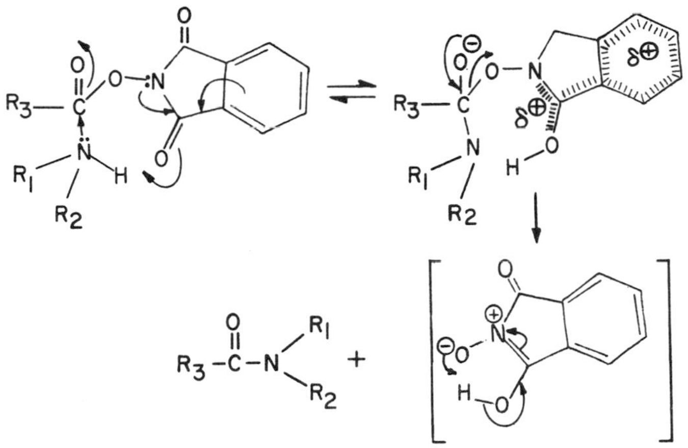

FIG. 26

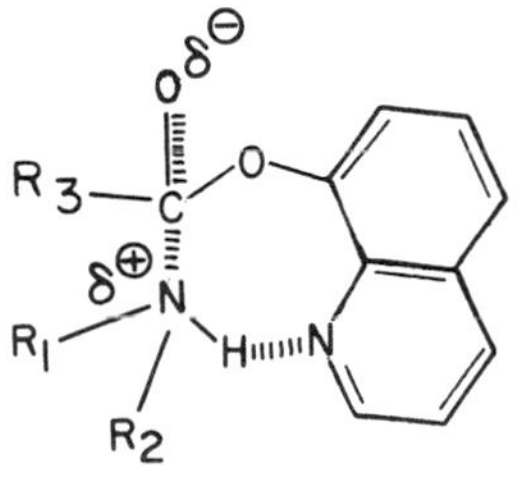

27-a

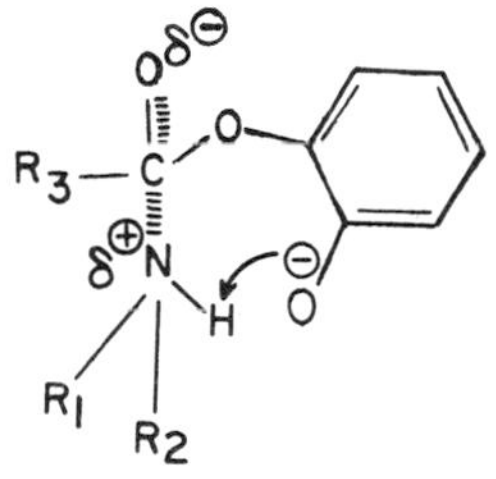

27-b

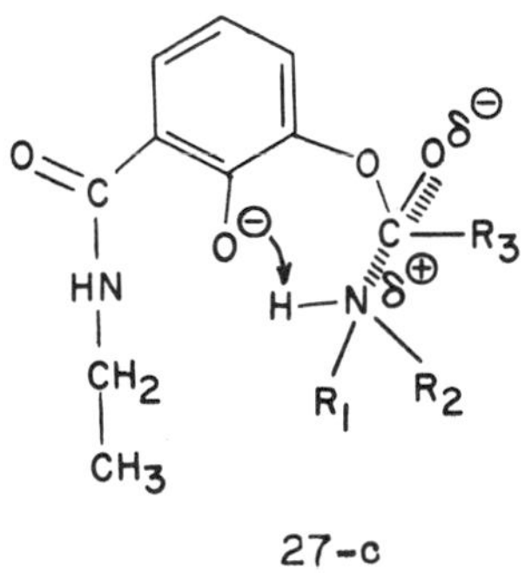

27-c

FIG. 27

aminolysis studied. On the basis of the normal $B_{AC}2$ mechanism the expected order of aminolysis is quinoline-(3)-ester (pka for 3-hydroxyquinoline≈ 8.06) ≫ quinoline-(6)-ester (pka for 6-hydroxyquinoline≈ 8.88) > quinoline-(8)-ester (pka for 8-hydroxyquinoline =9.89). The actual rate of aminolysis was quinoline-(8)-ester ≫ quinoline-(3)-ester > quinoline-(6)-ester. This is consistent with the hydrogen-bonded transition state for the 8-hydroxyquinoline ester. In addition, it was pointed out that the use of activating groups with high pka values is important in preventing intramolecular attack to form oxazolone. Catechol (27-b) esters offer another similar approach to this problem[69]. Finally, the phenolic esters derived from 2-ethyl-7-hydroxyl-benzisoxazolium cation by the procedure of Kemp [70a, b] offer a particularly promising method for peptide coupling; here also, hydrogen-bonded intermediates appear to be of key importance (27-c).

A related approach to the hydrogen-bonded transition states is the use of bifunctional catalysts introduced into peptide chemistry by Beyerman and Maassen van den Brink [71]. These compounds posses both a weakly basic and a weakly acidic group situated so that a cyclic transition state may occur leading to a concerted displacement. Considerable acceleration is found in the aminolysis of various esters in the presence of these reagents. Imidazole is a bifunctional

compound that cannot act as a bifunctional catalyst since it
does not allow for a concerted cyclic pathway. It shows
considerably less acceleration than the compounds shown
in FIG. 28 which are examples of bifunctional catalysts
employed by these workers.

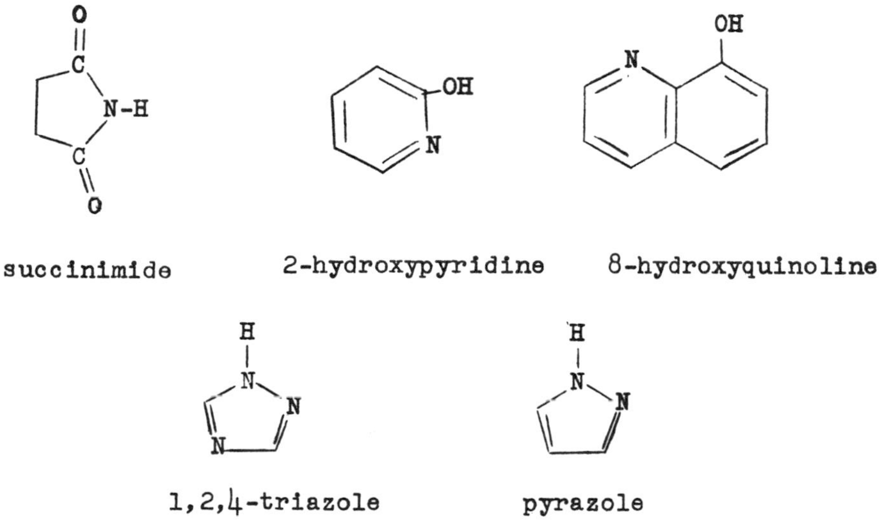

succinimide   2-hydroxypyridine   8-hydroxyquinoline

1,2,4-triazole   pyrazole

FIG. 28

In a related paper on racemization studies, it was
reported[72] that the aminolysis of various active esters in
the presence of 1,2,4-triazole proceeds without racemization. In contrast, imidazole leads to racemization in several
cases. The following, general acid-basic catalysis is consistent with these results[40]:

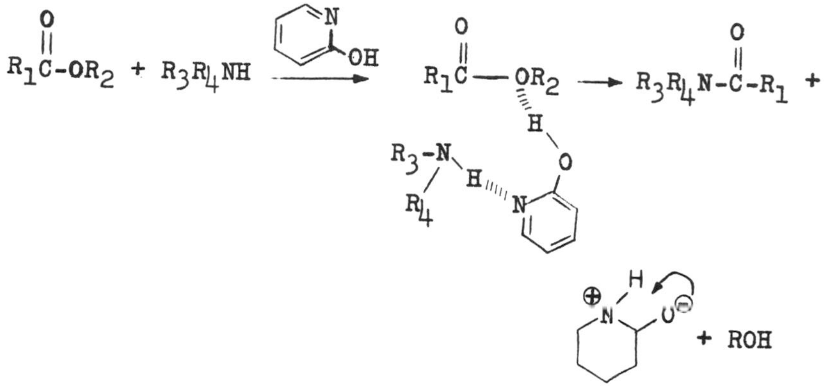

FIG. 29

Alternately, a nucleophilic-electrophilic catalysis can be viewed[40]:

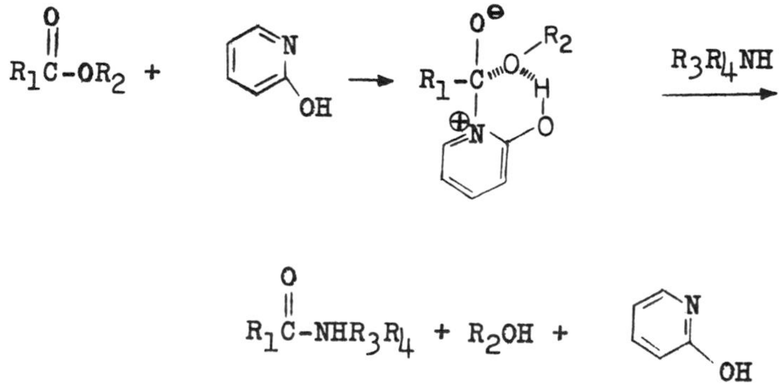

FIG. 30

OTHER APPROACHES TO COUPLING WITHOUT RACEMIZATION

The azide method is an approach to peptide coupling which does not generally involve racemization. It has been used extensively for the coupling of larger peptide fragments. The inability of azides to form oxazolones has been attributed to the special electrostatic nature of the molecule which does not allow for internal amide oxygen attack[45]. An analogous structure has been proposed for the acidic form of N-hydroxy-piperidine esters.

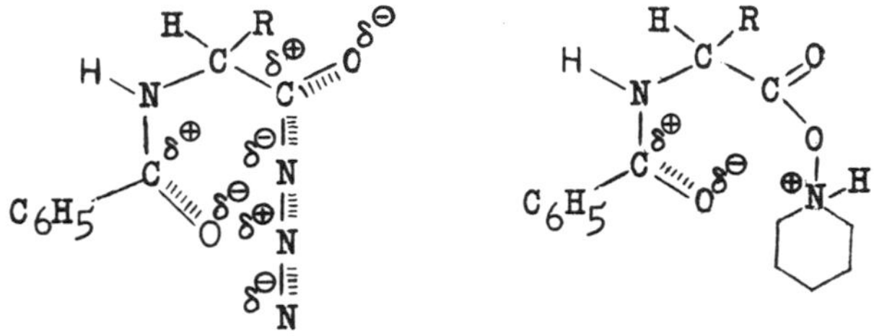

FIG. 31

Unfortunately, azides react sluggishly and are often accompanied by troublesome side reactions[73-75]. In addition there have been two reports of racemization in the azide method[17,76]. Anderson and his group[76] isolated 1.6% D, L-isomer in addition to 19% L-isomer after one equivalent of trimethylamine was allowed to react for twelve minutes at low temperature with benzyloxycarbonylglycyl-L-phenyl-alanyl azide before coupling with glycine ethyl ester. These false conditions are too extreme for any comparison to normal coupling reactions. Determan reported[17], however, some racemization in the coupling of benzoyl-L-alanyl azide with L-phenylalanine benzyl ester under normal azide coupling conditions. Benzyloxycarbonyl-L-alanine gives

317

pure L-isomer under similar conditions. The author attributes these results to racemization via oxazolone formation from benzoyl-L-alanyl azide. We believe another possibility deserves consideration. The resonance structures (32a-b) below are entirely reasonable and follow from Determan's own results (see FIG. 9 and accompanying discussion). No analogous resonance forms are possible for the benzyloxycarbonyl derivative. It may be that the azide group does not undergo ring closure to form oxazolone, as Young has suggested. Racemization can still occur for the benzoyl derivative via direct proton abstraction. The proton on the asymmetric carbon atom of the benzyloxycarbonyl derivative is much less acidic, and thus is not abstracted. Consequently, in the latter cases no racemization results.

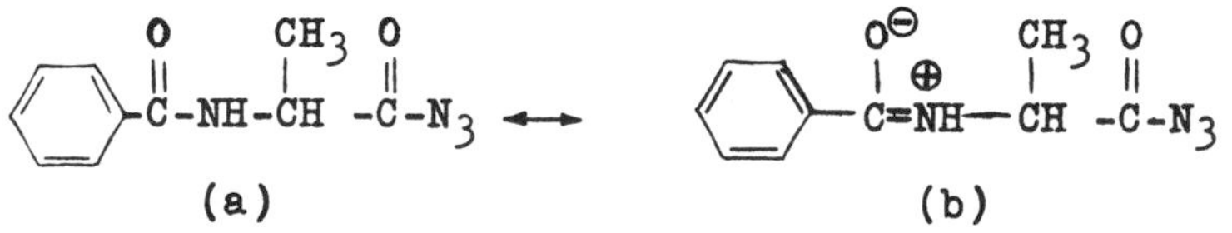

FIG. 32

Brenner[77], in an evaluation of coupling methods, offers another approach to the problem. He points out that in order to overcome the sluggishness of coupling reactions, ever more powerful activating groups have been used. The activation energy is lowered and the reactivity is greatly increased.

Unfortunately, selectivity is inevitably decreased and side products result. Decomposition of the active species, reaction with unprotected functional groups, or even acylation of peptide bonds may result. In addition, intramolecular attack leading to oxazolone formation and subsequent racemization becomes more probable. In other words, the increased reactivity often leads to an "overactivated" species.

Brenner points out that the sluggishness of a reaction could be overcome without lowering the activation energy if the frequency of collisions between the ester and the amine are increased. This can be accomplished via intramolecular ester aminolysis.

Several schemes of peptide synthesis have utilized this approach[78-80]. In each case, the amine component is converted into an active derivative capable of selective capture of the carboxyl group. This leads to an activated carboxyl function and subsequent amide bond formation via intramolecular attack. This can be illustrated for the isocyanate method of peptide synthesis[78].

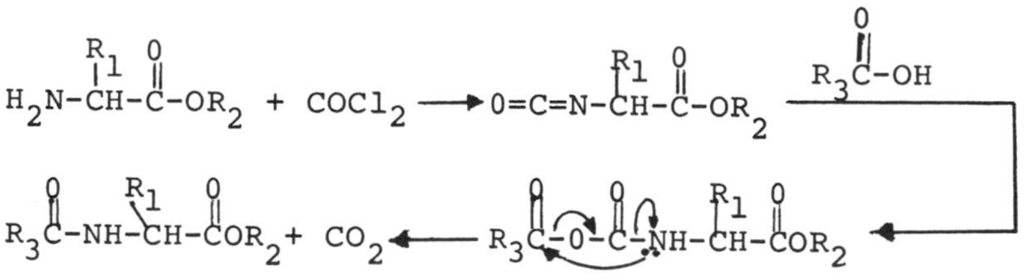

FIG. 33

Alternatively, some decomposition to free amine which reacts with anhydride to give amide, carbon dioxide and more amine can account for the racemization found and would not necessitate a four-membered ring transition state.

The established schemes[78-80] require rather severe conditions to bring about amino acid attachment and subsequent carboxyl activation. As a result, racemization is found.

A more promising method of amino acid insertion is the rearrangement of diacylhydrazines[81]. These compounds are prepared by the reaction of hydrazides with N-carboxyanhydrides in acetic acid. Rearrangement is achieved under the influence of weak organic acids such as propionic acid.

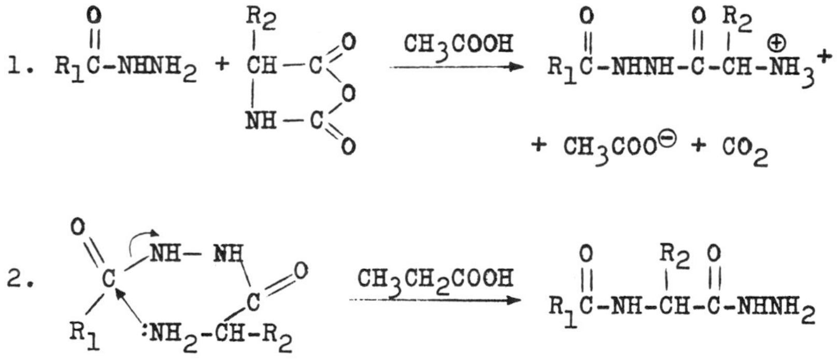

FIG. 34

This scheme has several promising features:

1) conditions are mild and there is considerable selectivity in the preparation of the diacylhydrazine,

2) each rearrangement generates a new hydrazide allowing a repetition of the process,

3) the hydrazides obtained can be used in coupling to a second peptide via the azide method,

4) the hydrazide group can be converted to free acid conveniently at any stage.

In an entirely different approach to the racemization problem, Anderson and coworkers[82] undertook an extensive investigation of the nature and scope of the mixed anhydride method of coupling. They demonstrated that with careful control of conditions (temperature, solvent, base, chloroformate, activation time and order of addition of reagents), optically pure products can be obtained in high yield. While the general applicability of this method for the synthesis of larger, optically pure peptides remains to be tested, the authors' comprehensive studies clearly illustrate the importance of reaction conditions.

Merrifield recently devised a new method of building peptide chains in which he relies heavily on the stereopurity of the single residue addition technique[83, 84]. The original method uses a single, insoluble support consisting of polystyrene crosslinked with 2% divinylbenzene and subsequently chloromethylated. A t-butyloxycarbonyl N-protected amino acid is allowed to couple at the chloromethylated substituent

from an alcoholic solution containing a tertiary amine. The
N-acyl protecting group is removed by acidic hydrolysis and
another t-butyloxycarbonyl N-protected amino acid residue
is added by the carbodiimide method. At each step, all impurities can be washed away with solvent, leaving only the
polymer support with its attached peptide chain. Finally the
peptide is removed from the benzylated anchorage on the polymer by treatment with hydrogen bromide in trifluoroacetic
acid.

Numerous modifications in the choice of blocking groups,
coupling agents, solvent, and cleavage reagents have been
reported since the introduction of the solid phase method[85].
In addition, automation has been achieved[85].

Other, related methods have been introduced based on
the principle of synthesis without isolation of intermediates
[85-92]. Some of these have made use of polymeric supports
[86-88]. Letsinger and Kornet[86, 87] make use of a popcorn
polymer of styrene with a very low degree of crosslinking
(0. 1-0. 5%) by divinylbenzene in order to avoid diffusion
problems. In addition, these authors employ the N-terminal
residue as the anchoring group and extend stepwise at the
carboxyl end. Shemyakin and colleagues[88] work with a
soluble polymer support of emulsion polystyrene (200, 000
average molecular weight) and run solution reactions in
order to get more complete reaction at each step. After

each amino acid addition cycle, the dimethylformamide solution is poured into water. All excess reagents remain in solution and can be washed away, while the polymer with its peptide chain precipitates.

The solid-phase method, at present, relies primarily on the building up of the peptide one amino acid unit at a time in order to avoid racemization. This has practical limitations for the synthesis of larger peptides. Since 100% coupling at each step is unrealistic, the final product must always be separated from peptide impurities which may have quite similar physical-chemical properties. As the synthesis of larger and more complex materials is undertaken, separation techniques are bound to reach a point of diminishing returns. How, for example, can one cleanly separate a random peptide of 60 amino acid units from one with 59 amino acid units.

Application of racemization-free coupling methods to the solid-phase technique will be of tremendous importance. It could enable coupling of blocks of peptides at a time. The smaller number of coupling steps leads to a much smaller number of peptide impurities. In addition, impurities should be significantly different from the desired compound in physical-chemical properties to enable ready separation. Difficultly synthesizable fragments can be handled separately, and introduced into the larger peptide as a unit.

323

Other stepwise syntheses have been undertaken without isolation of intermediates using water-soluble carbodiimides, both by carboxyl end chain extension[89,90] and amino acid chain extension[91]. Finally, Denkewalter and his associates[92] were able to carry out the controlled stepwise synthesis of peptides by rapidly mixing a solid α-amino acid N-carboxy-anhydride with an aqueous solution of an amino acid or peptide with close control of temperature and pH. The condensation to form a peptide carbamate is carried out in a pH 10.2 buffer at $0^{\circ}C$ and is complete in two minutes. Decarboxylation at pH 3-5 produces the free peptide, which can be immediately extended in length by repetition of the process with a new N-carboxyanhydride or can be isolated and purified before continuing. The method was found to be general for amino acids. No racemization was found using a very sensitive tracer method, and yields were good.

RACEMIZATION VIA DIRECT PROTON EXCHANGE

Considerable experimental evidence points to an alternate route to racemization where oxazolone formation is not possible[93-101]. In order to explain the racemization of benzyloxycarbonyl and phthaloyl amino acid acitve esters in base, Liberek and coworkers, in a series of communications[93-98] proposed direct proton abstraction followed by resonance stabilization of the carbanion by conjugation with the π- electrons on the beta substituted groups.

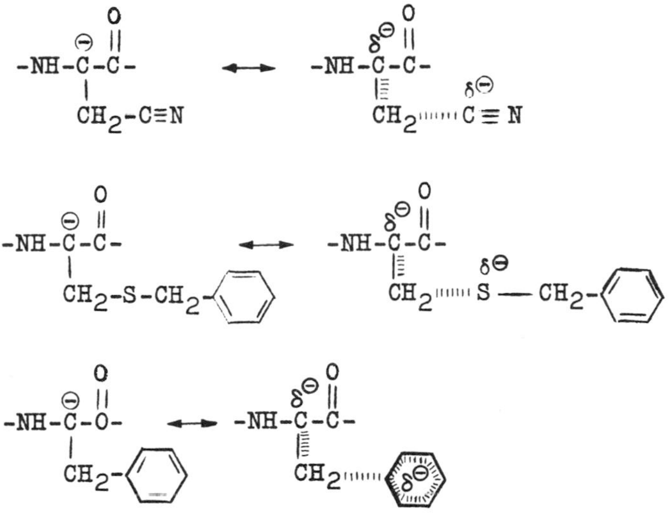

FIG. 35

Alternately, the racemization can be viewed as a reversible, beta-elimination reaction[99,100]. Kovacs and colleagues[101] investigated the proposed "β -elimination-readdition"
mechanism. They allowed the pentachlorophenyl and p-nitrophenyl active esters of N-benzyloxycarbonyl-S-benzylcysteine
to react with triethylamine in the presence of benzyl $[^{35}S]$
thiol. In each case, no radioactive sulphur was incorporated
at the asymmetric carbon, indicating that racemization proceeds by direct proton abstraction rather than reversible,
beta-elimination.

In addition to this stabilization, we attribute the
greater rate of racemization found for phthaloyl amino acid
esters as compared to benzyloxycarbonyl amino acid esters

[93,98] to the stabilization of the resulting carbanion by the strong inductive electron-withdrawing effect (indicated by arrow in Fig. 36) of the phthaloyl group.

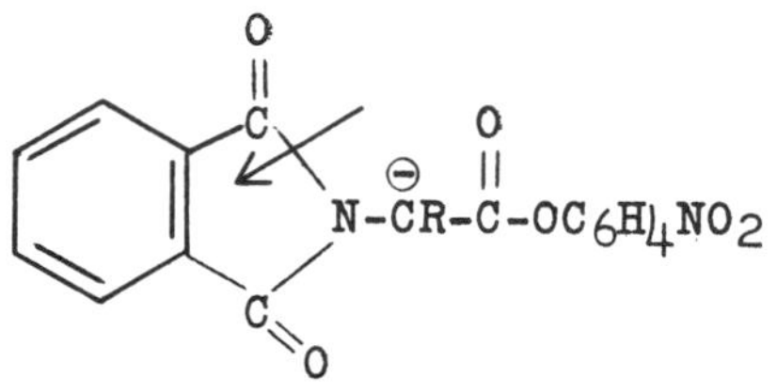

FIG. 36

The derivatives of aromatic amino acids have an increased tendency for racemization, since the negative charge resulting from proton abstraction can be delocalized into the ring[102].

Matsuo and coworkers[103] studied the base catalyzed D-H exchange and racemization of several amino acids, their derivatives and related model compounds. D-H exchange was measured by NMR. Percent racemization and percent exchange were found to be the same in every case. While the free amino group has a retarding effect on base-catalyzed deuteration compared with the corresponding de-amino compounds, N-acylation did not only cancel the NH_2-retarding effect but also accelerated significantly the α-deuteration effect. Carboxylate anion has a considerable retarding effect. The carboxamide has a striking accelerating effect. An ester group has less retarding effect than a carboxylate. The order of racemizability of α-amino acid derivatives found

is $R_1CONHCHR_2CONR_3R_4 \gg R_1CONHCHR_2COOH >$
NH_2CHR_2COOH.

CONCLUSIONS

Our review deals primarily with the role of oxazolones in racemization mechanisms involved in peptide synthetic manipulations.

We have traced the chemistry of optically active oxazolones from the dates when they appeared as elusive unisolable compounds to present research efforts which have led to isolation and characterization of crystalline optically pure materials. In the majority of techniques of peptide synthesis, oxazolones appear to be the route to racemic product. In our laboratory we have demonstrated the effects of solvent, temperature, structure of the oxazolones and the nature of the nucleophiles on the extent of racemization.

Other routes are briefly discussed in this review. We have shown cases where direct hydrogen abstraction from the asymmetric center of β-elimination reactions must occur to explain observed racemization. Liberek's group has shown that amino acid derivatives blocked at the amino end with urethane or phthaloyl groups can racemize by direct abstraction. Specific cases have been observed where serine, cysteine and related amino acid derivatives may racemize by β-elimination.

327

Our review also deals with more recent methods of peptide synthesis involving α -dinucleophiles and other reagents which can attack activated amino acid or peptide derivatives by biphilic mechanisms. We showed that in all of these cases part of the attacking reagent functions as an electrophile while the other serves as a nucleophile. In this manner intramolecular cyclization reactions to form oxazolones are repressed. Even if oxazolones are formed, they ring-open by biphilic mechanisms which involve a reduced basicity or enhanced nucleophilicity for the attacking reagent. In this manner hydrogen abstraction from the asymmetric center of the oxazolone does not compete favorably with ring-opening reactions.

We have noted some special cases where some racemization is observed using the azide method of peptide synthesis. All in all, this route remains the safest if worry about racemization is a prime factor in the peptide synthetic scheme. By its nature the azide route cannot be applied to the modern automated methods since the azide method requires low temperature and much time to insure high yield and absence of extensive side reactions.

Recent methods discussed in our review require careful study to obtain their real scope and limitations.

Anderson and Young pioneered in comparative studies on the numerous synthetic methods in the literature. As a result, Anderson has been able to improve and expand the utility of the mixed anhydride method. In a similar fashion, Young's work has led to the development of hydroxypiperidine and related methods which appear to be highly racemization resistant.

Peptide chemists are still awaiting or searching for a panacea. We desire a facile, simple, high yield, non-racemizing reaction which is generally applicable to problems of a complex synthetic nature. Although many improvements are obvious in examining the developments over the past decade, we remain with the belief that the synthesis of proteins and related biologically important materials requires tedious operations and brute force approaches.

REFERENCES

1. M. Bergmann and L. Zervas, Biochem. Z., 203, 280 (1928).

2. V. du Vigneaud and C. E. Meyer, J. Biol. Chem., 98, 295 (1932).

3. V. du Vigneaud and R. R. Sealock, ibid., 96, 511 (1932).

4. V. du Vigneaud and C. E. Meyer, ibid., 99, 143 (1932).

5. H. E. Carter and C. M. Stevens, ibid., 133, 117 (1940).

6. F. A. Csonka and B. H. Nicolet, ibid., 99, 213 (1932).

7. H. E. Carter, Org. Reactions. Vol. III, John Wiley, New York, 1946, p. 198.

8. M. Goodman and K. C. Stueben, J. Org. Chem., 27, 3409 (1962).

9. M. W. Williams and G. T. Young, J. Chem. Soc., 3701 (1964).

10. I. Antonovics and G. T. Young, ibid., 595 (1967).

11. D. S. Kemp and S. W. Chien, J. Am. Chem. Soc., 89, 2745 (1967).

12. I. Antonovics and G. T. Young, Chem. Commun., 398 (1965).

13. A. L. Heard and G. T. Young, J. Chem. Soc., 5809 (1963).

14. N. A. Smart, G. T. Young, and M. W. Williams, ibid., 3902 (1960).

15. M. W. Williams and G. T. Young, ibid., 881 (1963).

16. a)I. Z. Siemion and D. Konopinska, Proc. 8th European Peptide Symp., Noordwijk, 1966, p. 79; cf. I. Z. Siemion, Tetrahedron Letters, 4807 (1966).
b)K. Blaha, I. Fric, and J. Smolikova, Coll. Czech. Chem. Commun., 33, 3170, 1968.

17. H. Determan, Proc. 8th European Peptide Symp., Noordwijk, 1966, p. 73; cf. H. Determan, J. Heuer, P. Pfaender, and M. L. Reinartz, Ann., 694, 190 (1966).

18. R. W. Jackson and W. M. Cahill, J. Biol. Chem., 126, 37 (1938).

19. H. E. Carter and C. M. Stevens, ibid., 133, 117 (1940).

20. J. W. Cornforth and D. F. Elliott, Science, 112, 534 (1950).

21. J. L. O'Brien and C. Niemann, J. Am. Chem. Soc., 79, 80 (1957).

22. R. Huisgen, H. Gotthardt, H. O. Bayer, and F. C. Schaefer, Angew. Chem. Internat. Edit., 3, 136 (1964).

23. M. Goodman and K. C. Stueben, J. Am. Chem. Soc., 81, 3980 (1959).

24. H. T. Clarke, The Chemistry of Penicillin, Princeton University Press, Princeton, 1949, p. 730.

25. M. Goodman and L. Levine, J. Am. Chem. Soc., 86, 2918 (1964).

26. I. Z. Siemion and A. Dzugaj, Roczniki Chemii, 40, 1699 (1966).

27. M. T. Leplawy, D. J. Jones, G. W. Kenner and R. C. Sheppard, Tetrahedron, 11, 39 (1960).

28. W. J. McGahren and M. Goodman, ibid., 23, 2017 (1967).

29. I. Z. Siemion and K. Nowak, Roczniki Chemii, 34, 1479 (1960).

30. M. Goodman and W. J. McGahren, Tetrahedron, 23, 2031 (1967).

31. J. Kovacs, unpublished results.

32. D. F. DeTar, R. Silverstein, and F. F. Rogers, Jr., J. Am. Chem. Soc., 88, 1024 (1966).

33. M. Goodman and C. Glaser, unpublished results.

34. G. W. Anderson and F. M. Callahan, J. Am. Chem. Soc., 80, 2902 (1958).

35. J. O. Edwards, ibid., 78, 1819 (1956).

36. R. G. Pearson, Chem. Brit., 3, 103 (1967).

37. R. F. Hudson, Chimica, 16, 173 (1962).

38. K. M. Ibne-Rasa, J. Chem. Ed., 44, 89 (1967).

39. W. P. Jencks and J. Carriuolo, J. Am. Chem. Soc., 82, 1778 (1960).

40. M. L. Bender, Chem. Rev., 60, 53 (1960).

41. T. C. Bruice, A. Donzel, R. W. Hoffman, and A. R. Butler, J. Am. Chem. Soc., 89, 2106 (1967).

42. J. O. Edwards and R. G. Pearson, ibid., 84, 16 (1962).

43. I. Z. Siemion and J. Morawiec, Bull. Acad. Polon. Sci., ser. sci. chim., 12, 295 (1964).

44. S. Bittner, Y. Knobler, and M. Frankel, Tetrahedron Letters, 95 (1965).

45. S. M. Beaumont, B. O. Handford, and G. T. Young, Proc. 7th European Peptide Symp., Budapest, 1964, p. 37.

46. F. Weygand and W. Konig, Z. Naturforsch., 20b, 710 (1965).

47. J. H. Jones, B. Liberek, and G. T. Young, Proc. 8th European Peptide Symp., Noordwijk, 1966, p. 15.

48. G. H. L. Nefkens and G. I. Tesser, J. Am. Chem. Soc., 83, 1263 (1961).

49. G. H. L. Nefkens, G. I. Tesser, and R. J. F. Nivard, Rec. Trav. Chim., 81, 683 (1962).

50. G. W. Anderson, J. E. Zimmerman, and F. M. Callahan, J. Am. Chem. Soc., 85, 3039 (1963); also, 86, 1839 (1964).

51. E. Wunsch and F. Drees, Chem. Ber., 99, 110 (1966).

52. F. Weygand, D. Hoffman and E. Wunsch, Z. Naturforsch., 21b, 426 (1966).

53. J. E. Zimmerman and G. W. Anderson, J. Am. Chem. Soc., 89, 7151 (1967).

54. E. Taschner, B. Rzeszotarska, and L. Lubiewska, Chem. and Ind., 402 (1967).

55. M. J. Gregory and T. C. Bruice, J. Am. Chem. Soc., 89, 2327 (1967).

56. M. J. Gregory and T. C. Bruice, ibid., 89, 4400 (1967).

57. K. M. Ibne-Rasa and J. O. Edwards, ibid., 84, 763 (1962).

58. O. Hassal and K. O. Strome, Acta Chem. Scand., 13, 275 (1959).

59. I. Z. Siemion, Roczniki Chemii, 42, 237 (1968).

60. D. F. DeTar and R. Silverstein, J. Am. Chem. Soc., 88, 1013 (1966).

61. D. F. DeTar and R. Silverstein, ibid., 88, 1020 (1966).

62. M. M. Botvinik, S. N. Kara-Murza, S. M. Avaeva, and V. Ya. Nikitin, Dokl. Akad. Nauk. SSSR, 88 (1964).

63. W. D. Cash, J. Org. Chem., 27, 3329 (1962).

64. B. O. Handford, J. H. Jones, G. T. Young, and T. F. N. Johnson, J. Chem. Soc., 6814 (1965).

65. S. M. Beaumont, B. O. Handford, and G. T. Young, Acta Chim. Acad. Sci. Hung., 44, 37 (1965).

66. J. H. Jones and G. T. Young, Chem. Commun., 35 (1967).

67. H. D. Jakubke and A. Voigt, Chem. Ber., 99, 2419 (1966).

68. H. D. Jakubke, A. Voigt, and S. Burkhardt, Chem. Ber., 100, 2367 (1967).

69. G. T. Young, Proc. 8th European Peptide Symp., Nordwijk, 1966, p. 53.

70. a) D. S. Kemp and S. W. Chien, J. Am. Chem. Soc., 89, 2743 (1967); b) D. S. Kemp, this publication.

71. H. C. Beyerman and W. Maassen van den Brink, Proc. Chem. Soc., 266 (1963).

72. H. C. Beyerman and W. Maassen van den Brink, and F. Weygand, A. Prox, W. Konig, L. Schmidhammer and E. Nintz, Rec. Trav. Chim., 84, 213 (1965).

73. E. Schnabel, Ann., 659, 168 (1962).

74. J. Rudinger, Pure Appl. Chem., 7, 335 (1963).

75. J. Honzl and J. Rudinger, Coll. Czech. Chem. Commun., 26, 2333 (1961).

76. G. W. Anderson, J. E. Zimmerman, and F. M. Callahan, J. Am. Chem. Soc., 88, 1338 (1966).

77. M. Brenner, Proc. 8th European Peptide Symp., Nordwijk, 1966, p. 1.

78. S. Goldschmidt and M. Wick, Ann., 575, 217 (1952).

79. S. Goldschmidt, Coll. Czech. Chem. Commun., 24, 15 (1959).

80. G. W. Anderson, A. D. Welcher, and R. W. Young, J. Am. Chem. Soc., 73, 501 (1951).

81. M. Brenner and W. Hofer, Helv. Chim. Acta, 44, 1794 (1961); M. Brenner and W. Hofer, Helv. Chim. Acta, 44, 1799 (1961).

82. G. W. Anderson, J. E. Zimmerman, and F. M. Callahan, J. Am. Chem. Soc., 89, 5012 (1967).

83. R. B. Merrifield, ibid., 85, 2149 (1963).

84. R. B. Merrifield, Biochemistry, 3, 1385 (1964).

85. R. B. Merrifield, Recent Prog. Hormone Res., 23, 451 (1967), and references cited therein.

86. R. L. Letsinger and M. J. Kornet, J. Am. Chem. Soc., 85, 3045 (1963).

87. R. L. Letsinger, M. J. Kornet, V. Mahadevan, and D. M. Jerina, ibid., 86, 5163 (1964).

88. M. M. Shemyakin, Y. A. Ovchinnikov, A. A. Kinyushkin, and I. V. Kozhevnikova, Tetrahedron Letters, 2323 (1965).

89. D. G. Knorre and T. N. Shubina, Dokl. Akad. Nauk. SSSR, 150, 559 (1963).

90. D. G. Knorre and T. N. Shubina, Acta Chim. Acad. Sci. Hung., 44, 77 (1965).

91. J. C. Sheehan, J. Preston, and P. A. Cruickshank, J. Am. Chem. Soc., 87, 2492 (1965).

92. R. G. Denkewalter, H. Schwam, R. G. Strachan, T. E. Beesley, D. F. Veber, E. F. Schoenwaldt, H. Barkemeyer, W. J. Paleveda, Jr., T. A. Jacob, and R. Hirschmann, ibid., 88, 3163 (1966).

93. B. Liberek, Tetrahedron Letters, 925 (1963).

94. B. Liberek, A. Nowicka, and Z. Grzonka, ibid., 22, 1479 (1963).

95. B. Liberek and Z. Grzonka, ibid., 3, 159 (1964).

96. B. Liberek, Z. Grzonka, and A. Michalik, Bull. Acad. Polon. Sci., ser. sci. chim., 14, 375 (1964).

97. B. Liberek and A. Michalik, Acta Chim. Acad. Sci. Hung., 44, 71 (1965).

98. B. Liberek, Tetrahedron Letters, 1103 (1963).

99. J. A. Maclaren, W. E. Savige, and J. M. Swan, Austral. J. Chem., 11, 345 (1968).

100. M. Bodansky and A. Bodansky, Chem. Commun., 591, (1967).

101. J. Kovacs, G. L. Mayers, R. H. Johnson, and U. R. Ghatak, ibid., 1066 (1968).

102. M. Bodansky and C. A. Birkhimer, Chimia (Switz.), 14, 368 (1960).

103. H. Matsuo, Y. Kawazoe, M. Sato, M. Ohnishi, and T. Tatsuo, Chem. Pharm. Bull. (Tokyo), 15, 391 (1967).

ON THE RACEMIZATION OF AMINO ACID ACTIVE ESTERS

J. Kovacs, G. L. Mayers, R. H. Johnson and U. R. Ghatak

Department of Chemistry
St. John's University, Jamaica, New York

In continuation of our studies on polypeptides with known repeating sequence of amino acids, we investigated the synthesis of the sequential polypeptides containing cysteinyl residues. The use of pentachlorophenyl active esters for the preparation of sequential polypeptides has proved to be most satisfactory in our experiences[1,2]. Protected polyglutathione (III) has been prepared by polycondensation of the tripeptide pentachlorophenyl ester derivative (II), obtained through (I), in concentrated dimethylformamide solution in the presence of N-methylmorpholine or triethylamine.

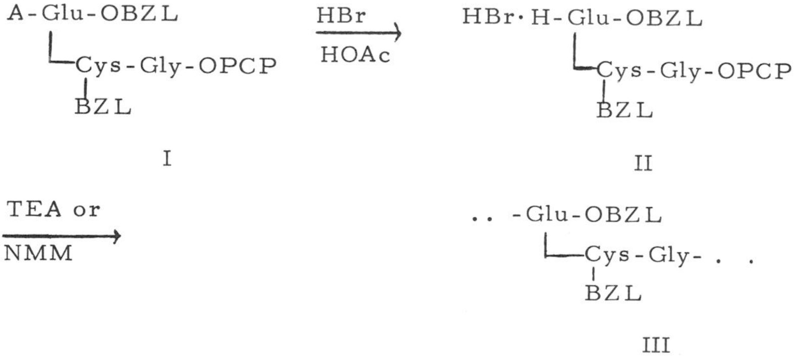

A - Glu - OBZL
   └─ Cys - Gly - OPCP
      BZL

$\xrightarrow[\text{HOAc}]{\text{HBr}}$

HBr· H - Glu - OBZL
    └─ Cys - Gly - OPCP
       BZL

I

II

$\xrightarrow{\text{TEA or NMM}}$

.. - Glu - OBZL
    └─ Cys - Gly - . .
       BZL

III

337

The use of cysteine containing intermediates for polymerization requires thorough investigation since any incipient racemization that occurs during the synthesis of high molecular weight sequential polypeptides is permanently incorporated in the product and is impossible to separate by known procedures. Thus, a study of the mechanism and the rate of racemization of cysteine active ester derivatives in the basic medium used in polymerization was undertaken.

Carboxyl activation of even N-carbobenzyloxy-L-cysteine derivatives leads to various degrees of racemization in the presence of strong base[3,4]. The racemization has been proposed to proceed either by resonance stabilization of the anion (IVa and IVb) formed by α-hydrogen abstraction[5] or by reversible

$$-NH-\overset{\ominus}{\underset{|}{C}}-CO- \underset{CH_2-S-BZL}{} \qquad \longleftrightarrow \qquad -NH-\overset{\delta-}{\underset{\vdots}{C}}-CO- \underset{CH_2\cdots\overset{\delta-}{S}-BZL}{}$$

IVa   IVb

β-elimination of benzyl mercaptan[4,6] as shown below:

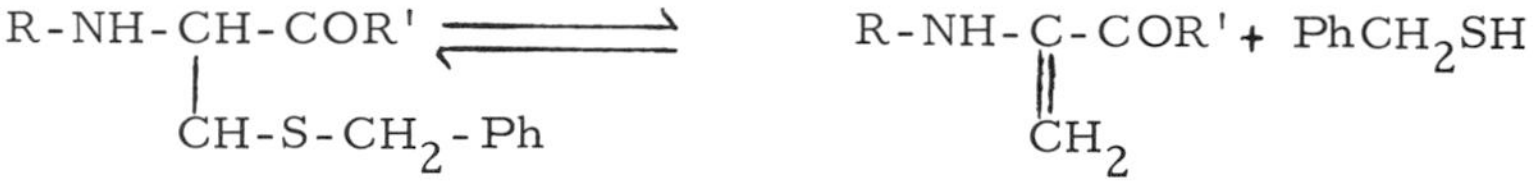

$$R-NH-\underset{CH-S-CH_2-Ph}{\overset{|}{C}H}-COR' \underset{\longleftarrow}{\longrightarrow} R-NH-\underset{CH_2}{\overset{\|}{C}}-COR' + PhCH_2SH$$

V   VI   VII

In a recent communication,[6] it was proposed that the second mechanism is operative in the racemization of N-carbobenzyl-oxy-S-benzyl-L-cysteine p-nitrophenyl ester in the presence of excess tertiary amines.

Since we had used N-carbobenzyloxy-S-benzyl-L-cysteine pentachlorophenyl ester (VIII) for the synthesis of several peptide intermediates, and in view of the above observations, we investigated the racemization of this compound. The active ester (VIII) was found to racemize in the presence of benzyl mercaptan-S^{35} with excess of triethylamine without incorporation of S^{35} as summarized below:

$$\begin{array}{ccc}
\text{Z-Cys-OPCP} & \xrightarrow[\substack{\text{NEt}_3 \ (3.6 - 7.2 \ \text{equiv.}) \\ \text{CHCl}_3, \ 1.5 \ \text{hr.}}]{\text{PhCH}_2 S^{35}\text{-H (1 equiv.)}} & \text{Z-Cys-OPCP} \\
\ \ \ \ | & & \ \ \ \ | \\
\text{BZL} & & \text{BZL} \\
\text{VIII} & &
\end{array}$$

$[\alpha]_D \ -41.05$ $[\alpha]_D \ -3.45$

mp $171\text{-}172^{\text{o}}$ mp $168\text{-}169^{\text{o}}$

-OPCP = $-\text{O-C}_6\text{Cl}_5$ no incorp. of S^{35}

Under identical conditions N-carbobenzyloxydehydroalanine pentachlorophenyl ester (IX) yielded racemic (VIII).

Z-NH-C-COOPCP   PhCH$_2$SH (1 equiv.)   VIII

$$\text{Z-NH-C-COOPCP} \xrightarrow[\substack{\text{NEt}_3 \ (7.2 \ \text{equiv.}) \\ \text{CHCl}_3}]{\text{PhCH}_2\text{SH (1 equiv.)}}$$

‖
CH$_2$

IX

yield 79%

mp 132-134°   mp 164-165°

These experiments demonstrated that the "β -elimination-readdition mechanism" does not explain the racemization of (VIII) under these conditions.

Due to the discrepancy between these observations and the previously mentioned literature,[4, 6] we deemed it necessary to investigate the mechanism of racemization of other active esters of N-carbobenzyloxy-S-benzyl-L-cysteine.

Racemization of N-carbobenzyloxy-S-benzyl-L-cysteine p-nitrophenyl ester (X) in the presence of S^{35}-labeled benzyl mercaptan yielded 82% of the partially racemized carbobenzyloxy-S-benzyl cysteine thiobenzyl ester (XI) in which one equivalent of benzyl mercaptan-S^{35} was incorporated. To locate the position of the radioactive sulfur in compound (XI) it was hydrazinolyzed. The resulting hydrazide (XII), isolated in 98% yield, did not contain any S^{35}.

Z-NH-CH-COONP $PhCH_2S^{35}$-H(1 equiv.)
| _____→
CH_2-S-CH_2Ph NEt_3 (7.2 equiv.)
                   $CHCl_3$, 1.5 hr.

X

Z-NH-CH-COS^{35}-CH_2Ph NH_2NH_2 Z-NH-CH-CONH-HN_2
| _____→ |
CH-S-CH_2Ph CH_2-S-CH_2Ph

XI   XIII

                                           no S^{35} present

The structure of (XI) was established by comparison with

an authentic sample. Similarly, under the conditions

described for the corresponding pentachlorophenyl ester

(IX), N-carbobenzyloxydehydroalanine p-nitrophenyl ester

yielded racemic (X) as one of several products when treated

with benzyl mercaptan.

These experiments clearly confirm that 'β -elimination-

readdition" is not the mechanism for the racemization of

N-carbobenzyloxy-S-benzyl-L-cysteine active esters under

these basic conditions[7].

Our second aim was to determine the rates of racemi-

zation of the active esters of N-carbobenzyloxy-S-benzyl-L-

cysteine used in peptide synthesis and to correlate these

rates with the "activity" of the ester groups. These data are

summarized in FIG. 1. It appears from this figure that the

rates of racemization of these active esters are not strictly

parallel to the "activity" assuming that the relative rates

are similar to those found for aminolysis of N-carbobenzy-loxy-L-phenylalanine active esters.[8]

During this work, it was observed that the reaction of the pentachlorophenyl ester (VIII) and the p-nitrophenyl ester (X) with benzyl mercaptan in the presence of base was surprisingly different. The pentachlorophenyl ester

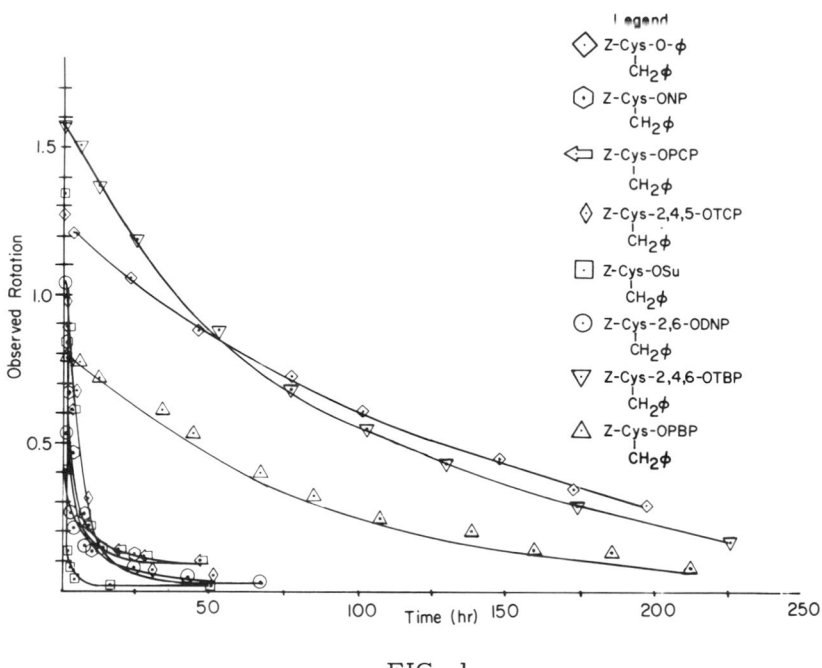

FIG. 1

Racemization of N-carbobenzyloxy-S-benzyl-L-cysteine active esters in the presence of 7 equivalents of triethylamine in tetrahydrofuran solution; the ester concentration was 0.05M and the temperature was $22° \pm 2°$. Anderson et al.[9] have also recorded the racemization of the p-nitrophenyl and N-hydroxysuccinimide esters under different conditions.

did not react with benzyl mercaptan, while the p-nitrophenyl ester afforded 82% of the corresponding thiobenzyl
ester. Thus, we decided to study other esters of N-carbobenzyloxy-S-benzyl-L-cysteine. The following esters,
p-nitrophenyl, 2,4,5-trichlorophenyl, pentafluorophenyl,
N-hydroxysuccinimide, and 2,4- and 2,6-dinitrophenyl
esters, when treated with one equivalent of benzyl mercaptan in the presence of 7 equivalents of triethylamine
in chloroform solution, yielded the corresponding thiobenzyl ester in high yield. However, under similar
reaction conditions, the pentachlorophenyl, pentabro-
mophenyl, 2,4,6-tribromophenyl, 2,4,6-trichlorophenyl,
phenyl and ethyl esters were recovered unchanged.
Examination of the data on the halogenated phenyl esters
seems to indicate that steric effects may play an important part in this ester exchange reaction, for example,
the difference between 2,4,5-trichlorophenyl and 2,4,6-
trichlorophenyl esters. However, in the case of the other
esters, we could not offer a plausible explanation for their
differences in reactivity towards benzyl mercaptan.

In the cases where the ester exchange reaction takes
place, the ester carbonyl absorption disappears in the infrared spectra during racemization. Also it should be mentioned that the recovery of the racemized compounds in this
group is only in the range of 40-70%, whereas in the other

group, where ester exchange does not take place, the recovery of the racemized ester is almost quantitative. These phenomena were found to result from hydrolysis of the active ester catalyzed by base. When strict anhydrous conditions were maintained, the carbonyl absorption did not disappear and we were able to recover the racemized active ester in high yield.

In conclusion, these results indicate that racemization rate studies followed in a polarimeter for these amino acid derivatives should be evaluated with extreme caution, unless rigorous anhydrous conditions were observed.

ACKNOWLEDGMENT

This work was supported by grants from the National Institutes of Health, Public Health Service (GM06579 and 08795).

REFERENCES

1. J. Kovacs, R. Gionnotti and A. Kapoor, J. Am. Chem. Soc., 88, 2282 (1966).

2. H. Kovacs, G. N. Schmidt and U. R. Ghatak, Biopolymers, 6, 817 (1968).

3. B. Iselin, M. Feurer, R. Schwyzer, Helv. Chim. Acta, 38, 1508 (1955).

4. J. A. Maclaren, W. E. Savige and J. M. Swan, Austral. J. Chem. 11, 345 (1958); J. A. Maclaren, ibid., 11, 360 (1958).

5. B. Liberek, Tetrahedron Letters, 925 (1963).

6. M. Bodanszky and A. Bodanszky, Chem. Comm., 591 (1967).

7. Some of the results presented in this lecture have been reported in a preliminary communication; J. Kovacs, G. L. Mayers, R. H. Johnson and U. R. Ghatak, Chem. Comm., 1066 (1968).

8. J. Pless and R. A. Boissonnas, Helv. Chim. Acta., 46, 1609 (1963).

9. G. W. Anderson, F. M. Callahan and J. E. Zimmerman, Acta Chim. Hung., 44, 51 (1965).

A NEW RACEMIZATION TEST
FOR PEPTIDE SYNTHESIS

Nobuo Izumiya and Masako Muracka

Laboratory of Biochemistry
Faculty of Science
Kyushu University, Fukuoka, Japan

I would like to describe our experiments in the detection of racemization by the use of an amino acid analyzer. By way of introduction, I shall talk briefly of our studies in the separation of dipeptide diastereomers.

Since 1960, we have studied the separation of diastereomeric mixtures of amino acids and peptides through column chromatographic procedures. There are several reports of the analytical separation of dipeptide diastereomers. In a recent paper by Wieland and Bende[1], the preparative separation of 200 mg of Ala-Tyr diastereomers by Sephadex has been described. The methods we shall describe may be used either analytically or preparatively.

We selected four leucyl dipeptide diastereomers for initial study[2]. Analytical separation was performed on a Dowex 50x8 column of 0.9 x 50 cm with ammonium acetate as the eluting solvent in most cases. We studied many factors influencing the separation pattern; the different cross linkages in Dowex 50, temperature, and type and concentration of solvent. Among the factors studied, the variation in pH of the solvent gave the most remarkable influence. The separation patterns of diastereomeric Leu-Val are shown in FIG. 1 as an example. We found an interesting reversal in the order of elution of the L-L and D-L peptides between pH 5 and 4. 5 (FIG. 1). Similar reversals were observed also for other leucyl dipeptide diastereomers. The explanation for the phenomenon was suggested by the pH-titration curves of the separated diastereomers. It was found that the curves of the two peptides crossed each other between pH 4. 5 and 5, as shown in FIG. 2.

I shall now turn to the preparative separation of Leu-Val diastereomers. By a conventional procedure, L-leucine was coupled with DL-valine, and L-Leu-DL-Val was obtained as a crude powder. We found that 1. 1 g of this crude material was sufficiently resolved by a 1. 8 x 110 cm Dowex 50 column, elutions with 0. 2 M ammonium acetate at pH 7. We obtained pure L-Leu-L-Val in a yield of 0. 44 g from the faster peak (110-170 ml), and pure L-Leu-D-Val in a yield of 0. 63 g from the slower peak (175-270 ml)[2].

We then applied a diastereomeric mixture of Leu-Val to the column of the amino acid analyzer. As expected, sufficient separation was observed. Although there were

already several publications dealing with the separation of
dipeptide diastereomers by an amino acid analyzer[3], our
own experiences encouraged us to use this method to develop
a simplified racemization test. Our proposed procedure is
shown in the following reaction sequence:

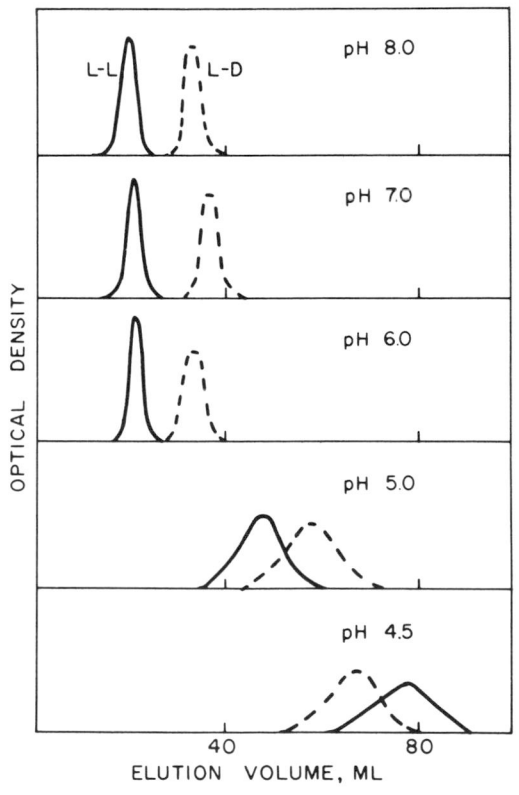

FIG. 1

Effect of pH of 0. 2 M ammonium acetate on separation of
Leu-Val.

Z-Gly-L-A-OH + H-L-B-OBzl $\xrightarrow{\text{(with partial or complete}}$
racemization of A residue)

Z-Gly-A-B-OBzl(LL isomer + DL isomer) $\xrightarrow{H_2}$

H-Gly-A-B-OH (LL isomer + DL isomer)

The crude Z-tripeptide benzyl ester is subjected directly to hydrogenolysis, and the hydrogenated material is submitted to an amino acid analyzer.

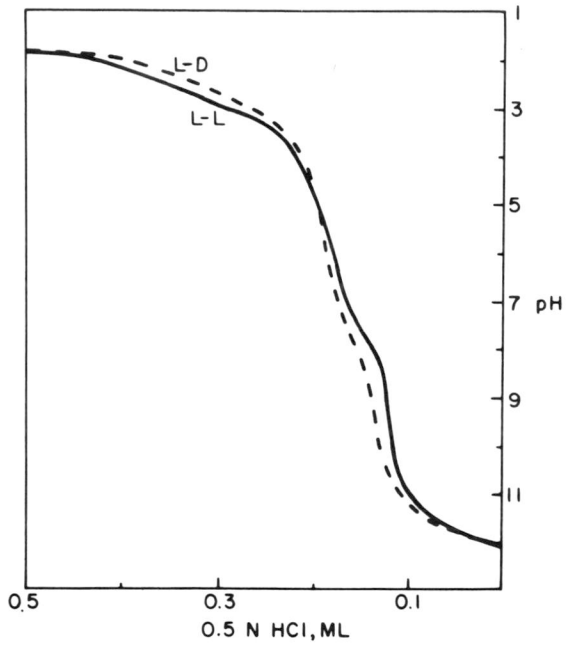

FIG. 2

pH Titration curves of Leu-Val.

RACEMIZATION TEST FOR PEPTIDE SYNTHESIS

Our first task was to discover a good system of glycyl-tripeptide diastereomers for separation by an amino acid analyzer. Initially we selected several tripeptides, all composed of glycine, a basic and an acidic amino acid residue, with the surmise that a diasteromeric mixture of a polyfunctional neutral tripeptide might be efficiently separated under appropriate conditions. We synthesized the pure L-L and D-L isomers of Gly-Lys-Glu, Gly-Lys-Asp, Gly-Orn-Glu, Gly-Orn-Asp, Gly-Glu-Lys and Gly-Asp-Lys[4]. Diastereomeric mixtures of each tripeptide were applied to the Hitachi amino acid analyzer with Dowex spherical resin. We observed that all mixtures gave incomplete separation, using several different conditions. Among the conditions employed, the following was the best system for the separation; with a short column (0.9 x 10 cm), the elution was initiated with 360 ml of pH 3.25 buffer (standard citrate buffer), followed by pH 4.25 buffer. FIG. 3 is a summary of the patterns obtained by this procedure[4].

We observed that DL-Lys-L-Glu was separated better than Gly-DL-Lys-L-Glu by the amino acid analyzer. This fact indicates that dipeptide diastereomers are separated more efficiently than related tripeptides. Therefore, we chose a coupling system of α-acetyl-ε-Z-L-lysine and H-L-B-OBzl. Several model α-acetyl-dipeptides were synthesized as the materials for the amino acid analyzer.

FIG. 4 is a summary of the patterns obtained for diastereomeric mixtures of α -acetyl-lysyl-amino acids with the 0.9
x 50 cm column and pH 4.25 buffer[5]. We still were not
satisfied with the results in FIG. 4 and went to the next
trial.

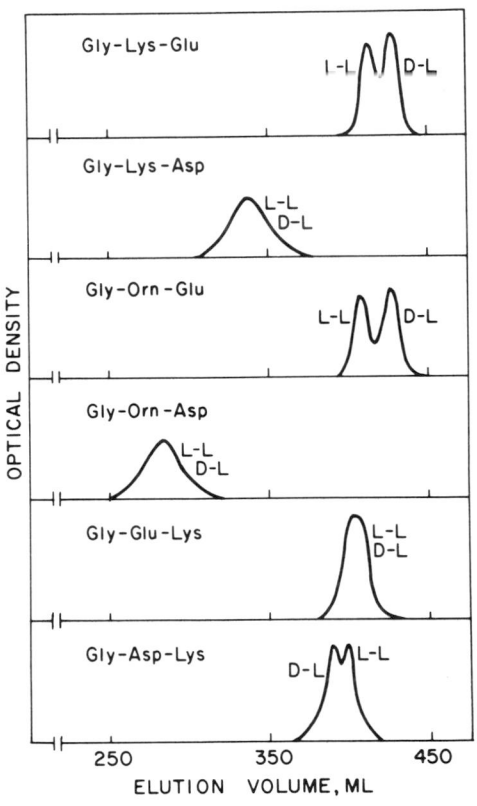

FIG. 3

Elution pattern of tripeptides composed of basic and acidic
amino acid.

This time, we selected a few simple tripeptide systems and prepared several Gly-DL-Ala-B tripeptides. In these studies, some diastereomers were separated completely (0.9 x 50 cm column, pH 4.25 buffer, 55°C) as shown in FIG. 5. Valine and leucine tripeptides both showed complete separation. But, Gly-Ala-Leu is our preferred system

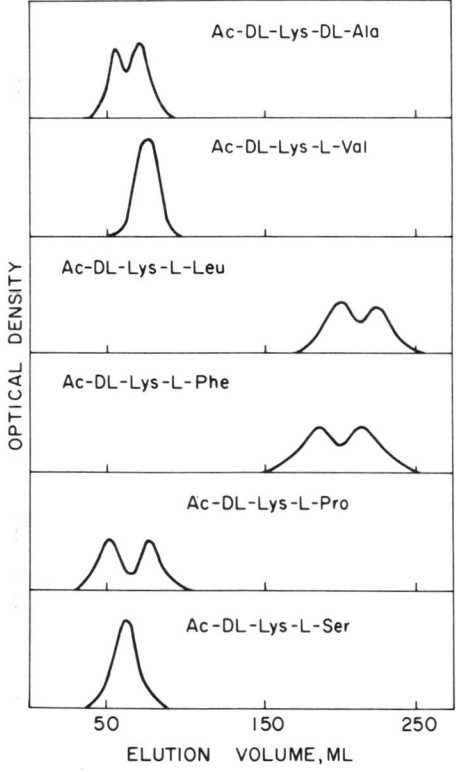

FIG. 4

Elution pattern of α-acetyl-DL-lysyl-amino acids.

for the racemization test because it is not overlapped by either leucine or Gly-Ala (FIG. 6). We prepared pure L-L and L-D Gly-Ala-Leu by the azide method. The azide derived from Z-Gly-L-Ala-NHNH$_2$ was coupled with L (or D)-leucine benzyl ester, and the Z-tripeptide benzyl ester was subjected to hydrogenolysis. The L-L or L-D

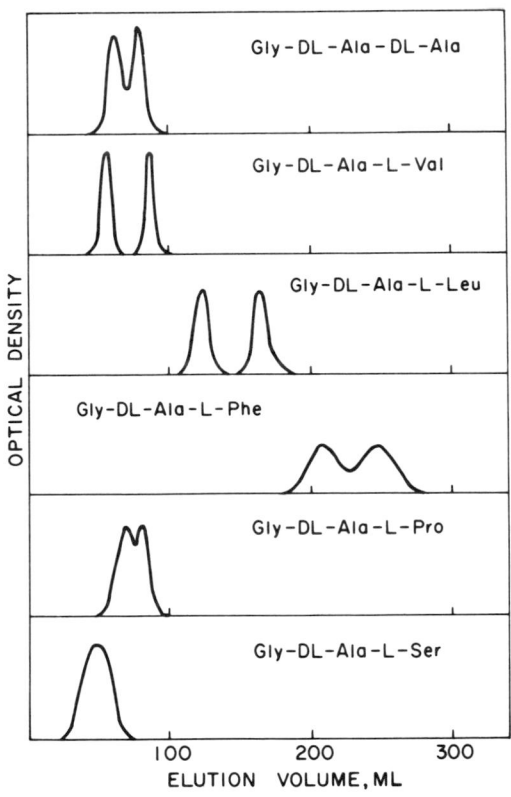

FIG. 5

Elution pattern of glycyl-DL-alanyl-amino acids.

tripeptides thus obtained both showed only single peaks on
the amino acid analyzer, using loads of up to 6 μmole. The
results agreed with the fact that no racemization has ever
been reported in coupling with the azide method. The limit
of detection of the L-D isomer in the L-L isomer was
studied with a synthetic mixture of both isomers. When a
mixture of 100 parts L-L isomer (6 μmole) and 1 part L-D

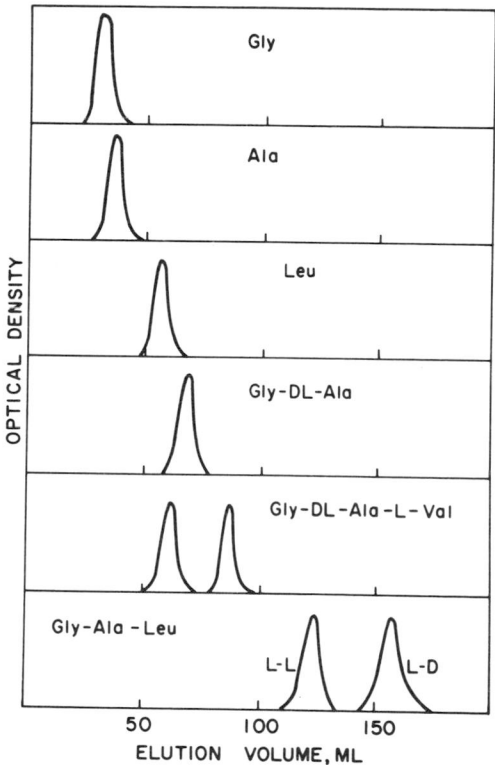

FIG. 6

Elution pattern of related compounds to Gly-Ala-Leu.

TABLE 1

Detection of Racemization by Different Methods

Amine (eq used)	HOSu (eq used)	Isobutylchloro-formate (eq used)	DCC (eq used)	Yield of tripeptide			
				by Anderson or Weygand method [a]		by Izumiya - Muraoka method [b]	
				DL	L	DL-L	L-L
TEA (1)		(1)		8	82[c]	10.7	61
NMM (1)		(1)		0	92[c]	2.1	69
TEA (1)	(1)	(1)				1.3	50.5
NMM (1)	(1)	(1)		0	94[c]	0.2	52.8
TEA (1)	(2)		(1.4)	0	90[d]	0.7	94.2
NMM (1)	(1)		(1)	0	90[c]	0	93.5

a) Z-Gly-L-Phe-OH +H-Gly-OEt $\longrightarrow$ Z-Gly-Phe-Gly-OEt (I), then fractional crystallation of DL-I from L-I (Anderson); Z-L-Leu-L-Phe-OH + H-L-Val-OBu^t $\longrightarrow$ Z-L-Leu-Phe-L-Val-OBu^t (II), then gas chromatography of Phe-Val derivative (Weygand).

b) Z-Gly-L-Ala-OH+H-L-Leu-OBzl $\longrightarrow$ Z-Gly-Ala-L-Leu-OBzl $\xrightarrow{H_2}$ Gly-Ala-L-Leu (III), then analysis of III by amino acid analyzer.

c) The data are from Anderson et al. (6, 7, 9).

d) The data are from Weygand et al. (8).

isomer was analyzed, a distinct peak of the L-D isomer

was observed. Even at a mixture of 1000 parts L-L and 1 part

part L-D isomer, a very small peak of the L-D isomer could

still be recognized. Therefore, this procedure for the detec-

tion of racemization is more sensitive than the methods

using fractional crystallization or measurement of optical

rotation.

We are now applying this method in the examination

of several coupling procedures. Anderson and his colleagues

have reported a series of important experiments to minimize

the degree of racemization during peptide bond formation.

In the case of the useful mixed anhydride procedure, they

found that the use of NMN (N-methylmorpholine) instead of

TEA (triethylamine) minimizes the degree of racemization[6].

Furthermore, it was reported   that the addition of HOSu

(N-hydroxysuccinimide) in the coupling by the mixed anhy-

dride[7] or the DCC method[8,9] was very useful in minimizing

the degree of racemization. We carried out the coupling of

Z-Gly-L-Ala-OH with L-leucine benzyl ester following

the same conditions described in the literature, and applied

the final hydrogenated material to the amino acid analyzer.

As reported, we found that the degree of racemization was

diminished when HOSu was used. However, we found that

either method did give a very small peak of Gly-D-Ala-L

Leu in many cases (Table 1). We carried out the coupling

357

using one equivalent each of HOSu and DCC, the stirring being continued for 48 hours at 0°C. The result was excellent from the standpoint of total yield and degree of racemization in other coupling procedures, including the use of Woodward's reagent[10], and EEDQ[11].

ACKNOWLEDGMENT

We wish to express our thanks to Professor B. Belleau for a generous gift of EEDQ reagent.

REFERENCES

1. T. Wieland and H. Bende, Chem. Ber., 98, 504 (1965).

2. K. Noda, H. Okai, T. Kato and N. Izumiya, Bull. Chem. Soc. Japan, 41, 401 (1968).

3. F. C. Neuhaus, J. Biol. Chem., 237, 778 (1962); K. Harada and S. W. Fox, Arch. Biochem. Biophys., 109, 49 (1965).

4. M. Muraoka, N. Yoshida, K. Noda and N. Izumiya, Bull. Chem. Soc. Japan, in press.

5. M. Muraoka and N. Izumiya, Bull. Chem. Soc. Japan, in preparation.

6. G. W. Anderson, J. E. Zimmerman and F. M. Callahan, J. Am. Chem. Soc., 89, 5012 (1967).

7. G. W. Anderson, F. M. Callahan and J. E. Zimmerman, J. Am. Chem. Soc., 89, 178 (1967).

8. F. Weygand, D. Hoffman and E. Wunsch, Z. Naturforsch., 21b, 426 (1966).

9. J. E. Zimmerman and G. W. Anderson, J. Am. Chem. Soc., 89, 7151 (1967).

10. R. B. Woodward and R. A. Olofson, J. Am. Chem. Soc., 83, 1007 (1961).

11. B. Belleau and G. Malek, J. Am. Chem. Soc., 90, 1651 (1968).

DETERMINATION OF THE OPTICAL PURITY AND CONFIGURATION[1] OF AMINO ACIDS BY GAS CHROMATOGRAPHY OF DIASTEREOISOMERS

John W. Westley[2]

Genetics Department
Stanford Medical School, Palo Alto, California

Since the optical resolution of camphor by Casanova and Corey[3] in 1961, there have been many reports of the GLC resolution of enantiomers[4] either as diastereoisomeric derivatives or on an optically active stationary phase. The technique was first applied in the peptide field by Weygand in his study of racemization in peptide synthesis[5]. Our work in this area developed out of an interest in the stereospecifity of biochemical processes[6]. Here the advantages of the GLC technique over conventional polarimetry in the determination of optical purity are that chemical and optical impurities are separated on the column and analyses can be carried out on the microgram scale. The choice of N-trifluoroacetyl-(TFA)-S-prolyl chloride[7] (FIG. 1) as a resolving agent for amino acid esters was based on its ready availability in optically pure form and the observation that proline does not racemize during acylation or peptide synthesis (oxazalone formation is not possible). In addition,

the coupling reaction was rapid and quantitative, and the
rigid conformation of prolyl peptide bonds was expected to
enhance differences in physical properties of its diastereoisomers.

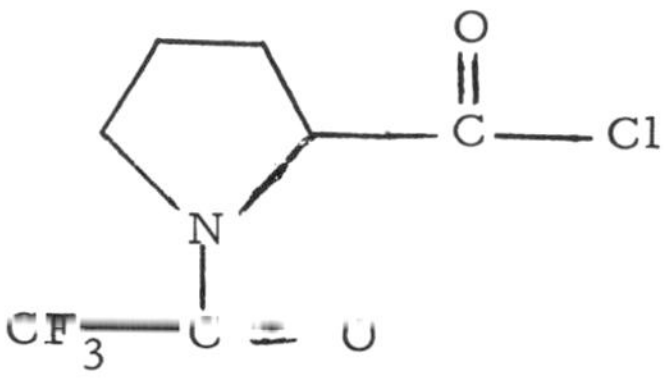

FIG. 1

N-Trifluoroacetylprolyl chloride

The N-TFA-S-prolyl derivatives of amino acid esters
are prepared by coupling N-TFA-S-prolyl chloride with the
amino acid ester in chloroform using excess triethylamine.
In the case of the hydroxy amino acids, it was necessary
to prepare the trimethylsilyl ether before coupling with the
resolving agent. Some typical analyses are indicated in
Table 1, and it should be noted in all cases examined that
the SR diastereoisomer had a shorter retention time than
the SS compound[8,9].

The chromatographic behaviour of the diastereoisomers
is in agreement with Wieland and Bende's conclusion that the
SR dipeptides exist in a stabilized ring form, while the SS
dipeptides prefer an open chain conformation[10]. The
smaller molecular volume of the SR isomer would result in

TABLE 1

Gas Chromatographic Separation of Racemic Amino Acids as Their
N-trifluoroacetyl-S-prolyl peptide methyl esters*

Amino acid	Column conditions	Amino acid derivative	Retention times (minutes) of diastereoisomers SR	SS	Ratio of retention times, SS/SR
Alanine	A		4.4	5.0	1.14
Valine	A		6.6	7.6	1.15
Leucine	A		8.7	9.45	1.09
Proline	A		13.3	14.8	1.11
Serine	B	O-TMS	5.6	6.85	1.22
Threonine	B	O-TMS	5.1	6.25	1.23
γ-Hydroxyproline	B	O-TMS	18.3	22.1	1.21
Aspartic acid	B		18.0	19.4	1.08
Glutamic acid	B		29.3	33.7	1.15
Methionine	B		25.7	29.3	1.14
Phenylglycine	C		4.1	4.6	1.12
Phenylalanine	C		8.1	8.4	1.04

*GLC analyses were carried out on 5 feet by 1/8-inch columns using a flame ionization detector. Column A: 5 per cent. SE-30 on Chromosorb W at 176°C and N_2 flow 28 ml/ minute. Column B: 0.5 per cent. EGA on Chromosorb W at 185°C and N_2 flow 46 ml/ minute. Column C: 0.5 per cent. EGA on Aeropak 30 at 220°C and N_2 flow 30 ml/minute.

TABLE 2

Correlation of the Rule of Six with Ratio of Retention Times of Diastereoisomers of a Series of N-chloralkanoyl Valine Methyl Esters on FFAP*

$$R_1\!-\!C\!-\!CH\!-\!CO\!-\!NH\!-\!CH\!-\!COOCH_3$$

with R_2, R_3 on the R_1 carbon, Cl substituent, and CH — CH_3, CH_3 group

Chloro acid	Retention times of diastereoisomers SR	Retention times of diastereoisomers SS	Ratio of retention times SS/SR	No. of atoms of resolving agent in position† 5	6	7
2-Chloropropanoic acid $R_1=R_2=R_3=H$	5.75	6.3	1.13	3	0	0
2-Chlorobutanoic acid $R_1=R_2=H$; $R_3=CH_3$	6.3	7.95	1.17	3	3	0
2-Chloro-4-methylpentanoic acid $R_1=R_2=H$; $R_3=CH(CH_3)_2$	10.15	12.0	1.18	3	3	6
2-Chlorohexanoic acid $R_1=R_2=H$; $R_3=CH_3CH_2CH_3$	12.4	14.7	1.18	3	3	3
2-Chloro-3-methylbutanoic acid $R_1=H$; $R_2=R_3=CH_3$	8.1	9.9	1.22	3	6	0
2-Chloro-3-methylpentanoic acid $R_1=H$; $R_2=CH_3$; $R_3=CH_2CH_3$	10.35	12.9	1.25	3	6	3
Allo-2-chloro-2-methylpentanoic acid $R_1=H$; $R_2=CH_2CH_3$; $R_3=CH_3$	10.5	12.85	1.22	3	6	3
2-Chloro-3-dimethylbutanoic acid $R_1=R_2=R_3=CH_3$	9.6	12.5	1.30	3	9	0

*Chromatographic analyses were carried out on 5 feet by 1/8-inch column packed with 5 per cent. FFAP on Chromosorb W. The separation temperature was 161°C and during analyses the nitrogen flow was 28 ml/minute.

†See Fig. 2.

both an increased volatility and a lower interaction with the stationary phase. The consistency in the order of retention times of diastereoisomeric peptides suggested that the method might be applicable to the assignment of absolute configuration to other asymmetric compounds. To check the general applicability of this technique, α-amino acids were converted to their α-chloro analogues using a procedure which was known to lead to compounds of known configuration. The chloro acids were then coupled with valine methyl ester and the products examined by GLC (Table 2). Again the SR diastereoisomers consistently had the shorter retention time[11].

Many different types of diastereoisomeric amides and esters have now been analysed using this technique and in all cases the order of retention of diastereoisomers within an homologous series was consistent (Table 3). These results clearly establish the technique as a very sensitive addition to the ORD, CD, NMR and enzymatic methods of determining absolute configuration[4,12].

It is worth noting here the factors influencing the degree of resolution of diastereoisomers. In the case of the N-α-chloroalkanoyl valine methyl esters (Table 2), there was a striking correlation between the steric bulk of the alkanoyl group and the efficiency of resolution. Thus Newman's

TABLE 3

The Order of Gas Chromatographic Elution of Various
Diastereoisomeric Amides and Esters

Diastereoisomer	First GLC peak	Second GLC peak	Reference
N-TFA-prolyl-amino acid esters	SR	SS	8, 9
α-Chloralkanoyl-amino acid esters	SR	SS	11
N-TFA-prolyl-1-methylalkylamides	SR	SS	12
N-TFA-prolyl-1-amino-1-phenylethanes	SR	SS	12
N-TFA-prolyl-2-amino-1-phenylpropanes	SR	SS	12
N-TFA-α-amino acid-2-alkylesters	SR	SS	13, 14, 15
α-Acetoxy-alkanoic acid 2-alkyl esters	SR	SS	16
α-Hydroxy-alkanoic acid 2-alkyl esters	SR	SS	16
α-Alkylphenylacetyl-2-methylamino-1-phenylpropanes	SS	SR	17
N-TFA-prolyl derivatives of cyclic α-alkyl amines	SS	SR	12

"six number" (FIG. 2) is in good agreement with the ratio of retention times of the diastereoisomers[18].

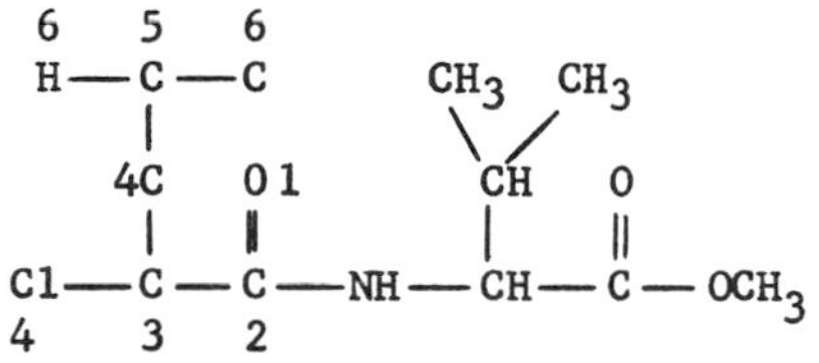

FIG. 2

The six number for the resolving agent is obtained by summing the number of atoms in the six position[19, 20].

It follows that in selecting a resolving agent, the three groups attached to the asymmetric center (along with the functional group) should have a large size differential. Alternatively, cyclic compounds with a functional group adjacent to the asymmetric center such as proline also serve as excellent resolving agents. In general, the more rigid the diastereoisomeric molecule close to the asymmetric centers, the larger will be the separation[21].

From the consideration of these factors, menthyl chloroformate (FIG. 3) was selected as being a potential resolving agent for the simultaneous analysis of amino and hydroxy acid methyl esters, the resulting diastereoisomeric urethanes and carbonates were found to be resolvable by GLC (Table 4). In both classes, the RS diastereoisomer had the shorter retention[22].

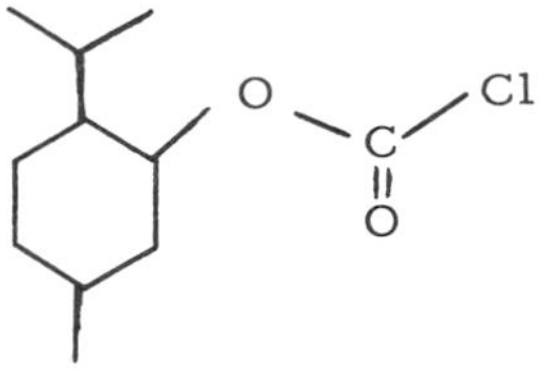

FIG. 3

Menthyl chloroformate

Finally, it should be pointed out that this technique does not require both enantiomers for assignment of configuration. In the case of natural products where usually only one optical form is available, assignment is made by coupling with optically pure and with racemic reagents prior to GLC analysis. This is possible because the gas chromatograph does not distinguish SS from RR or SR from RS diastereoisomers (see below).

Schematic procedure for the determination of configuration:

Preparation of Diastereoisomers		GLC Analysis	
Resolving agent	Unknown	1st peak	2nd peak
S, R	S	RS	SS
S	S		SS
S, R	R	SR	RR
S	R	SR	

Absolute configuration of the unknown compound is therefore simply determined by comparing the order of retention of its diastereoisomeric derivative with the same

TABLE 4

Gas Chromatographic Separation of α-hydroxy and α-amino Acid Methylesters as their R-(-)-menthoxycarbonyl Diastereoisomeric Derivatives*

Acid	Separation temperature (°C.)	Retention time of diastereoisomers (min.)		Ratio of retention times $\frac{RR}{RS}$
		R.S.	R.R.	
Lactic	170	3.85	4.2	1.09
α-Hydroxyisovaleric	170	5.00	5.7	1.14
α-Hydroxyisocaproic	170	6.8	7.8	1.15
3-Phenyllactic	200	8.5	9.7	1.14
Alanine	170	6.6	7.0	1.06
Valine	170	9.05	10.0	1.10
Leucine	170	11.9	12.75	1.07
Phenylalanine	200	13.1	14.4	1.10

*GLC analyses were carried out on 5 ft x 1/8 in column packed with 5% QF-1 on Aeropak 30. The nitrogen flow during analyses was 30 ml/min.

derivative of a homologue of known configuration. An

analagous approach has been made using thin layer chroma-

tography and NMR, and the three methods compared in the

configurational assignment of diketopiperazines[23].

CONCLUSION

There are two useful applications for this technique

in peptide chemistry. The first is the optical purity

determination of the amino acids used in peptide synthesis.

The second is the assignment of configuration to novel

amino acids isolated from natural sources such as peptide

antibiotics.

ACKNOWLEDGEMENT

This work was carried out in collaboration with

Dr. B. Halpern and was supported in part by a grant from

the National Aeronautics and Space Administration

(NSG 81-60).

REFERENCES

1. The R-S system of configurational assignment is used
   throughout this paper. See R. K. Cahn, C. K. Ingold and
   V. Prelog, Experentia, 12, 81 (1956).

2. Present address: Department of Microbiology, Hoffmann-
   La-Roche Inc., Nutley, New Jersey.

3. J. Casanova and J. Corey, Chem. Ind. (London), 1664
   (1961).

4. M. Raban and K. Mislow in Topics in Stereochemistry,
   (N. L. Allinger and E. L. Eliel, eds.), Vol. 2,
   Interscience, New York, 1967, p. 199.

5. F. Weygand, _Angew Chem. Intern. Ed._, 2, 183 (1963).

6. J. W. Westley, _Advances in the Astronautical Sciences_, 22, 213 (1967).

7. F. Weygand, P. Klinke, and I. Eigen, _Chem. Ber._, 90, 1896 (1957).

8. B. Halpern and J. W. Westley, _Biochem. Biophys. Res. Commun._, 19, 361 (1965).

9. B. Halpern and J. W. Westley, _Tetrahedron Letters_, 2283 (1966).

10. T. Wieland and E. Bende, _Chem. Ber._, 98, 504 (1965).

11. B. Halpern and J. W. Westley, _Chem. Comm._, 246 (1965).

12. J. W. Westley and B. Halpern, Seventh International Symposium on Gas Chromatography, Copenhagen, June 25-28, 1968.

13. R. Charles, G. Fischer, and E. Gil-Av, _Israel J. Chem._, 1, 234 (1963).

14. S. V. Vitt, M. B. Saporovskaya, I. P. Gudkova, and V. M. Belikov, _Tetrahedron Letters_, 2575 (1963).

15. G. E. Pollock and V. I. Oyama, _J. Gas Chromatog._, 4, 126 (1966).

16. B. L. Karger, R. L. Stern, H. C. Rose, and W. Keane, in _Gas Chromatography 1966_, (A. B. Littlewood, ed.), Institute of Petroleum, London, 1967, p. 240.

17. B. Halpern and J. W. Westley, _Chem. Comm._, 237 (1967).

18. B. Halpern, J. W. Westley, and B. Weinstein, _Nature_, 210, 837 (1966).

19. M. S. Newman, in _Steric Effects in Organic Chemistry_, (M. S. Newman, ed.), John Wiley, New York, 1956, p. 206.

20. R. E. Whitfield, _Science, 142_, 577 (1963), has used the rule of six to interpret conformations of polypeptides and proteins and to explain hydrolysis rates of di- and poly-peptides.

JOHN W. WESTLEY

21. J. W. Westley, B. Halpern, and B. L. Karger, Anal. Chem., 40, 2046 (1968).

22. J. W. Westley and B. Halpern, J. Org. Chem., 33, 3978 (1968).

23. J. W. Westley, V. A. Close, D. Nitecki, and B. Halpern, Anal. Chem., 40, 1888 (1968).

DETECTION OF RACEMIZATION IN PEPTIDE SYNTHESIS BY NUCLEAR MAGNETIC RESONANCE SPECTROSCOPY

Boris Weinstein

Department of Chemistry
University of Washington
Seattle, Washington

A problem of considerable importance in practical peptide chemistry involves the evaluation of racemization during the coupling of amino-acid components. Such techniques as counter-current distribution[2], deuterium exchange[3], fractional crystal-lization[4-6], gas-liquid partition[7-10], ion-exchange[12], optical rotation[16], paper[17,18] and thin-layer chromatography[19-21], and thiohydantoin formation[22] have been used to detect and to measure the extent of racemization in a typical synthetic route. Other studies on the subject concern the effects of activating agents, acyl protecting groups, amino components, bases, salts, solvents, and temperature on the optical purity of the condensation reaction[23-27]. However, a general solution to this present vexing situation is hindered by the paucity of resolvable or separable diastereoisomeric peptide pairs.

Although the introduction of nuclear magnetic resonance (n. m. r.) spectroscopy as a tool for racemization studies is

371

relatively new, observations based on the n. m. r. spectra of peptides have been common for the last decade. For example, a shielding phenomenon was seen in peptides containing adjacent aromatic and aliphatic amino-acid residues[28]. In the diastereoisomeric pair L-leucyl-L-tyrosine and D-leucyl-L-tyrosine, the resonances of the leucyl side-chain were shifted to higher field in the D-L compound. This change was attributed to a closer proximity of the leucyl and tyrosyl side-chains in the second diastereoisomer. A similar effect was found in the n. m. r. spectra of D-alanyl-L-tyrosine and L-alanyl-L-tyrosine[29]. Here, most of the resonance peaks are identical or only slightly different from each other, yet the methyl group in D-alanyl-L-tyrosine is upfield from the equivalent L-L isomer. Alkyl shielding was again noted on comparing the related diastereoisomers L-valyl-L-tyrosine and L-alanyl-L-phenylalanine.

These results led to the idea of a more compact form for the D-L dipeptide, as compared to the L-L dipeptide in aqueous solution. Assuming a trans planar amide bond, the tendency for maximal approach of differently charged groups, as well as a stabilizing effect due to hydrogen bonding, then one could initially propose a cyclic conformation in the L-L compound. However, the cis side-chains would hinder each other, so this action causes a loss of the intramolecular hydrogen bridge, and instead produces a stretched molecule (FIG. 1).

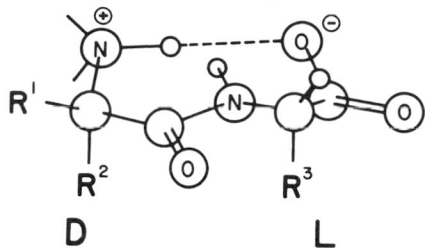

R^2 = H, R^1 and R^3 <u>trans</u> side chains

FIG. 1

D-L Dipeptide in Deuterium Oxide

In the D-L compound, according to the same model, the side-chain residues are <u>trans</u> and there is no steric hindrance, so the molecule is found in a coiled form (FIG. 2).

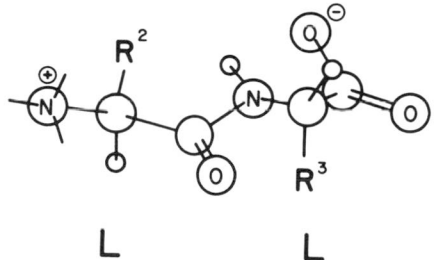

R^2 and R^3 side chains

FIG. 2

L-L Dipeptide in Deuterium Oxide

Thus, in the L-L linear state, the aliphatic side-chain is deshielded relative to the D-L conformation by the charged amino species. The alternative explanation that assumes direct interaction of the side-chains through diamagnetic shielding of the aliphatic chain by the aromatic ring was

373

TABLE 1.   Methyl Resonances of Alanyl Peptides

Peptide[a]	N-Terminal	Central	C-Terminal
L-Alanyl-L-alanine	92.8	- - -	80.9
D-Alanyl-D-alanine	93.0	- - -	80.0
L-Alanyl-D-alanine	91.1	- - -	81.1
L-Alanyl-L-alanyl-L-alanine	93.1	84.1	79.6
L-Alanyl-D-alanyl-L-alanine	91.2	83.0	78.9
D-Alanyl-L-alanyl-L-alanine	91.5	83.9	79.6
D-Alanyl-D-alanyl-L-alanine	92.9	83.4	79.0

[a]All spectra were determined on a Varian A-60 spectrometer with the center of gravity of the chemical shift given in hertz downfield from sodium dimethylsilapentylsulfonic acid. The compounds were dissolved in deuterium oxide and the pH values were adjusted to 5-6 with addition of deuterio-acetic acid or sodium deuterioxide.   The error of measurement was ± 0.5 Hz.

avoided because, in both of the diastereomers, the signal of the protons of the benzene ring coincide exactly.

    The first application of magnetic non-equivalence in diastereoisomeric pairs was in a study of alanyl di- and tripeptides, for which it was concluded that these compounds have identical n.m.r. spectra[29].   However, a reexamination of a more complete series revealed a small net change in the chemical shift resonances of the methyl resonances between the L-L and L-D peptides (Table 1)[30].

Although variations in spectra between the various diastereoisomeric alanyl-alanines and alanyl-alanyl-alanines were only slight (0-2 Hz.), the methyl resonances of various blocked N-acyl peptide derivatives of alanine containing an aromatic ring had sufficient differences between the L-L (or D-D) and D-L (or L-D) compounds to be used as a convenient tool for the analysis of racemization. As in previous studies, the methyl doublet signal in a L-L compound is at a lower field than the equivalent signal for the D-L (or L-D) analog. The visual presence of two sets of doublets (an L-L doublet and a D-L or L-D doublet) in the aliphatic region of the spectra of a sample indicates the presence of a racemate (Table 2).

Using this technique with N-acyl-alanyl-phenylalanine methyl esters or N-acyl-phenylalanyl-alanine methyl esters, it was possible to examine the influence of several coupling agents and N-acyl protecting groups on the extent of racemization during peptide synthesis. By area integration of the separated L-L and D-L (or L-D) resonances in a racemized sample, a quantitative analysis was easily achieved without the need to physically separate the individual diastereoisomers (Table 3)[31].

TABLE 2. Methyl Resonances of Various N-Acyl Peptide Derivatives

Peptide[a]	L-L(or D-D)[b]	D-L(or L-D)
N-Acetyl-L(or D)-alanyl-O-benzyl-L-tyrosine methyl ester	78.0	74.0
N-Acetyl-L(or D)-alanyl-L-phenylalanine methyl ester	78.4	70.4
N-Benzoyl-L(or D)-phenylalanyl-L-alanine methyl ester	79.5	74.5
N-Boc-L-phenylalanyl-L(or D)-alanine methyl ester	80.9	75.4
N-Formyl-L-alanyl-L(or D)-phenylalanine methyl ester	80.5	74.8
N-Cbz-glycyl-L(or D)-alanyl-L-phenylalanine	75.5	74.5
N-Cbz-glycyl-L(or D)-phenylalanyl-D-alanine benzyl ester	77.5	69.5

[a]Compounds listed here were prepared by standard procedures and had physical constants in agreement with literature values.

[b]All spectra were determined on a Varian A-60 spectrometer with the center of gravity of the chemical shift given in hertz downfield from tetramethylsilane. The compounds were dissolved in deuteriochloroform.

TABLE 3. Degree of Racemization During Peptide Bond Formation

Component Activated[a,b]	Condensed With[a,b]	%D-L or L-D in Product with Coupling Agent[c]				Methyl Resonance	
		CDI	K	DCC	EDC	L-L	D-L or L-D
For-L-Ala	L-Phe-OMe	3	3	3	3	80.5	74.3
For-L-Phe	L-Ala-OMe	3	3	3	3	79.5	72.5
Ac-L-Ala	L-Phe-OMe	3	3	35	27	79.0	71.5
Ac-L-Phe	L-Ala-OMe	16	6	50	41	81.0	73.5
Bz-L-Ala	L-Phe-OMe	19	3			84.5	79.5
Bz-L-Phe	L-Ala-OMe	35	3			79.5	74.5
Bz-L-Phe	L-Ala-OMe	3	5	10	12	78.0	71.0
Z-Gly-L-Phe	L-Ala-OMe	3	9	17	17	77.5	70.5
Z-Gly-Gly-L-Phe	L-Ala-OMe	10	15	25	20	81.5	72.0

[a]For = formyl; all other abbreviated designations of compounds follow IUPAC-IUB rules.

[b]The optical purity of the starting materials was verified by gas-liquid partition chromatography: N-acetyl and N-benzoyl compounds were converted to the menthyl ester derivatives, while the N-formyl compounds were hydrolyzed and analyzed as the N-trifluoroacetyl-L-prolyl peptide esters; the methyl ester compounds were assayed similarly. [c]The limit of measurement was generally 3%, although in some cases a more accurate value was obtained by duplicate procedures. [d]All spectra were determined on a Varian A-60 spectrometer with the center of gravity of the chemical shift given in hertz downfield from tetramethylsilane (J=7.2 ± 0.3 Hz). The compounds were dissolved in deuteriochloroform (deuterioethanol for the tetrapeptide).

In order to extend this work, a related diastereoisomeric series has been prepared that involves the remaining aromatic amino-acids histidine, tryptophan, and tyrosine. It appears a similar alanyl shift exists in these systems, too (Table 4)[32].

At this time, no elaborate discussion will be given as to the precise conformational shape that those dipeptides take in solution. Yet, one must note that the factors illustrated in FIGS. 1 and 2 do not apply here, as they are derived from the shape of the zwitterionic species in deuterium oxide, and the current data concerns blocked peptides in deuteriochloroform. It is believed that the results of Table 4 are a combination of both steric hindrance and dimagnetic shielding. For example, N-benzyloxycarbonyl-L-alanyl-L-tyrosine methyl ester and N-benzyloxycar-bonyl-D-alanyl-L-tyrosine methyl ester exhibit identical spectra - - a somewhat unexpected result - - but, this situation is possibly due to steric requirements that prevent the juxtaposition of the side-chains in either isomer. One additional case merits discussion at this time. The aliphatic shift for the L-D isomer relative to the L-L isomer in the N-benzyloxycarbonylhistidylalanine methyl esters is downfield instead of upfield as in all other dipeptide pairs. It may be surmised the aliphatic side-chain is diamagnetically shielded by the aromatic ring in the L-L isomer rather than the L-D isomer. Again, steric hindrance is the probable factor.

TABLE 4. Methyl Resonances of N-Acyl Peptide Derivatives

Compound	Methyl Resonance[a]	Shift Difference LL-LD(or D-L)
Z-L(or D)-ala-L(orD)-ala-OMe	83.5	0
Z-L-his-L-ala-OMe	76.5 ⎫	2.5
Z-L-his-D-ala-OMe	74.0 ⎭	
N^{α}-Z-N^{im}-bz-L-his-L-ala-OMe	73.0 ⎫	-4.5
N^{α}-Z-N^{im}-bz-L-his-D-ala-OMe	77.5 ⎭	
Z-L-phe-L-ala-OMe	79.5 ⎫	6
Z-L-phe-D-ala-OMe	73.5 ⎭	
Z-L-ala-L-phe-OMe	78.0 ⎫	2
Z-D-ala-L-phe-OMe	76.0 ⎭	
Z-L-try-L-ala-OMe	74.0 ⎫	8
Z-L-try-D-ala-OMe	66.0 ⎭	
Z-L-ala-L-try-OMe	77.5 ⎫	2
Z-D-ala-L-try-OMe	75.5 ⎭	
Z-L-tyr-L-ala-OMe	79.5 ⎫	4
Z-D-tyr-L-ala-OMe	75.5 ⎭	
Z-L-ala-L-tyr-OMe	79.5 ⎫	0
Z-D-ala-L-tyr-OMe	79.5 ⎭	
N,O-di-Z-L-tyr-L-ala-OMe	79.0 ⎫	5.5
N,O-di-Z-L-tyr-D-ala-OMe	73.5 ⎭	

[a]All spectra were determined on a Varian A-60 spectrometer with the center of gravity of the chemical shift given in hertz downfield from tetramethylsilane. The compounds were dissolved in deuteriochloroform (deuteriodimethylsulfoxide for the last two products) and the concentration was 7.5% (weight/volume).

If there are objections to the use of aromatic residues in this type of analysis, then the dipeptides N-benzyloxy-carbonyl-L-alanyl-L-alanine benzyl ester and N-benzyloxycarbonyl-L-alanyl-D-alanine benzyl ester may be of interest, since a related shift is found for the methyl group in the second alanyl residue due to the proximity of the benzyl ester ring[33].

The basic method discussed here has been adopted by other workers to determine both the amount of racemization occurring in the formation of L-alanyl-L-phenylalanine through use of 2, 5-thiazolidinediones[34] and to verify the configuration of some alanyl-cycloserine derivatives[35].

As a model compound for future racemization studies, the derivative N-acetyl-phenylalanyl-alanine methyl ester is suggested for further applications. The advantages are as follows: the acetyl group is known to be very poor from the protection viewpoint - - thus, a true index of racemization can be built for a large array of coupling agents; next, the phenylalanyl-alanine unit gives a satisfactory shielding value, which allows integration of methyl doublet areas to be done without difficulty; and, the acetyl and methyl ester singlets in the n. m. r. spectrum provide convenient, internal standardization values. A typical such spectrum is illustrated in FIG. 3.

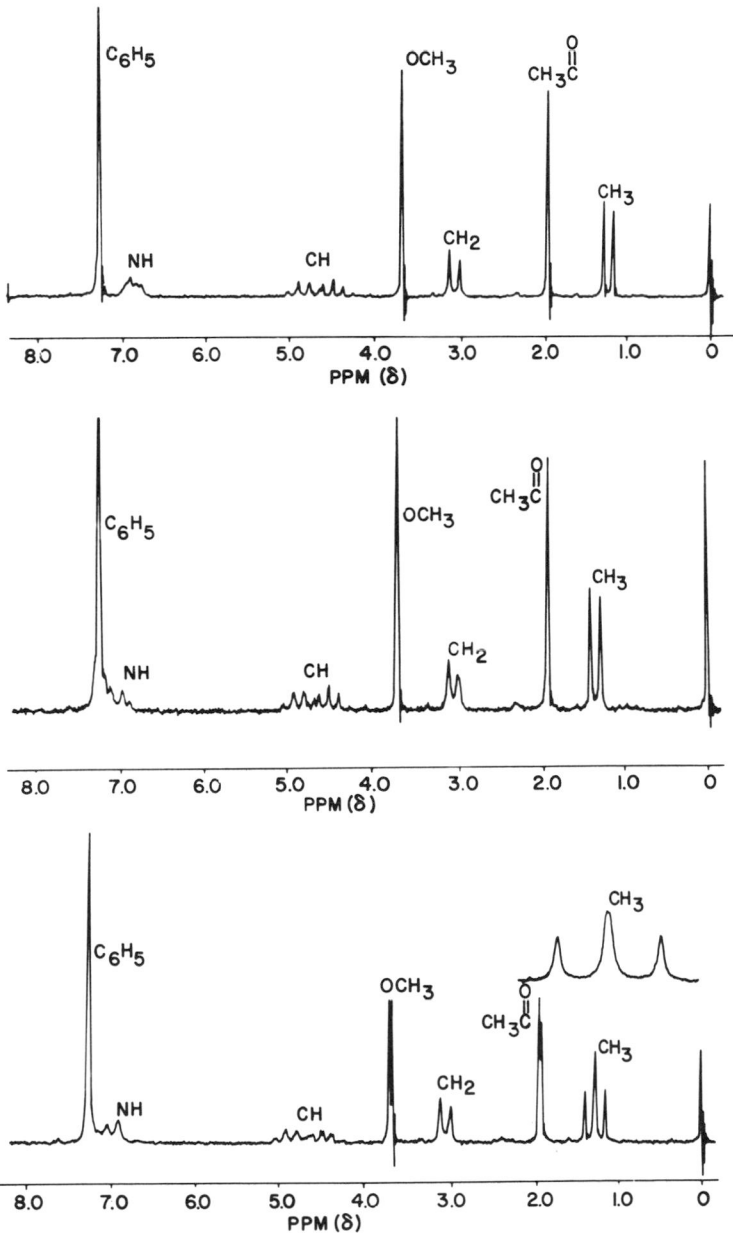

FIG. 3

N. M. R. Spectra of Diastereoisomers of N-Acetyl-Phenylalanine-alanine Methyl Ester: D-L (top); L-L (middle); 50% L-L and 50% D-L (bottom)

In a general experiment, a solution of N-acetyl-L-phenylalanine and L-alanine methyl ester is coupled with the aid of some suitable agent. The organic phase is then washed one or more times with dilute acid, dilute base, water, and dried, so as to remove any extraneous n. m. r. signals in the aliphatic region. After removal of the solvent, the dipeptide is dissolved in deuteriochloroform for measurement purposes. To prevent a preferential concentration or fractionation of one of the optical isomers, the solid or oily product is not crystallized.

With a racemic product, three peaks are seen in the aliphatic region of the n. m. r. spectrum, which is a result of an overlap of the L-L and D-L doublets. The signals are integrated to obtain the areas of the first two (downfield) peaks (due to the L-L doublet plus one-half of the D-L doublet) and the area of the third (upfield) peak (due to one half of the D-L doublet). Twice the area of the third (upfield) peak (the total area of the D-L doublet) divided by the total area of all three peaks (the total L-L plus D-L) gives the fraction of D-L isomer in the racemate. The integration can be done several times and the results averaged for a statistical treatment. To test the validity of the results, artificial mixtures were prepared with a known percent of the D-L isomer. The integrations were taken and the percent D-L isomer calculated as indicated here. The precision among the measured values was found to be 3%. For mixtures with less than 10% D-L isomer, the T-60 n. m. r. spectrometer was used, instead of the older A-60, since the better signal-to-noise ratio permitted detection of racemization as low as 3% D-L isomer.

In summary, the n. m. r. procedure for the analysis of racemization in peptide synthesis has several practical and theoretical advantages over other schemes found in the literature:

a. Convenience - - There is no need to isolate or to crystallize individual diastereoisomeric peptides.

b. Generality -- Any N-protecting, ester blocking group or coupling agent can be evaluated in a facile fashion.

c. Models -- At least eight alanyl dipeptides and sixteen glycyl-alanyl or alanyl-glycyl tripeptides can furnish methyl doublet data.

d. Rapidity -- Excluding the time needed for the reaction and various work-up procedures, a typical n. m. r. scan takes only a few minutes, which includes area integration, too.

e. Sensitivity -- A typical value is useful to within ± 3%; however, a comparison with the aid of a ^{13}C side-band peak increases the accuracy by at least ten times.

f. Standardization -- By choosing a suitable di- or tri-peptide, a host of secondary factors involved in racemization, such as changes in solvent or base concentration can be studied at leisure.

Finally, we might mention that another method for the analysis of racemization by n. m. r. spectroscopy could involve the use of a solvent effect -- for example, an optically active solvent that binds, coordinates or shields the dipeptide amide bond in a special manner. Trideuteriomethylphenyl sulfoxide, $CD_3SOC_6H_5$, has been evaluated in this respect and some evidence has been accumulated that the desired separation is being seen; however, a definite method must be developed before additional claims are made at this time[36].

ACKNOWLEDGMENT

We wish to thank the National Aeronautics and Space Administration (NsG 81-60), National Science Foundation (GB 3208) and National Institutes of Health (AM 12241 and AM 12616) for partial support of this work.

REFERENCES

1. E. Schröder and K. Lübke, The Peptides, Vol. 1, Academic Press, New York, N. Y. , 1965, p. 319; M. Bodanszky and M. A. Ondetti, Peptide Synthesis, Interscience Publishers, New York, N. Y. , 1966, p. 137.

2. D. W. Clayton, J. A. Farrington, G. W. Kenner, and J. M. Turner, J. Chem. Soc. , 1398 (1957).

3. H. Matsuo, Y. Kawazoe, M. Sato, M. Ohnishi, and
    T. Tatsuno, Chem. Pharm. Bull., 15, 391 (1967).

4. G. W. Anderson and F. M. Callahan, J. Am. Chem. Soc.,
    80, 2902 (1958).

5. N. A. Smart, G. T. Young, and M. W. Williams,
    J. Chem. Soc., 3902 (1960); M. W. Williams and
    G. T. Young, ibid., 881 (1963).

6. S. Goldschmidt and K. K. Gupta, Chem. Ber., 98,
    2831 (1965).

7. F. Weygand, A. Prox, L. Schmidhammer, and W. König,
    Angew. Chem., 75, 282 (1963); F. Weygand, A. Prox,
    and W. König, Chem. Ber., 99, 145 (1966);
    F. Weygand, D. Hoffmann, and A. Prox., Z. Naturforsch.,
    23b, 279 (1968).

8. B. Halpern and J. W. Westley, Biochem. Biophys. Res.
    Commun., 19, 361 (1965); B. Halpern, L. F. Chew,
    and J. W. Westley, Anal. Chem., 39, 399 (1967).

9. S. Lande and R. A. Landowne, Tetrahedron, 3085 (1966).

10. B. Feibush and E. Gil-Av, J. Gas Chromatog., 5, 257
    (1967); E. Gil-Av and B. Feibush, Tetrahedron Letters,
    3345 (1967).

11. G. E. Pollock and V. I. Oyama, J. Gas Chromatog.,
    4, 126 (1966).

12. M. Muraoka, N. Yoshida, K. Noda, and N. Izumiya,
    Bull. Chem. Soc. Japan, 41, 2134 (1968); N. Izumiya,
    Proceedings of the First American Peptide Symposium
    (B. Weinstein and S. Lande, eds.) Marcel Dekker,
    New York, 1970, this volume.

13. M. Bodanszky and L. E. Conklin, Chem. Commun.,
    773 (1967).

14. N. Inukai, K. Nakano, and M. Murakami, Bull. Chem.
    Soc. Japan, 41, 182 (1968).

15. W. R. Waterfield, J. Chem. Soc., 1964, 541.

16. M. W. Williams and G. T. Young, J. Chem. Soc.,
    1963, 881; A. L. Heard and G. T. Young, ibid.,
    1963, 5807.

17. E. Taschner, T. Sokolowska, J. F. Biernat,
A. Chimiak, C. Wasielewski, and B. Rzeszotarska,
Ann., 663, 197 (1963); T. Skolowska and
J. F. Biernat, J. Chromat., 13, 269 (1964).

18. G. Losse, H. Raue, and K. Koehler, Z. Chim.,
7, 105 (1967).

19. Z. Pravda, K. Poduška, and K. Bláha, Collection
Czech. Chem. Commun., 29, 2626 (1964).

20. T. Wieland and H. Bende, Chem. Ber., 98, 504
(1965).

21. H. Feltkamp and H. Pfrommer, J. Chromatog., 18,
403 (1965).

22. E. Taschner, L. Lubiewska, M. Smulkowski, and
H. Wojciechowska, Experientia, 24, 521 (1968).

23. S. Sakakibara and M. Itoh, Bull. Chem. Soc. Japan
40. 656 (1967).

24. M. Bodanszky and A. Bodanszky, Chem. Commun.,
591 (1967).

25. G. T. Young, in Peptides, Proceedings of the Eighth
European Peptide Symposium (H. C. Beyerman, A.
van de Linde, and W. Maassen van den Brink, eds.),
North - Holland, Amsterdam, 1967, p. 55.

26. N. Nakamizo, Tampakushitsu Kakusan Koso, 13,
586 (1968).

27. C. Glaser and M. Goodman, Proceedings of the First
American Peptide Symposium (B. Weinstein and
S. Lande, eds.), Marcel Dekker, New York, 1970, thi
volume.

28. F. A. Bovey and G. V. D. Tiers, J. Am. Chem. Soc.,
81, 2870 (1959).

29. M. van Gorkom, Tetrahedron Letters, 5433 (1966).

30. B. Halpern, D. E. Nitecki, and B. Weinstein,
Tetrahedron Letters, 3075 (1967).

31. B. Halpern, L. F. Chew, and B. Weinstein, J. Am.
Chem. Soc., 89, 5051 (1967).

32. B. Weinstein and A. E. Pritchard, unpublished data.

33. B. Weinstein and H. -H. Chang, unpublished data.

34. R. S. Dewey, E. F. Schoenewaldt, H. Joshua, W. J. Paleveda, Jr., H. Schwam, H. Barkemeyer, B. H. Arison, D. F. Veber, R. G. Denkewalter, and R. Hirschmann, J. Am. Chem. Soc., 90, 3254 (1968).

35. R. A. Payne and C. H. Stammer, J. Org. Chem., 33, 2421 (1968).

36. B. Weinstein, K. C. Das, and A. E. Pritchard, unpublished data.

STRUCTURAL STUDIES ON NISIN

Erhard Gross and John L. Morell

National Institutes of Health
Bethesda, Maryland

The isolation of an inhibitory substance from
Streptococcus lactis[1] which prevents the growth of
Streptococci[1a] and Lactobacillus bulgaricus[1b], predated
that of penicillin[2] by one year. The producing strain of the
microorganism belongs to the Lancefield Group N[3] which is
reflected in the name of the antibiotic (Nisin = Group N
Inhibitory Substance + in, the terminating letters in names
given antibiotics).

Thus far, nisin has not shared the prominence of penicillin
as antibacterial agent. This, no doubt, is in part the result
of the reported poor solubility of nisin. Nisin does, however,
reserve for itself a distinct role as unique food preservative
in European countries and in other parts of the world, but
not in the United States.

By its very origin nisin would appear to be a substance
producing few or no side effects when consumed by man.
It has actually been shown that nisin occurs in various concentrations in milk and in milk products as the result of

E. GROSS AND J. L. MORELL

contamination with nisin-producing strains of Streptococcus lactis. Nisin must therefore have been consumed for centuries by millions of people over their normal life span, evidently without ill effects.

The protein or polypeptide nature of nisin was recognized early[4]. As many as five different polypeptides have been claimed[5] to be present in nisin. This is not necessarily the case and will have to await clarification in view of our findings to be discussed subsequently.

The presence of lanthionine[5] and β-methyllanthionine[6] in nisin was initially of interest to us. We contemplated extension of the Cyanogen Bromide Reaction[7] to these thioether amino acids, found, however, that lanthionine and β-methyllanthionine do not react with cyanogen bromide under the conditions commonly employed[7,8].

A more interesting observation was made during the purification of commercially available nisin[9]. The material represented by the last peak of FIG. 1 is pyruvyllysine which originates from the COOH-terminal sequence dehydro-alanyllysine of nisin[10].

One might have been tempted to discard the low molecular weight components from gel chromatography on SEPHADEX as contaminants. However, passage over a 60-cm column of the amino acid analyzer[11] showed the material to be eluted as a distinct moiety (of FIG. 2B). Total hydrolysis

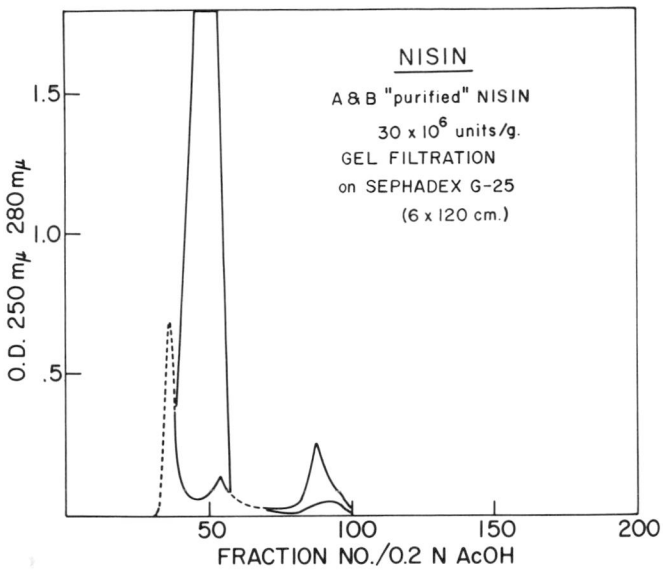

FIG. 1

Purification of Nisin. Gel chromatography on Sephadex
G-25 (6 x 120 cm; 0. 2 N acetic acid)

yielded only lysine, dinitrophenylation and hydrolysis

N-dinitrophenyllysine.   The α -H_2N-group of lysine,

obviously, is acylated.   Our working hypothesis of a

precursor in nisin in the form of an α , β -unsaturated

amino acid[12] and the attachment of an α -ketoacyl group to

the α -amino group of lysine was supported when treatment

of the low molecular weight material with o-phenylene

diamine[13] resulted in the liberation of lysine.   The

α -ketoacyl group was characterized by oxime formation

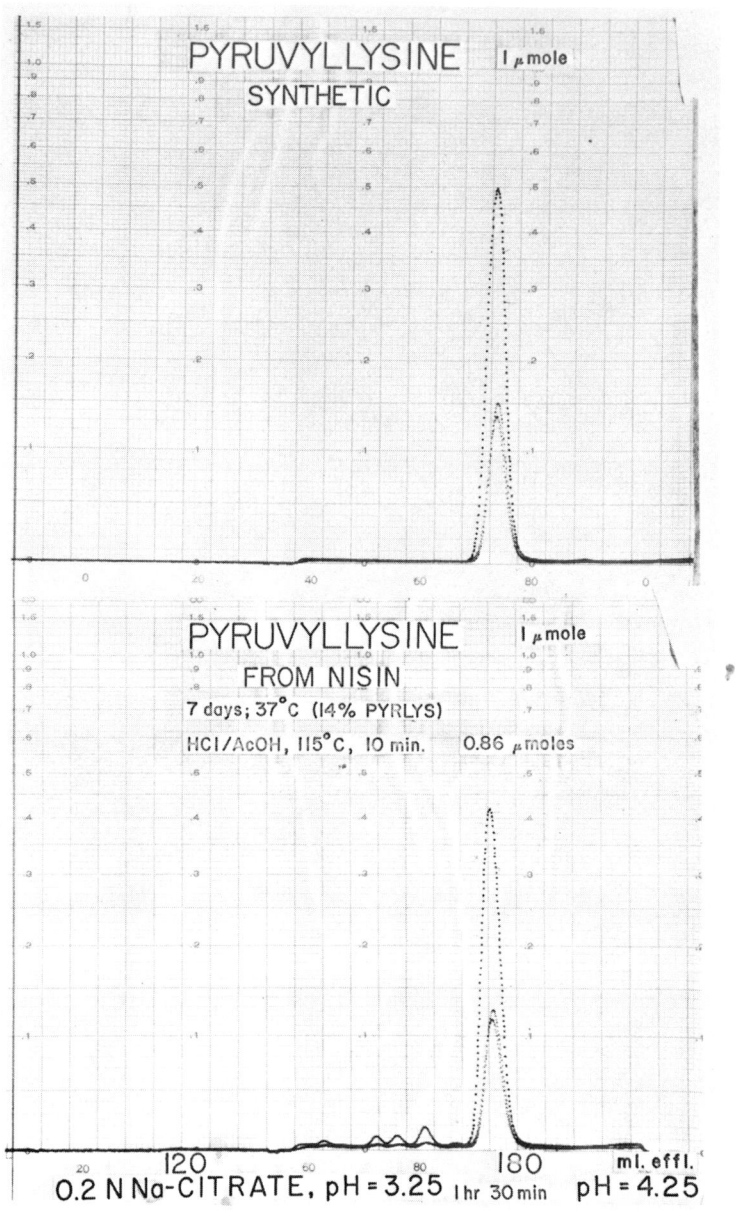

FIG. 2

Chromatography of Pyruvyllysine on Beckman Custom Resin
AA 15

    A. synthetic pyruvyllysine
    B. pyruvyllysine isolated from nisen.

and reduction to <u>alanine</u> under acylating conditions:

$$O=C-\underset{\underset{CH_3}{|}}{\overset{\overset{O}{\|}}{C}}-NH-\underset{\underset{COOH}{|}}{CH}-CH_2-CH_2-CH_2-CH_2-NH_2$$

$\downarrow +H_2NOH$

$$HON=C-\underset{\underset{CH_3}{|}}{\overset{\overset{O}{\|}}{C}}-NH-\underset{\underset{COOH}{|}}{CH}-CH_2-CH_2-CH_2-CH_2-NH_2$$

$\downarrow$ Pd-black/ H_2

acetic acid

$$H_3C-\underset{\underset{O}{\|}}{C}-HN-\underset{\underset{CH_3}{|}}{CH}-\overset{\overset{O}{\|}}{C}-NH-\underset{\underset{COOH}{|}}{CH}-CH_2-CH_2-CH_2-CH_2-\underset{\underset{H_3C-C=0}{|}}{NH}$$

$\downarrow H_2O/H^{\oplus}$

$$H_3C-\underset{\underset{O}{\|}}{C}-OH + H_2N-\underset{\underset{CH_3}{|}}{CH}-\overset{\overset{O}{\|}}{C}-OH \ + \ H_2N-\underset{\underset{COOH}{|}}{CH}-CH_2-CH_2-CH_2-\underset{\underset{NH_2}{|}}{CH_2}$$

ACETIC ACID   ALANINE   LYSINE   +

$$H_3C-\underset{\underset{O}{\|}}{C}-OH$$

ACETIC ACID

Pyruvyllysine was synthesized[10] following a procedure reported by Bergmann and Grafe[14], and compared with the product isolated from nisin (cf. Figs. 2 A+B).

$$H_3C-\overset{\overset{O}{\|}}{C}-NH_2$$

$$+ \quad O=C\overset{CH_3}{\underset{COOH}{\diagdown}}$$

$$H_3C-\underset{\underset{O}{\|}}{C}-NH_2$$

acetamide   pyruvic acid

$\downarrow$ 115° C
20 mm; 2-3 hrs

$$H_3C-\overset{\overset{O}{\|}}{C}-NH \diagdown \qquad CH_3$$
$$C$$
$$H_3C-\underset{\underset{O}{\|}}{C}-NH \diagup \qquad COOH$$

α,α-diacetaminopropionic acid

$\downarrow$ $(CH_3-\overset{\overset{O}{\|}}{C}-O)_2O$, 100°C , 4 hrs.

Finally, the presence of dehydroalanine in nisin was proved directly by the addition of mercaptans to the α , β -unsaturated amino acid. The addition of mercapto-acetamide, for instance, resulted in the formation of a product which yielded S-carboxymethylcysteine after total hydrolysis.

Methylmercaptan was added to nisin with the intention of forming S-methylcysteine for subsequent reaction with cyanogen bromide[12]. However, at 0°C the reaction does not proceed with the formation of serine[15].

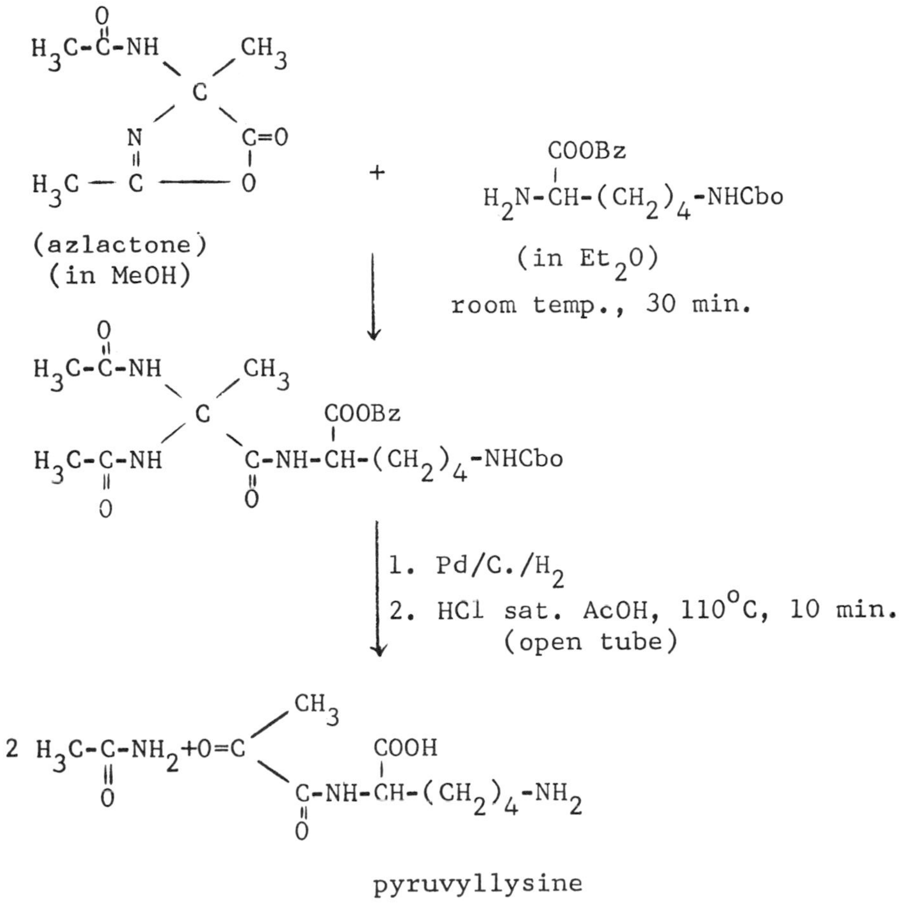

(azlactone)
(in MeOH)

+

COOBz
H_2N-CH-$(CH_2)_4$-NHCbo

(in Et_2O)
room temp., 30 min.

1. Pd/C./H_2
2. HCl sat. AcOH, $110^{\circ}C$, 10 min.
   (open tube)

pyruvyllysine

Subtilin[16], a peptide antibiotic from Bacillus subtilis

contains also lanthionine and β-methyllanthionine. We

asked the question: does it also contain dehydroalanine?

Indeed, it does. Not only that, the COOH-terminal sequence

is identical with that of nisin[17], namely dehydroalanyllysine,

which indicates interesting phylogenetic aspects for the

395

peptides from different microorganisms. Both antibiotics are inactivated[18] by nisinase[19]; the mode of action of this enzyme may well be that of dehydropeptidase.

The partial substitution technique of Battersby and Craig[20] proved to be the method of choice to establish the molecular weight of nisin. From the extinction of mono-dinitrophenylated nisin[10] at 360 mµthe molecular weight of nisin was calculated to be 3500, rather than 7000 as pre-viously reported[21]. There is no major component of molecular weight 7000[22] in purified nisin, nor is there room or the need for subunit consideration[22] and/or formation of such under alkaline conditions.

We decided the question of fragmenting nisin in favor of the application of the Cyanogen Bromide Reaction[7]. We had also considered tryptic digestion, but felt, that the poor solubility of nisin at pH~7 alone would stand in the way of satisfactory fragment formation.

From the presence of two residues of methionine in nisin, one may expect three fragments upon cleavage of the methionyl peptide bonds by cyanogen bromide. Only two are obtained. Two of the possible fragments are cross-linked by lanthionine residues.

The fragmentation is schematically presented in Fig. 3. Cleavage of the methionyllysyl bond is exceedingly slow at

$0°C$[23] and the cleavage of the methionylglycyl bond[24] alone

does not result in fragmentation at all. In order to bring

about more extensive cleavage of the methionyllysyl bond,

the reaction was continued at $0°C$ for 48 hours or allowed

to proceed at $37°C$ (cf. FIG. 4) for a total of 24 hours.

Continuation of the reaction at $0°C$ is to be preferred,

since it assures preservation of the additional α , β -unsatu-

rated amino acids[25] in nisin, which we intend to utilize

for fragmentation via amide and keto acid formation.

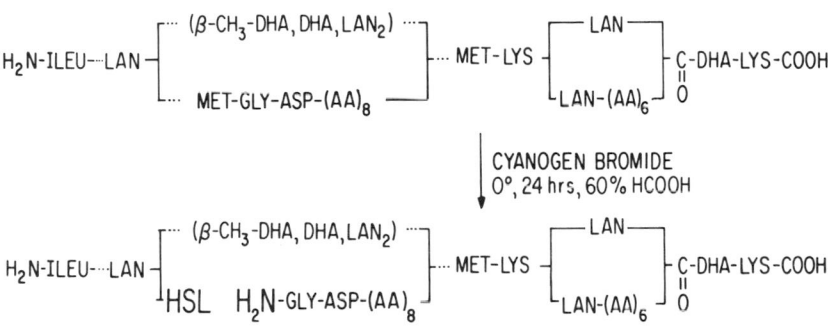

FIG. 3
The Action of Cyanogen Bromide on Nisin. Conditions:
$0°C$, 24 hrs, 60% formic acid. DHA=dehydroalanine;
β -CH_3-DHA=β -methyldehydroalanine HSL=homoserine
lactone; LAN=lanthionine or β -methyllanthionine,
AA=other amino acids.

The fragments resulting from cleavage of the methionyl

peptide bonds of nisin with cyanogen bromide were separated

by gel chromatography and counter current distribution.

The reaction mixture was first passed over a column of

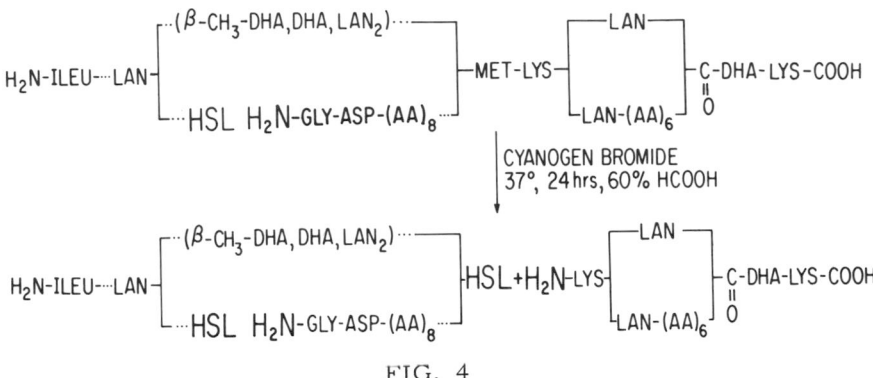

FIG. 4

The Action of Cyanogen Bromide on Nisin. Conditions: 37°C, 24 hrs, 60% formic acid; DHA = dehydroalanine, β -CH_3 — DHA = β -methyldehydroalanine, HSL = homoserine lactone; -LAN = lanthionine or β -methyllanthionine, AA = other amino acids.

Sephadex G-25. The resulting chromatogram is shown in FIG. 5. From left to right we encounter a peak representing material of distinctly high molecular weight, a second peak representing nisin in which only the methionylglycyl bond has been cleaved [mono-(MET → HSL) nisin] and of polymers of nisin and fragments of nisin. The third peak represents the two fragments of nisin identified as H_2N-terminal and COOH-terminal fragment.

The components of the mixture of H_2N-terminal and COOH-terminal fragments were separated by counter current distribution in the solvent system (v/v): water (2.0), n-butanol (1.5), glacial acetic acid (0.5). The distribution pattern is shown in FIG. 6. From left to right the first

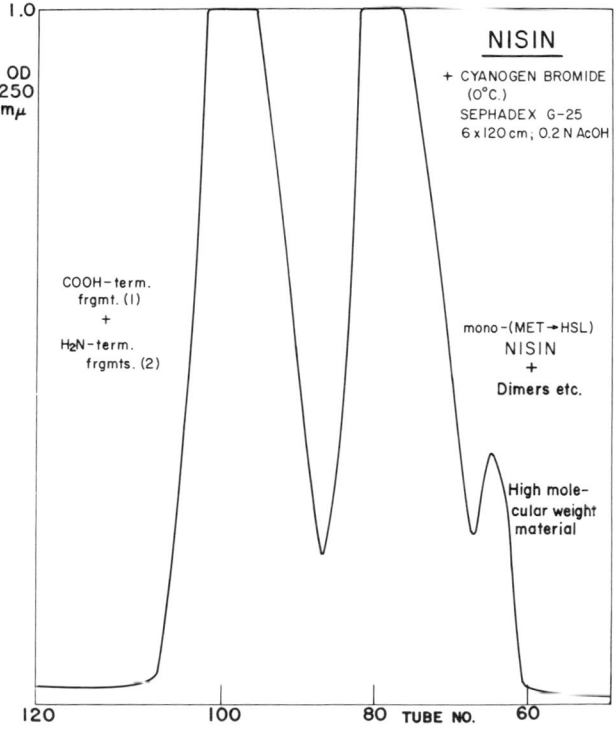

FIG. 5

Separation of Fragments of Nisin Resulting from Cleavage with Cyanogen Bromide. Sephadex G-25, 6 x 120 cm, 0.2 N acetic acid.

peak represents the COOH-terminal fragment, the second peak the NH_2-terminal fragment in which the methionylglycyl bond has been cleaved [MET - GLY - → -HSL GLY -) - H_2N-terminal fragment]. The third peak represents a small amount of H_2H-terminal fragment, in which the MET - GLY bond has not been cleaved[27].

399

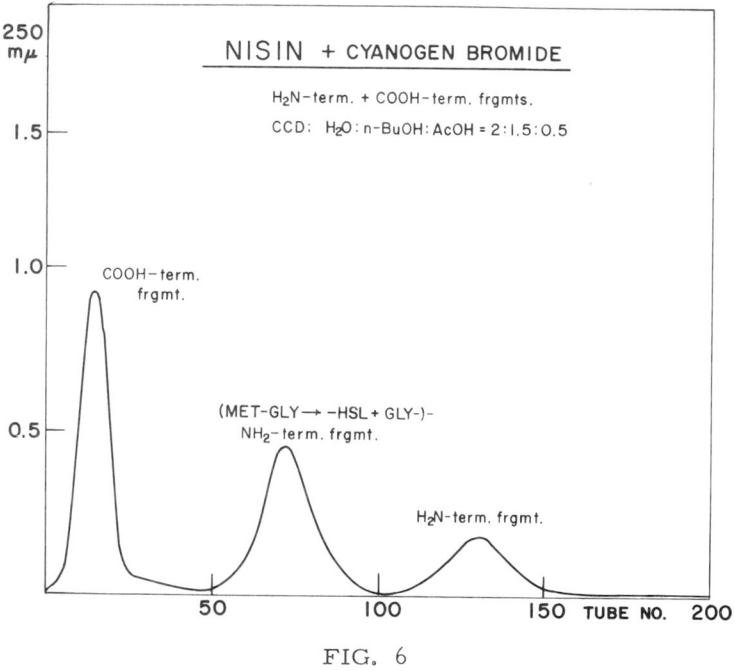

FIG. 6

Separation of Fragments of Nisin Resulting from Cleavage with Cyanogen Bromide. Counter current distribution; solvent system (v/v): water (2.0), n-butanol (1.5), glacial acetic acid (0.5).

The amino acid compositions of the H_2N-terminal and COOH-terminal fragment are recorded in Table 1. The amino acid composition of nisin is presented for the purpose of comparison.

Similar results were obtained when mono-dinitrophenylated nisin from the molecular weight determination was allowed to react with cyanogen bromide. One significant difference encountered during gel chromatography of the

TABLE 1. Amino Acid Composition of Nisin and of Fragments
of Nisin Obtained by Cleavage with Cyanogen
Bromide.

AMINO ACID	NUMBER OF RESIDUES		
	NH₂-terminal FRAGMENT	COOH-terminal FRAGMENT	NISIN
ASPARTIC ACID	1	—	1
THREONINE	—	—	—
SERINE	—	1	1
GLUTAMIC ACID	—	—	—
PROLINE	1	—	1
GLYCINE	3	—	3
ALANINE	1	1	2
1/2 CYSTINE	—	—	—
VALINE	—	1	1
METHIONINE	—	—	2
ISOLEUCINE	2	1	3
LEUCINE	2	—	2
TYROSINE	—	—	—
PHENYLALANINE	—	—	—
TRYPTOPHAN	—	—	—
LYSINE	1	2	3
HISTIDINE	—	2	2
AMMONIA	(3)	(1)	(4)
ARGININE	—	—	—
LANTHIONINE	1	—	1
β-CH₃-LANTHIONINE	2	2	4
DEHYDROALANINE	1	1	2
β-CH₃-DEHYDROALANINE	1	—	1
HOMOSERINE HOMOSERINE LACTONE	} 2	—	—
	18	11	29

fragments was the separation of the mono-dinitrophenyl

derivative of the COOH-terminal fragment from the H_2N-

terminal fragments (cf. FIG. 7). The presence of the

dinitrophenyl group enhances adsorption to Sephadex thus

delaying the elution of the COOH-terminal fragment. We

know already that the NH_2-group of one of the lysine residues

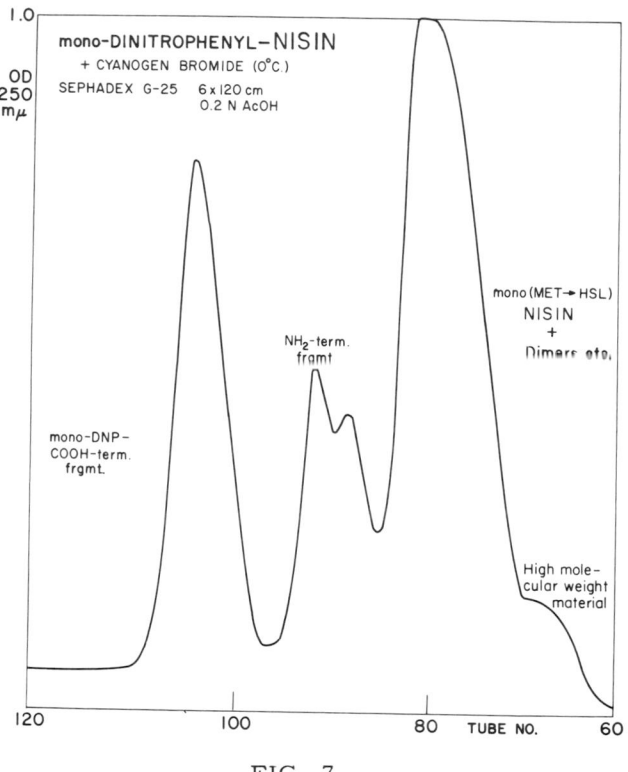

FIG. 7

Separation of Fragments of mono-Dinitrophenylnisin
Resulting from Cleavage with Cyanogen Bromide.
Sephadex G-25, 6 x 120 cm., 0.2 N acetic acid.

was the carrier of the dinitrophenyl group[10]. Since pyruvyllysine may still be released from the mono-dinitrophenylated
COOH-terminal fragment the lysine carrying the dinitrophenyl
group is identified as that of the methionyllysyl peptide bond
(cf. FIGS. 3 and 4).

The presence of α, β -unsaturated amino acids in nisin
imposes a high degree of lability (chemical reactivity) upon

the molecule. One type of possible chemical interaction is

shown in FIGS. 8 and 9. α , β -Unsaturated amino acids may

be degraded with the formation of amides and keto acids.

The reaction is reversible and α , β -unsaturations may be

generated as the result of amide addition to keto groups.

It should be observed that the generation of α , β -unsaturations

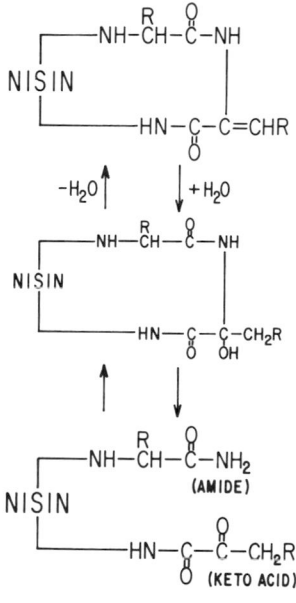

FIG. 8

The Intramolecular Interaction of α , β -Unsaturated Amino
Acids, Keto Acids, and Amides in Nisin.

may proceed in a strictly reversible fashion, i. e. intra-

molecularly. However, new α , β -unsaturations may also

be generated intermolecularly (cf. FIG. 9, where the

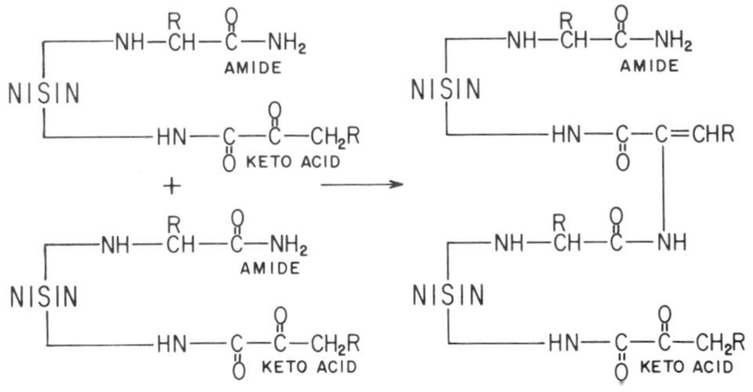

FIG. 9

The Intermolecular Interaction of α , β -Unsaturated Amino Acids, Keto Acids, and Amides in Nisin.

dimerization of two nisin molecules is indicated). The latter interaction explains many observations made in the course of our studies on nisin and demonstrates the significance of amides and keto acids at the peptide and possibly the protein level.

If, for instance, we inspect the distribution pattern of a large amount (1000 mg) of nisin (FIG. 10), we notice a difference in the slopes of the peak of the major component. If we redistribute the material indicated by the cross-hatched area of FIG. 10, we find that the experimental and theoretical curve do not match, the difference in slopes is still present (FIG. 11A). We may redistribute material represented by the right hand half of the curve of FIG. 11A and now find matching experimental and theoretical curves

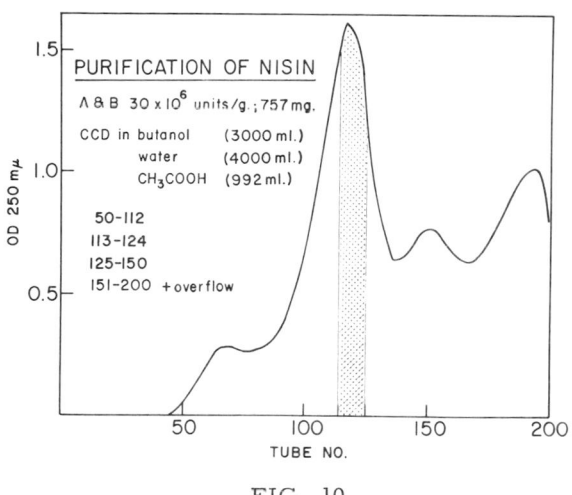

FIG. 10

Purification of Nisin. Counter current distribution; solvent system (v/v): water (2.0), n-butanol (1.5), glacial acetic acid (0.5).

in FIG. 11B. This, however, is misleading. By now, the amount of material has been reduced to such an extent that the differences are no longer observable. If we combined the material of several of the distributions of the type shown in FIG. 11B we would again produce a pattern, reminiscent of that shown in FIG. 11A.

What is the cause of this phenomenon? It is simply the type of interactions discussed earlier, the conversion of α, β -unsaturated amino acids to amides and keto-acids and the regeneration of dehydroalanine and/or β -methyldehydroalanine, either intra- or intermolecularly.

The intermolecular type of interaction is clearly demonstrated by material of the second peak of FIG. 5.

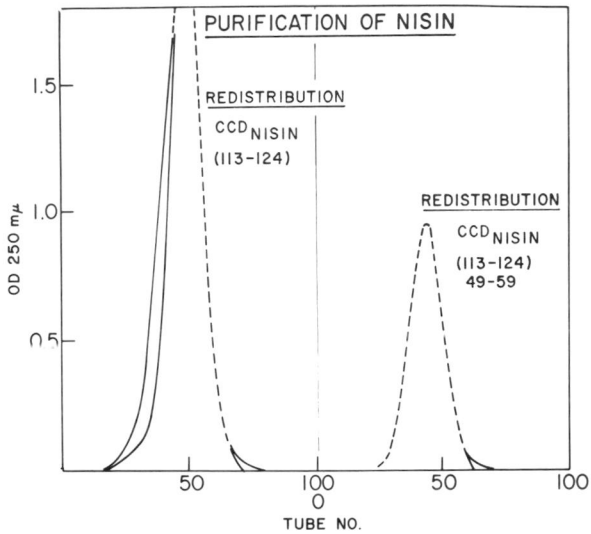

FIG. 11

Purification of Nisin. A. Redistribution of major nisin component (cf. cross-hatched area of Fig. 10).
B. Redistribution of material represented by the right hand half of the peak of A. Solvent system (v/v): water (2.0), n-butanol (1.5), glacial acetic acid (0.5).

Such material was cleaved exhaustively with cyanogen bromide, but eluted still in the same position. Only after treatment with hydrogen chloride in glacial acetic acid (100°C, 100 min.) was it eluted at the volumes of the H_2N-terminal and COOH-terminal fragments and identified as those after counter current distribution.

The ease of peptide bond formation from amides and keto acids, no doubt, is significant in the biosynthesis of antibiotics such as nisin, subtilin, and others of their class. It is interesting that three α, β-unsaturations are preserved in nisin and have not been consumed by mercaptan addition[28]. Whether other nucleophiles are added to dehydroalanine and whether amides are added to other keto acids, followed by reduction, is presently being studied in our laboratory.

Several enzymes containing keto acids[29] have been reported. It will be interesting to see whether the interplay of α, β-unsaturated amino acids, keto acids, and amides extends to proteins.

It was obvious to invoke participation of the α, β-unsaturated amino acids in the mechanism of action of nisin. Malaria parasites are known to depend upon coenzyme A supplied by the host organism. Would nisin be capable of intercepting coenzyme A and deprive the parasite of its vital supply? We are as yet not able to answer this question to its full extent. However, the growth of parasites in mice was greatly reduced when nisin was administered either intraperitoneally or orally.[10]

The structure-function relationship in nisin is not that simple that it is to be answered by the presence of dehydroalanine residues. Other physical parameters are of great significance, among them most likely the presence of lysine. Another impressive demonstration to this effect

is the antobiotic activity of fragments of nisin. The mono-

dinitrophenylated derivative of the COOH-terminal fragment

is more active than the parent molecule.

The two fragments of nisin described here serve

presently as starting material in studies aiming at the

elucidation of the structure of nisin.

REFERENCES

1. a. L. A. Rogers and E. O. Whittier, J. Bact., 16, 211 (1928);
    b. L. A. Rogers, ibid., 16, 321 (1928).

2. A. Fleming, Brit. J. Exptl. Pathol., 10, 226 (1929).

3. A. T. R. Mattick and A. Hirsch, The Lancet, ii, 5 (1947).

4. H. R. Whitehead, Biochem. J., 27, 1793 (1933).

5. N. J. Berridge, G. G. F. Newton, and E. P. Abraham, Biochem. J., 52, 520 (1952).

6. G. G. F. Newton, E. P. Abraham, and N. J. Berridge, Nature, 171, 603 (1953).

7. E. Gross, "The Cyanogen Bromide Reaction", in Methods in Enzymology, C. H. W. Hirs, ed., Academic Press, New York, New York, Vol. XI, p. 238.

8. The action of cyanogen bromide on lanthionine is the subject of a separate study.

9. From Aplin & Barrett, Yeovill, England.

10. E. Gross and J. L. Morell, J. Am. Chem. Soc., 89, 2791 (1967).

11. D. H. Spackman in Serum Proteins and Dysproteinemias, (F. W. Sunderman and F. W. Sunderman, Jr., eds.), Lippincott, Philadelphia, 1964, pp. 166-173.

12. Cf. Mechanism B of the reaction of cyanogen bromide with S-alkylcysteine in the course of which dehydroalanine is formed prior to decomposition to amide and keto acid. E. Gross, J. L. Morell, and P. Q. Lee, Seventh International Congress of Biochemistry, Tokyo, August 1967, Abstracts III, p. 535.

13. H. B. T. Dixon and V. Moret, Biochem. J., 94, 463 (1965).

14. M. Bergmann and K. Grafe, Z. Physiol. Chem., 187, 187 (1930).

15. Cf. mechanism A of ref. 12; studies are presently under way to determine whether this difference in reaction is due to unusual conformation or configuration or has yet other reasons. E. Gross and J. L. Morell, unpublished data.

16. A. Stracher and L. C. Craig, J. Am. Chem. Soc., 81, 696 (1959).

17. E. Gross, J. L. Morell, and L. C. Craig, in preparation.

18. B. Jarvis, J. Gen. Microbiol., 47, 33 (1967).

19. R. Alifax and R. Chevallier, J. Dairy Res., 29, 233 (1962).

20. A. R. Battersby and L. C. Craig, J. Am. Chem. Soc., 74, 4023 (1952).

21. G. C. Cheeseman and N. J. Berridge, Biochem. J., 71, 185 (1959).

22. B. Jarvis, J. Jeffcoat, and G. C. Cheeseman, Biochim. Biophys. Acta, 168, 153 (1968).

23. We are presently exploring conditions for the suppression of the cleavage of the methionyllysyl peptide bond and those of methionine with other basic amino acids.

24. Sequence established by dinitrophenylation and stepwise degradation, E. Gross and J. L. Morell, 1968.

25. There are a second residue of dehydroalanine and one residue of β-methyldehydroalanine. E. Gross and J. L. Morell, publication in preparation.

26. The formation of polymers of nisin and of fragments of nisin will be discussed subsequently.

27. At 0°C the cleavage of the methionyglycyl bond is also slower than at 37°C. This is the reason for the formation of this material. The amount of this material decreases gradually with increasing reaction time. Cleavage of the methionylglycyl bond is complete after 48-60 hours of reaction time.

28. By lanthionine formation; vide infra, the contribution of the α , β -unsaturated amino acids to the activity of nisin.

29. For instance pyruvic acid in D-proline reductase, of cf. D. Hodgins and R. H. Abeles, J. Biol. Chem., 242, 5158 (1967).

SYNTHETIC STUDIES ON TRIS-CYSTINE PEPTIDES

Richard G. Hiskey, Robert L. Smith, A. M. Thomas,
J. T. Sparrow and W. C. Jones, Jr.

Venable Chemical Laboratory
University of North Carolina
Chapel Hill, North Carolina

As part of a long-range program designed to study the role of the sulfur-sulfur bond in natural polypeptides containing cystine, synthetic procedures for the selective formation of disulfide bonds were desirable. Earlier studies[1-4] indicated that the sulfenylthiocyanate method, discovered by Lecher and Wittwer[5], could be applied to the synthesis of cystine derivatives[6]. In these experiments cysteine, the corresponding S-trityl and S-benzhydryl thioether derivatives, or the S-tetrahydropyranylhemithioacetal could be treated with thiocyanogen to provide the intermediate sulfenylthiocyanate. Treatment of the sulfenylthiocyanate with a second thiol or suitably protected cysteine derivative afforded the unsymmetrical cystine peptide. Subsequently[7] the S-isobutyloxymethyl derivatives of cysteine were also found to be converted to sulfenylthiocyanates by the action of thiocyanogen.

$$X-SCN$$

$$Z.\ CyOH \xrightarrow{(SCN)_2} \left[\begin{array}{c} X-SCN \\ + \\ Z.\ CyOH \\ | \\ S-SCN \end{array} \right] \xrightarrow{R-SX} Z.\ Cy-S-S-R + X-SCN$$

(with $Z.\ CyOH$ bearing $S-X$ on the left, and OH on the right)

$$X = -H,\ -C(C_6H_5)_3,\ -CH(C_6H_5)_2, -\langle O \rangle,\ -CH_2OCH_2CH(CH_3)_2$$

The selectivity of the attack of thiocyanogen or sulfenylthiocyanates on various derivatives of cysteine was
examined concurrently. The selective oxidation[2,4] of an
S-trityl-L-cysteine thioether in a peptide containing both
S-benzhydryl and S-trityl-L-cysteine residues indicated the
sulfenylthiocyanate method could be applied to the synthesis
of peptides containing two or more cystine residues.
Additional studies[8] indicated that S-trityl thioether such
as I, could be oxidized with thiocyanogen in the presence of
a preformed disulfide bond to a bis-disulfide, II; disulfide
interchange was not observed in these experiments.

In order to test the sulfenylthiocyanate method with a
somewhat more complex model system, the synthesis of a
tris-cystine derivative containing two cross-linked peptide
chains was attempted. The synthesis of IX involved the
stepwise introduction of three disulfide bridges, and was
considered in four stages: (a) the production of the protected
octapeptide III; (b) the cyclization of III and the synthesis of

$$C_6H_5SH \xrightarrow[\text{2.} \quad HSCH_2CH_2CO_2H]{\text{1.} \quad (SCN)_2} C_6H_5S\text{-}SCH_2CH_2CO_2H$$

$$H_2NCH_2CH_2SC(C_6H_5)_3 \qquad DCC$$

$$C_6H_5S\text{-}SCH_2CH_2\overset{\overset{\displaystyle O}{\|}}{C}NHCH_2CH_2SC(C_6H_5)_3 \longleftarrow$$

I

S-SCN

Z. CyOH

$$\longrightarrow C_6H_5S\text{-}SCH_2CH_2\overset{\overset{\displaystyle O}{\|}}{C}NHCH_2CH_2S\text{-}S\overset{\overset{\displaystyle Z}{|}}{C}yOH$$

II

an "A-chain", VI, containing a preformed disulfide bond and
two cysteine residues of differing reactivity toward thiocyanogen; (c) the formation of the bis-disulfide, VIII, by
reaction of the sulfenylthiocyanate of the "B-chain, VII, with
the S-trityl-L-cysteine residue of VI; and (d) the formation of
the third disulfide bridge by oxidation of the remaining two
S-benzhydryl-L- cysteine residues.

The production[9] of III and the subsequent cyclization with
thiocyanagen[10] provided the cyclic disulfide, IV, in good
overall yield and high purity (FIG. 1). Formation of the
"A-chain", VI, likewise proceeded in reasonable yield. The
preparation of VIII, involved the selective oxidation of the
S-trityl-L-cysteine residue with the sulfenylthiocyanate, VII

```
        STr                    STr
         |                      |
    Z.Cy.Cy.Gly.Phe.Gly.Cy.Phe.GlyO^t Bu
         |
        SBzh       III
                          |  1.  (SCN)_2
                          |  2.  BF_3 ,AcOH
                          ↓

    S ─────────────── S
    |                 |
    Z.Cy.Cy.Gly.Phe.Gly.Cy.Phe.GlyOH
         |
        SBzh

            IV   76%
```

```
        STr                        S ─────────────── S
         |          DCC            |                 |
IV + H.Cy.Gly.ValO^t Bu ──────→  Z.Cy.Cy.Gly.Phe.Gly.Cy.Phe.Gly.Cy.Gly.ValOR
                     C_5H_5N        |                          |
                                   SBzh                       STr

                            VI  a,  R = ^t Bu,  74%
                                b,  R = H,  98%
```

FIG. 1

Synthesis of the A-Chain

(FIG. 2); this operation had precedent in the earlier conversion of I to II using the sulfenylthiocyanate generated from
N-carbobenzoxy-L-cysteine. The reaction product, VIII, was
obtained as a crystalline solid, m. p. 150-151°. No evidence

of disulfide interchange products could be detected by thin
layer chromatography of the reaction mixture; the molecular
weight (osmometric in o-chlorophenol), elemental analysis
and amino acid composition of the substance were consistent
with the formulation as VIII.

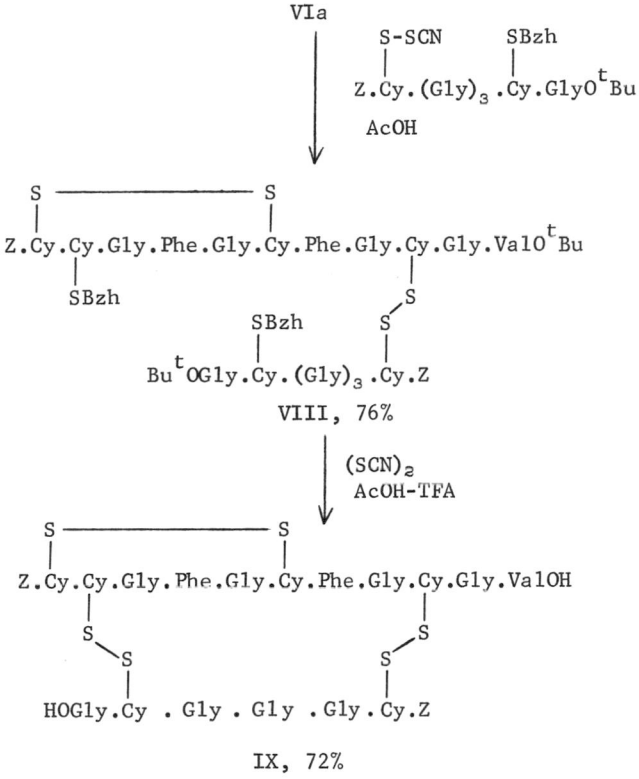

FIG. 2

Combination of A- and B-Chains

Introduction of the third disulfide bond (VIII⟶IX) required the oxidative removal of two S-benzhydryl groups in the presence of the preformed cystine residues. In order to determine the optimum reaction conditions for this conversion the oxidation of X was investigated[11]. When trifluoroacetic acid was employed as a solvent, disulfide interchange occurred and phenyl benzhydryl sulfide was isolated in 81% yield. Using

415

a trifluroacetic acid; acetic acid (1:1 v/v) system, however,

provided the <u>tris</u>-disulfide, XI, in 48% yield with no evidence

of disulfide interchange. Treatment of X with 2-naphthyl-

sulfenylthiocyanate ($R \rightleftharpoons C_{10}H_7$) afforded the bis-disulfide,

XII, in 51% yield; the use of other sulfenylthiocyanates,

generated <u>in situ,</u> gave somewhat lower yields of XII but no

disulfide interchange products could be detected.

$$C_6H_5\text{S-SCH}_2CH_2\overset{\overset{\displaystyle O}{\|}}{C}NHCH_2CH_2SCH(C_6H_5)_2 \xrightarrow{(SCN)_2}$$

X

$$\left[C_6H_5\text{S-SCH}_2CH_2\overset{\overset{\displaystyle O}{\|}}{C}NHCH_2CH_2S \right]_2$$

XI

$$\xrightarrow[\substack{\text{TRA-AcOH} \\ 0^\circ}]{\text{RS-SCN}} \quad C_6H_5\text{S-SCH}_2CH_2\overset{\overset{\displaystyle O}{\|}}{C}NHCH_2CH_2\text{S-SR}$$

XII

When these reaction conditions were applied to VIII, a

single product was obtained in good yield. Analytical evidence

including elemental analysis, amino acid analysis and mole-

cular weight (osmometric in <u>o</u>-chlorophenol) were in agree-

ment with structure IX. Although more rigorous proof of

structure will be required before IX can be regarded as the

correct formulation, the available evidence indicates this

structure. The synthesis of isomeric structures and the

application of the sulfenylthiocyanate method to more

complicated molecules is currently in progress.

SYNTHETIC STUDIES ON TRIS-CYSTINE PEPTIDES

ACKNOWLEDGMENT

This research was supported by grants AM-03416 and GM-07966 from the National Institutes of Health, U.S. Public Health Service. Amino acid analyses were performed by Mrs. M. W. Pendergraft and Mr. J. D. Morrisett. Stimulating discussions with Dr. J. A. Maclaren are gratefully acknowledged.

REFERENCES

1. R. G. Hiskey, F. I. Carroll, R. M. Babb, J. O. Bledsoe, R. T. Puckett and B. W. Roberts, J. Org. Chem., 26 1152 (1961).

2. R. G. Hiskey and W. P. Tucker, J. Am. Chem. Soc., 84, 4794 (1962).

3. R. G. Hiskey, T. Mizoguchi and E. L. Smithwick, Jr., J. Org. Chem., 32, 97 (1967).

4. R. G. Hiskey and E. L. Smithwick, Jr., J. Am. Chem. Soc., 89, 437 (1967).

5. H. Lecher and M. W. Wittwer, Ber. Dtsch. Chem. Ges., 55B, 1474 (1922).

6. A more detailed account of the earlier research and references to important contributions by other workers appears in Proc. Ninth European Peptide Symp., 1968, (E. Bricas, ed.), North Holland, Amsterdam, 1968.

7. R. G. Hiskey amd J. T. Sparrow, J. Org. Chem., in press,(1969).

8. R. G. Hiskey and D. N. Harpp, J. Am. Chem. Soc., 87, 3965 (1965).

9. R. G. Hiskey, J. T. Staples and R. L. Smith, J. Org. Chem., 32, 2772 (1967).

HISKEY ET AL.

10. R. G. Hiskey and R. L. Smith, J. Am. Chem. Soc., 90, 2677 (1968).

11. R. G. Hiskey and M. A. Harpold, Tetrahedron, 23, 3923 (1967).

SYNTHESIS OF ACTINOMYCIN D (C_1)

J. Meienhofer, Y. Sano, and R. P. Patel

The Children's Cancer Research Foundation,
The Children's Hospital Medical Center, and
Harvard Medical School, Boston, Massachusetts

Actinomycins are peptide antibiotics. They are some of the
most potent antitumor agents known. S. Farber initiated the use
of actinomycin D as an addition to x-ray treatment and surgery
in the therapy of Wilms' tumor, a kidney tumor prevalent in
young children. After an eight year period of Wilms' tumor
therapy in the Children's Cancer Research Foundation, Farber
reported cures in 89% of the patients who were treated by a
combination therapy of actinomycin D, irradiation and surgery,
in contrast to the previous 40% of cures when x-ray therapy
and surgery were available alone[1]. The very high toxicity of
the antibiotic has unfortunately prevented its wide clinical use
in the treatment of other tumors. It would therefore be very
desirable to develop a modified actinomycin with an improved
therapeutic index.

Actinomycin inhibits DNA controlled RNA synthesis, and
subsequently protein synthesis, through specific binding to
deoxyguanosine residues within the DNA double helix of the

cell nucleus[2]. The strength of this binding to DNA is con-

trolled - in yet unknown ways - by the pentapeptide lactones,

and it is correlated with the activity[3]. For this reason, and

because none of a large number of actinomycin derivatives

prepared by Brockmann and collaborators[4] through chromo-

phore substitution showed an improved therapeutic index, we

decided to synthesize peptide analogues and evaluate structure/

binding relationships.

The structure of actinomycin D (C_1)[5] is shown in FIG. 1.

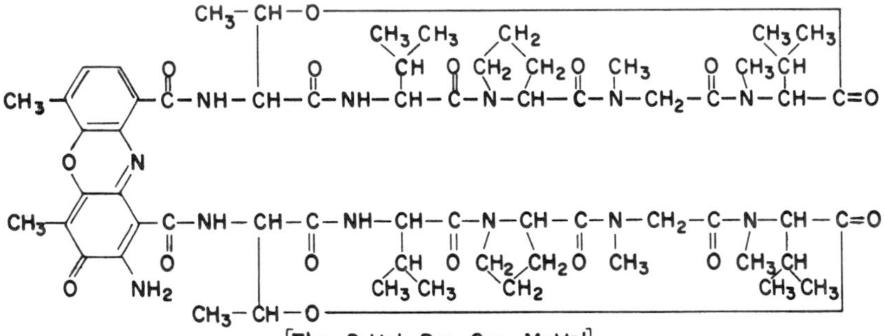

[Thr—D-Val—Pro—Sar—MeVal]

FIG. 1

Structure of actinomycin D (C_1) [6,7]

It consists of a phenoxazinone moiety (2-amino-4, 6-dimethyl-

phenoxazine-3-one-9, 11-bis-carbonyl) which is often referred

to as the "chromophore". Attached to it by amide bonds in

positions 9 and 11 are two identical cyclic pentapeptide lac-

tones with the amino acid sequence L-threonyl-D-valyl-L-

prolyl-sarcosyl-L-N-methylvalyl. The lactone rings are

closed between the C-terminal carboxyl group of N-methylvaline and the sec-hydroxyl group of threonine. The occurrence of three imino acids (Pro, Sar, MeVal) in sequence is
very remarkable.

To develop a synthetic pathway which would be useful for
preparative purposes, it was first necessary to synthesize a
parent natural actinomycin, and to evaluate the efficiency of
the synthesis on the basis of the known physicochemical and
biological characteristics. Much excellent work has been
done by Brockmann and collaborators who carried out several
total syntheses of actinomycins C_1[8] and C_3[9]. The key
step, ring closure to form the cyclic pentapeptide lactones,
was achieved either by peptide bond formation between sarcosine and N-methylvaline, or by lactonization of the pentapeptide chain using acetylchloride/acetylimidazole.

Some of our approaches for the synthesis of actinomycin
D are outlined below. We encountered many failures (due
perhaps to steric hindrance) during standard operations and
some of these will be pointed out.

Syntheses of actinomycinic acid[10] and its t-butyl ether-t-
butyl ester derivative are outlined in FIG. 2. It is known
that derivatives of N-methylamino acids are difficult to
crystallize and indeed many intermediates were obtained

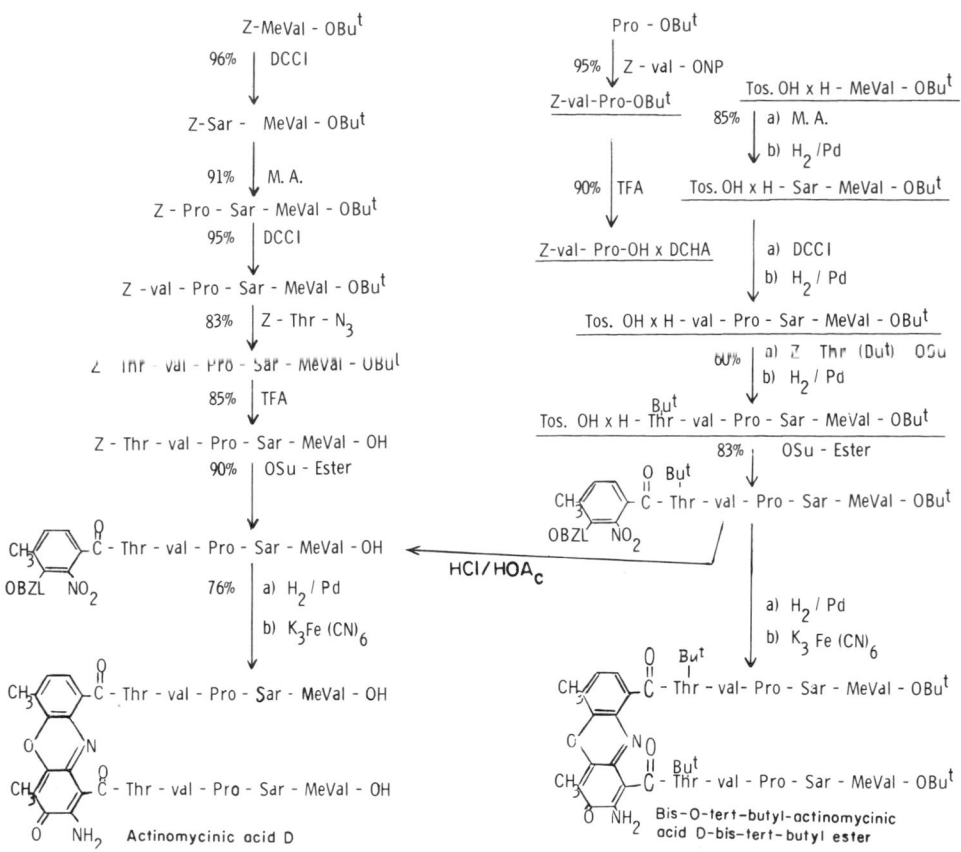

FIG. 2
Synthesis of actinomycinic acid D[10]

as oils only and had to be purified by countercurrent distribution. Attempts to cyclize by lactonization using various
reagents failed to yield more than 1-3% of actinomycin[11].

In subsequent approaches (FIG. 3) we planned to utilize
another of Brockmann's strategies, namely, ring closure by
peptide bond formation between sarcosine and N-methylvaline.

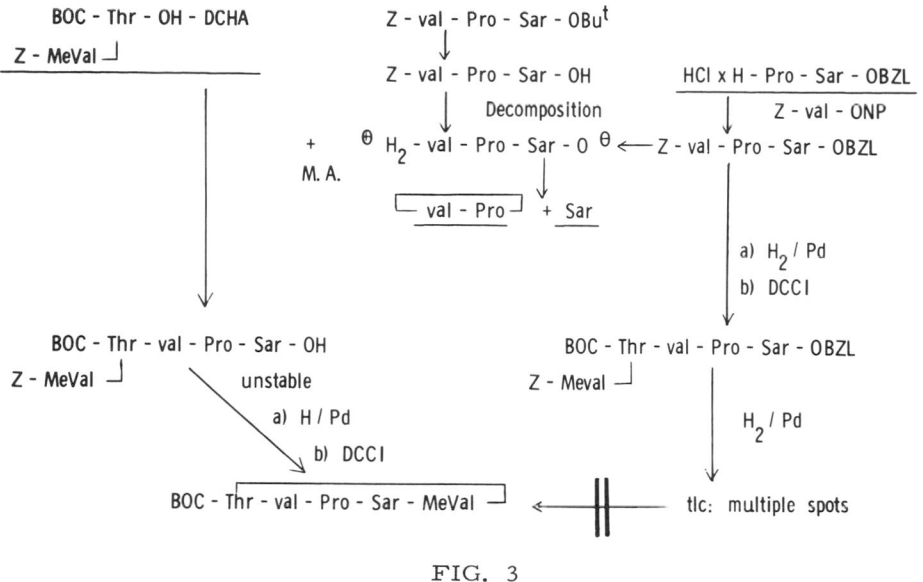

FIG. 3

Synthetic approaches employing ring closure between sarcosine
and N-methylvaline

Employing a tactic used by Ondetti for the synthesis of
vernamycin[12], Boc-Thr-OH was esterfied by the mixed
anhydride formed between Z-MeVal-OH and isobutylchloroformate. Two penta-β -depsipeptide derivatives were prepared.
Catalytic hydrogenation of O-(benzyloxycarbonyl-L-N-methylvalyl)-N-t-butyloxycarbonyl-L-threonyl-D-valyl-L-prolyl-
sarcosine-benzyl ester, using palladium black under
standard conditions, failed in a variety of solvents to go to
completion. Even after prolonged periods of time four major
fractions remained as shown by thin layer chromatography.
From O-(benzyloxycarbonyl-L-N-methylvalyl)-N-tert-
butyloxycarbonyl-L-threonyl-D-valyl-L-prolyl-sarcosine

the desired Boc-pentapeptide-lactone was obtained using
dicyclohexylcarbodiimide. However the yield was so low[13]
that this approach was abandoned.

Furthermore another complication arose with the tripeptide D-valyl-L-prolyl-sarcosine. It was prepared via two
different routes and obtained as a colorless oil, which gave
a correct elementary analysis and was found to be homogeneous by thin layer chromatography. Spontaneous crystallization of sarcosine was observed when the oil stood for
three weeks at room temperature in a closed flask. The
remaining material was ninhydrin negative and contained
valine and proline. It was apparently valyl-prolyl-diketo-
piperazine. The formation of diketopiperazines from
tripeptides, usually at elevated temperatures, has been
reported[14-16]. The spontaneous formation of D-valyl-L-
prolyl-diketopiperazine at room temperature suggests that
steric interaction of the pyrolidine ring of proline, the
bulky side chain of valine, and the N-methyl group of
sarcosine forces the C- and N-termini of D-valyl-L-prolyl-
sarcosine into close proximity, as shown in FIG. 4.
A very small amount of free amino function in equilibrium with
the zwitterion would attack the carbonyl carbon of the prolyl
moiety. The intermediate "semi-cyclol" would either reform
the tripeptide or split off sarcosine, thus forming the diketopiperazine.

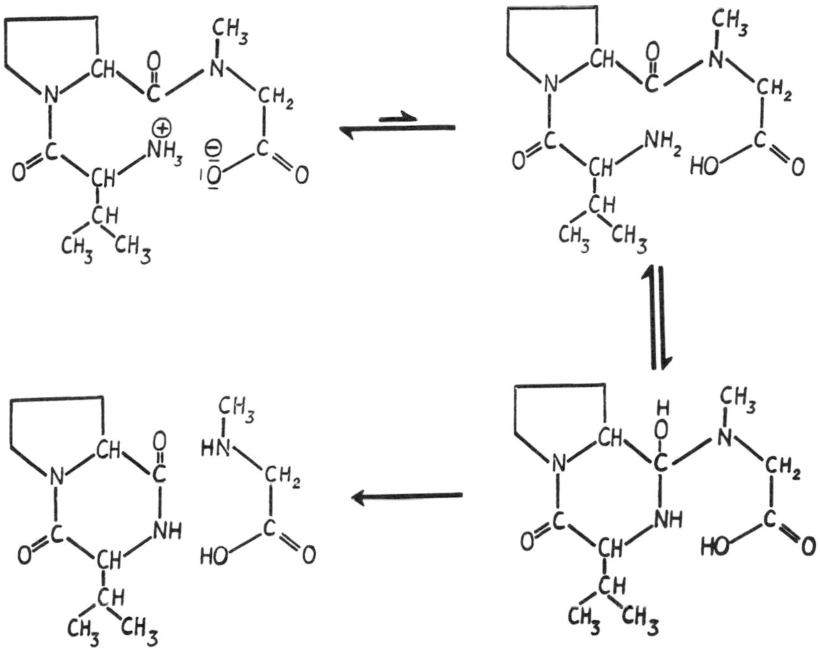

FIG. 4

Diketopiperazine formation from D-valyl-L-prolyl-sarcosine.

FIG. 5 outlines our successful synthesis of actinomycin D[17]. Attempts to improve the purity of O-(benzyloxycarbonyl-L-N-methylvalyl)-N-t-butyloxycarbonyl-L-threonine by prolonged countercurrent distribution failed. A multiplicity of peaks developed, resulting in rapidly decreasing recovery of the main product. The distribution system (toluene-chloroform-methanol-water, 5:5:8:2 [18]) contained methanol which might have caused transesterification. Catalytic hydrogenation of the above β-didepsipeptide derivative afforded the zwitterionic

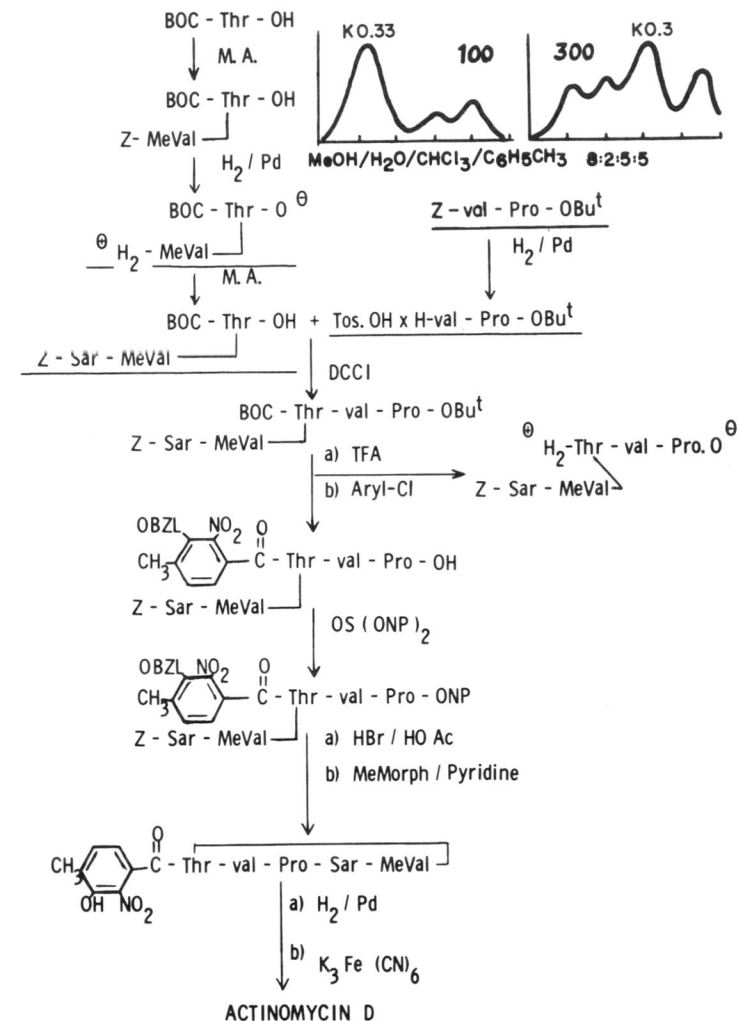

FIG. 5

Synthesis of actinomycin D via peptide cyclization between proline and sarcosine[17]

O-(L-N-methylvalyl)-N-t-butyloxycarbonyl-L-threonine
which crystallized readily and proved to be very stable
(m. p. 207°). Quantitative removal of the t- butyloxycarbonyl
and the t-butyl ester groups from O-(benzyloxycarbonyl-sarcosyl-L-N-methylvalyl)-N-t-butyloxycarbonyl-L-threonyl-D-
valyl-L-proline-t-butyl ester was achieved by treatment with
4 N HCl in dioxane for 3 hours at room temperature. Cleavage
by either trifluoroacetic acid or HCl in acetic acid remained
incomplete, even after many hours. The cyclization was
carried out with 30 - 31% yield via the nitrophenyl ester
method[19]. Subsequent hydrogenation and oxidation (with
$K_3Fe(CN)_6$ to form the chromophore[20]) afforded crystalline
actinomycin D in 80% yield, which was indistinguishable from
natural actinomycin D in its physiochemical characteristics
and its antimicrobial activity. Sephadex LH-20 chromatography
with methanol or ethyl acetate as eluents, proved to be a
powerful technique essential for the success of our synthesis,
especially for the purification of the pentapeptide derivatives.

The preparation of the p-nitrophenyl ester, namely, O-
(benzyloxycarbonyl-sarcosyl-L-N-methylvalyl)-N-(2-nitro-3-
benzyloxy-4-methyl-benzoyl)-L-threonyl-D-valyl-L-proline-
p-nitrophenyl ester, by the use of the p-nitrophenol/dicyclo-
hexylcarbodiimide method gave a low yield of impure product
containing three contaminants in almost equal amounts. Known

side products of carbodiimide reactions are, among others:
N-acylurea derivatives, symmetrical anhydrides and dehydration products[21]. However, by using di-p-nitrophenyl sulfite
in pyridine[22], and applying Sephadex LH-20/ethyl acetate
chromatography, an analytically pure p-nitrophenyl ester
derivative was obtained in 90% yield.

This considerable improvement in recovery and purity of the
above peptide-p-nitrophenyl ester derivative, prompted us
to reexamine the preparation of some acylamino acid-p-nitro-
phenyl esters, which could not previously be isolated or were
obtained as oils only. In a typical preparation, the acylamino
acid in pyridine was reacted with di-p-nitrophenyl sulfite for
1 to 3 hr at room temperature, the solvent removed in vacuo,
the residue dissolved in ethyl acetate, the solution washed with
1 M NaHCO$_3$, 1 M HCl or citric acid, and saline, and dried
over MgSO$_4$. The solution was then concentrated and placed
on a Sephadex LH-20 column. Elution with ethyl acetate,
removal of the solvent[5] and recrystallization afforded the
crystalline p-nitrophenyl esters listed below[23]: benzyloxy-
carbonyl-L-threonine-p-nitrophenyl ester** [69%, m. p.
93-95°,$[\alpha]_D^{20}$ -20.2° (c 1, dimethylformamide/1% acetic
acid); Lit.[24]: m. p. 93-95°,$[\alpha]_D^{22}$ -24° (c 2, dimethyl-
formamide/1% acetic acid); t-butyloxycarbonyl-L-threonine-
p-nitrophenyl ester**[59%, m. p. 98-100°, $[\alpha]_D^{20}$ -40°

(c 1, dimethylformamide/1% acetic acid); $\underline{t}$-butyloxycarbonyl-L-tyrosine-$\underline{p}$-nitrophenyl ester [57%, m. p. 162-164°, $[\alpha]_D^{20}$-7° (c, 1, dimethylformamide/1% acetic acid)] ; $\underline{t}$-butyloxycarbonyl-sarcosine-$\underline{p}$-nitrophenyl ester [59%, m. p. 46°]; $\underline{t}$-butyloxycarbonyl-L-glutamine-$\underline{p}$-nitrophenyl ester** [66%, m. p. 150-152°, $[\alpha]_D^{24}$ -41° (c 2, methanol); Lit. [25]): m. p. 145-146°, $[\alpha]_D^{22}$ -31° (c 1, ethyl acetate)] ; N-$\underline{t}$-butyloxycarbonyl-L-nitroarginine-$\underline{p}$-nitrophenyl ester* [35%, m. p. 126-128°, $[\alpha]_D^{20}$-30° (c 1, dimethylformamide/1% acetic acid)] ; and $\underline{p}$-toluenesulfonyl-L-valine-$\underline{p}$-nitrophenyl ester** [60%, m. p. 99-101°] . All compounds gave correct elementary analyses. $\underline{p}$-Nitrophenyl esters of N-tosylamino acids have not been reported in the literature before [26) and we therefore corroborated the identity of Tos-Val-ONP by converting it in good yield into the known tosyl-L-valyl-L-valine methyl ester[27).

The easy preparation of "difficult" $\underline{p}$-nitrophenyl esters with di-$\underline{p}$-nitrophenyl sulfite led us to try a more direct esterification. Thionyl chloride was added to pyridine at -40°, followed by a solution of $\underline{p}$-nitrophenol in tetrahydrofuran. After stirring for 1 - 2 hr at room temperature a solution of the acylamino acid in pyridine was added, the mixture stirred for 2 hr, and then worked up. Thus the following derivatives were obtained with physical data identical to those in the literature: t-butyloxycarbonyl-L-phenylalanine-p-nitrophenyl ester (78%), t-butyloxycarbonyl-L-proline-p-nitrophenyl ester (86%), benzyloxycarbonyl-L-alanine-p-nitrophenyl ester (88%); and also benzyloxycarbonyl-L-alanine-N-hydroxysuccinimide ester (77%), and benzyloxycarbonyl-L-alanine-pentachlorophenyl ester (51%) using N-hydroxysuccinimide and pentachlorophenyl in pyridine, respectively . For the preparation of p-nitrophenyl esters of trifunctional amino acids the use of the pre-isolated di-p-nitrophenyl sulfite was superior to the in situ method.

In conclusion, I should like to mention our analogue program. As pointed out in the beginning, our main effort will be the preparation and biological evaluation of peptide analogues of actinomycin. We are engaged at present in syntheses of actinomycin D lactam and thiolactone (see FIG. 6). To prepare isosteric analogues, α , β -diaminobutyric acid and α -amino-β -mercaptobutyric acid have to be employed. Both are not commercially available. L-α , β -Diaminobutyric acid was prepared as outlined in FIG. 6.

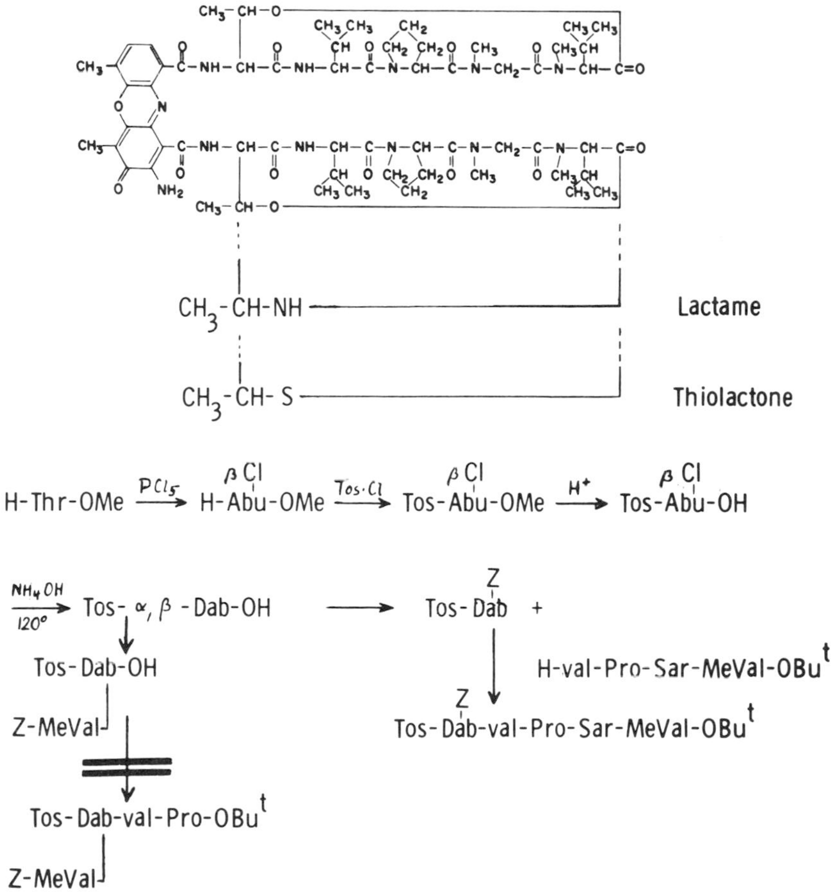

FIG. 6

Synthetic approaches toward the synthesis of actinomycin D
lactam

ACKNOWLEDGMENTS

The authors wish to thank Dr. S. Farber for his support of this work, Dr. C. H. Li and Dr. V. du Vigneaud for helpful discussions, Dr. G. E. Foley for the microbiological assays, and Mrs. A. Drischer-Fabis, Mrs. A. Seki-Viano, Mrs. E. Judkins, Mr. R. Cotton, and Mr. A. Trzeciak for technical help. This work was supported in part by Public Health Service research grants (C-6516 from the National Cancer Institute and FR-05526 from the Division of Research Facilities and Resources, National Institutes of Health), Albert and Mary Lasker Foundation, New York, N. Y. , and A. T. and V. D. Fuller Cancer Research Unit Grant, American Cancer Society (Massachusetts Division) Inc.

REFERENCES

1. S. Farber, J. Amer. Med. Assoc., 198, 826 (1966).

2. E. Reich and I. H. Goldberg, Progr. Nucleic Acid Research, 3, 183 (1964).

3. E. Reich, I. H. Goldberg, and M. Rabinowitz, Nature, 196, 743 (1962).

4. H. Brockmann, P. Hocks, and W. Muller, Chem. Ber., 100, 1051 (1967); H. Brockmann, J. Ammann, and W. Muller, Tetrahedron Letters, 3595 (1966); H. Brockmann and F. Seela, Tetrahedron Letters, 4803 (1965).

5. Designation D is according to L. C. Vining and S. A. W Waksman, Science, 120, 389 (1954); designation C_1 is according to H. Brockmann and H. Grone, Naturwissenschaften, 41, 65 (1954).

6. H. Brockmann, G. Bohnsack, B. Franck, H. Grone, H. Muxfeldt, and C. Suling, Angew. Chem., 68, 70 (1956).

7. E. Bullock and A. W. Johnson, J. Chem. Soc., 1602, 3280 (1957).

8. H. Brockmann and H. Lackner, Chem. Ber., 101, 1312 (1968); Naturwissenschaften, 51, 435 (1964); 51, 384 (1964).

9. H. Brockmann and H. Lackner, Chem. Ber., 100, 353 (1967); Naturwissenschaften, 48, 555 (1961); 47, 230 (1960).

10. J. Meienhofer, J. Org. Chem., 32 1143 (1967).

11. After experimental details of the acetylchloride/acetyl-imidazole method became known (H. Brockmann, private communication; reference 8 we obtained lactonization in good yield.

12. M. A. Ondetti and P. L. Thomas, J. Amer. Chem. Soc., 87, 4373 (1965).

13. We obtained about 3%; Brockmann and Lackner[9] reported 3.4% of cyclization by a mixed anhydride procedure.

14. J. C. Sheehan and D. N. McGregor, J. Amer. Chem. Soc., 84, 3000 (1962).

15. E. Wunsch, in Proc. Fifth European Symposium, (G. T. Young, ed., Pergamon Press, Oxford, London, 1963), pp. 89-91.

16. H. Hartmann and R. Brussau, Z. Naturforsch, 22B, 380 (1967).

17. J. Meienhofer, Experientia, 24, 776 (1968).

18. C. H. Li, J. Meienhofer, E. Schnabel, D. Chung, T.-B. Lo, and J. Ramachandran, J. Amer. Chem. Soc., 82, 5760 (1960); 83, 4449 (1961).

19. R. Schwyzer and P. Sieber, Helv. Chim. Acta., 40, 624 (1957).

20. W. G. Hanger, W. C. Howell, and A. W. Johnson, J. Chem. Soc., 496 (1958).

21. H. Zahn and J. F. Diehl, Z. Naturforsch., 12B, 85 (1957); E. Schnabel, Ann., 688, 238 (1965); C. Ressler, J. Amer. Chem. Soc., 78, 5956 (1956).

22. B. Iselin, W. Rittel, P. Sieber, and R. Schwyzer, Helv. Chim. Acta, 40, 373 (1957).

23. Yields are not optimal, since the nitrophenyl esters have been prepared once or twice only; *: washing of the ethyl acetate solution with acid and saline only; **: crystallized directly without LH-20 chromatography.

24. M. Bodansky and M. A. Ondetti, Chem. and Ind., 26 (1966).

25. H. Zahn, W. Danho, and B. Gutte, Z. Naturforsch, 21B, 763(1966).

26. C. Berse, T. Massiah, and L. Piche, J. Org. Chem., 26, 4514 (1961); E. Schroder and K. Lubke, The Peptides, Academic Press, New York, 1965, p. 100.

27. J. W. Hinman, E. L. Caron, and H. Christensen, J. Amer. Chem. Soc., 72, 1620 (1950).

γ -GLUTAMYL PEPTIDES

D. E. Nitecki and J. W. Goodman

Department of Microbiology
University   of California School of Medicine
San Francisco, California

The primary aim of this investigation was to obtain some information about the region on a protein antigen involved in reaction with antibody. One approach to this problem is to use the hapten inhibition technique. Reduced to its simpler terms, this can be described as follows. It is believed that an antibody molecule combines with only a small portion of a large protein antigen, designated the determinant group. Of course, a single protein antigen usually possesses at least several determinant groups, which contribute to the heterogeneity in the population of antibodies produced. If the antiserum is combined with a solution of the antigen, a precipitin reaction occurs, the magnitude of which can be determined by analyzing the amount of protein precipitated. However, if prior to such combination the antibody is exposed to a small molecule simulating the determinant group of the original antigen, this small molecule, or hapten, will be bound to antibody by essentially the same forces as the original antigen, and if the

hapten is sufficiently small no precipitation will occur. If
the original antigen is added to this antibody-hapten complex,
the precipitin reaction will be partially or entirely inhibited,
depending on the efficiency of the hapten. Thus, from the
relative efficiencies of a number of haptens tested, one may
deduce some information about the requirements of the
combining site of the antibody, such as the charges involved,
the size of the combining site, the hydrophobic areas, the
configurational requirements, etc. This, in turn, allows
some deductions concerning the determinant group in the
original antigen.

Kabat, in 1958[1], published one such investigation involving
a dextran-antidextran immunological system. Dextran is a
polymer of glucose, and by using oligosaccharides as haptens
Kabat found a progressive increase in hapten efficiency from
monosaccharide to heptasaccharide; larger haptens did not
show additional activity. Thus, it seems that the combining
site of the antibody molecule can accommodate no more than
a hexa- or hepta-saccharide, and, by the same token, this
is probably the maximum extent of the determinant group in
the dextran antigen.

This experimental approach can also be applied to immunological systems involving protein antigens. However, two
important complicating features appear here. First, the
exact composition and amino acid sequence of the antigen

must be specified. Secondly, the influence of the conformation (tertiary structure) of the determinant group as it
exists in the physiological medium while eliciting the antibody must be taken into account. Even if the exact primary
structure can be unraveled, there is very little definite
information available as yet about the conformation. Clearly,
a systematic choice of haptens for such complex systems
presents, at least at present, a very difficult task. This
difficulty has been partially circumvented by the selection
of polypeptide antigens of simplified structure, such as
synthetic amino acid polymers. These systems are at
present severely hampered by the lack of clear-cut information as to what makes a synthetic polypeptide immunogenic.
However, a number of successful inhibiting systems
employing oligopeptides of graded molecular size as haptens
have been demonstrated[2]. All these findings point to a
limited, well-defined area of the antibody molecule which can
accommodate haptens only up to a certain size, after which
increases in hapten size do not increase inhibitory efficiency.

In our investigation, the antigen used was poly- γ -D-
glutamic acid, produced as a capsule by Bacillus anthracis.
Antibodies can be produced in rabbits to this simple polypeptide composed of a single amino acid.

This immunological system has been extensively investigated for some twenty years by a Hungarian group[3,4],

D. E. NITECKI AND J. W. GOODMAN

and the structure of the polypeptide has been well established.
It has been shown that it is a γ-polypeptide by several schemes
of chemical degradation[4-7]. While none of these reactions
go to completion, in no case were any products found which
would arise from α-peptide bonds in the anthrax polymer.

Table 1 shows some of the results of the work done in our
laboratory[8]. The obvious choice of heptens for this system
are peptides of glutamic acid.

TABLE 1

Properties of Capsular Polypeptide Isolated

from __B. anthracis__ Strain M-36

Constituents (%)	
Glutamic acid	$\geqq 99.0$
Other amino acids	< 0.5
Hexose	< 0.5
Specific optical rotation of	-29.8
hydrolysate (deg)	
Molecular weight	$33,500 \pm 3800$

All eight possible dipeptides and four tripeptides of glutamic acid were synthesized[9] by the classical method. To
obtain higher oligopeptides, hydrolysis of anthrax polypeptide was undertaken. It was found that incubation in 3 N
hydrochloric acid for six days at room temperature results
in degradation of this polypeptide to glutamic acid and a

series of small peptides. The peptides were resolved by

high voltage electrophoresis on diethyl amino ethyl (DEAE)

cellulose sheets. FIG. 1 shows one such electropherogram

at pH 3.5. For preparative isolation, the hydrolysate was

streaked on DEAE cellulose sheets, electrophoresed at

pH 3.5, and guide slips developed with ninhydrin. Individual

bands were then eluted from the sheets, lyophilized, and

rechromatographed on a carboxymethyl cellulose column.

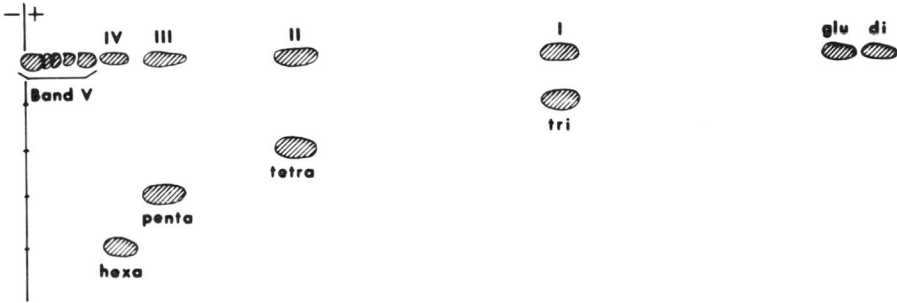

FIG. 1

Electropherogram of hydrolyzed anthrax polypeptide and
synthetic γ-glutamyl peptides; on DEAE cellulose, pH 3.5,
35 v/cm.

In this way, 40 - 50 mg of each of four peptides (bands

I - IV) were isolated[10]. Band V is obviously a mixture of

higher peptides. The identity of each peptide was established

by comparison with synthetic γ-glutamyl peptides and by

the quantitative ratio of the reactions of each peptide

before and after hydrolysis with ninhydrin and with 2, 4, 6-
trinitrobenzene sulfonic acid. When band V was eluted and
electrophoresed on DEAE-cellulose sheets at pH 1.85,
further separation could effected. The electrophoretic
pattern is shown in FIG. 2. It was possible to isolate peptides up to decapeptide (band 9). These bands also gave the

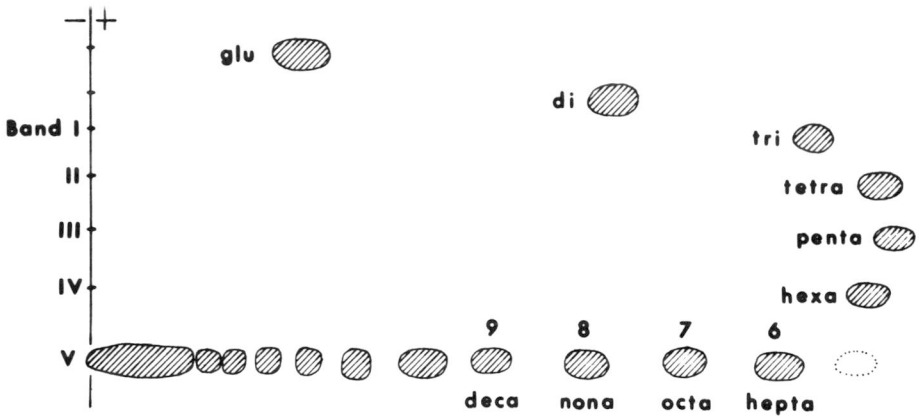

FIG. 2

Electropherogram of hydrolysis products of anthrax polypeptide; on DEAE cellulose, pH 1.85, 35 v/cm.

expected ninhydrin ratio before and after hydrolysis. FIG.
3 illustrates the inhibition of the precipitin reaction of these
peptides.

A synthetic scheme was undertaken for the synthesis of
higher γ-glutamyl peptides as well as for various modifications that would be desirable to build into these haptens.

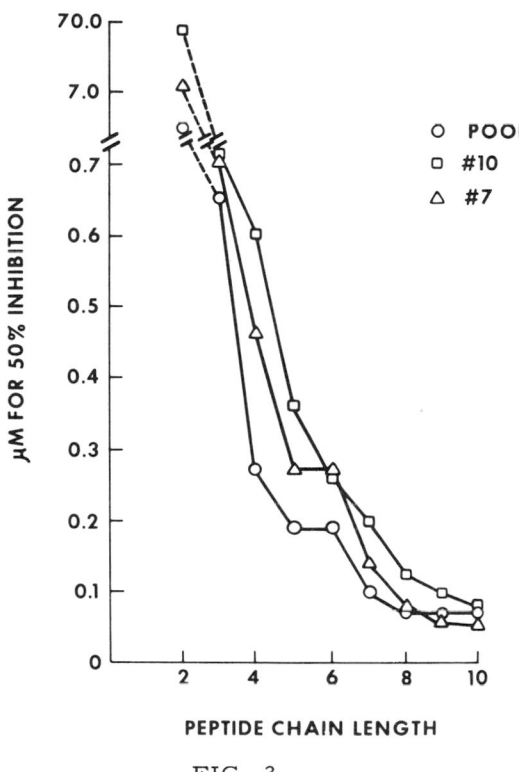

FIG. 3

Inhibition by homologous di- to decapeptides of the quantitative precipitin reaction between poly-γ-D-glutamic acid and
three rabbit antisera; O: serum pool from rabbits immunized
with killed B. anthracis; △ and ▱ : individual animals immunized
with polypeptide-methylated albumin complexes.

For this purpose solid phase synthesis of γ-glutamyl peptides

was chosen. In all cases the polymer used was from a single

batch of Bio-Rad X-2 polymer, containing 1.5 meq. of

chlorine per gram of polymer. Some forty hydrolyses were

done under various conditions of the esterification step with

the first glutamic acid derivative. The results were between

25-35% of complete reaction, yielding 0.35-0.50 meq of glutamic acid per gram of polymer. As monomers, t-boc-D-glutamic α -benzyl ester and α -p-nitrobenzyl ester were used. The synthesis of the latter goes through a t-boc-glutamic anhydride which is reacted with p-nitro-benzyl alcohol. This reaction invariably gives both esters, α and γ , but the α -ester can be easily separated by crystallization[11]. The purity of the monomers was investigated by high voltage electrophoresis as well as by TLC on silica gel, using a Clorox peptide spray for detection[9]. Investigation of steric purity by gas chromatography[12] showed little or no racemization.

In attempted syntheses of tri- and tetrapeptides, several byproducts were obtained, as shown on DEAE cellulose sheets. These byproducts did not correspond to the expected shorter peptide chains.

It is generally believed that γ -glutamyl peptide bonds are somewhat more labile to various hydrolytic agents than α -peptide bonds. In order to test the stability of γ -peptides, fully blocked γ -tetra and pentapeptides synthesized by classical methods were obtained (Fox Chemical Co.). These N-carbobenzoxy benzyl ester derivatives were subjected to various acid reagents used in solid phase synthesis for the total length of time that a pentapeptide would spend in these reagents. FIG. 4 shows TLC patterns on silica gel of the two blocked peptides treated with trifluoroacetic acid. Similar results were obtained when the same fully blocked peptides were subjected to 1N HCl in acetic acid for several hours. When these fully blocked peptides were kept in acids for designated times and then hydrogenated, there was little, if any, peptide bond destruction. Therefore, the effect of acids must essentially be removal of benzyl esters, not cleavage of peptide bonds.

When free γ-tetra and pentapeptides were treated under conditions of cleavage for 1.5 hrs, some destruction did take place; therefore, treatment with HBr was limited to 30 min. Considerably more destruction occurred when the fully blocked γ-pentapeptide was treated with 4N HCl in dioxane, including some peptide bond cleavage.

After ascertaining that peptide bond cleavage does not occur during the synthesis of the peptide or its cleavage from the polymer, a γ-decapeptide was synthesized by the solid phase method. Acetylation was performed after every coupling step in order to facilitate removal of byproducts due to incomplete coupling. The product, after hydrogenation, was subjected to electrophoresis on DEAE cellulose paper at pH 3.5, as shown in FIG. 5. There were no peptides smaller than about a hexapeptide in appreciable amounts.

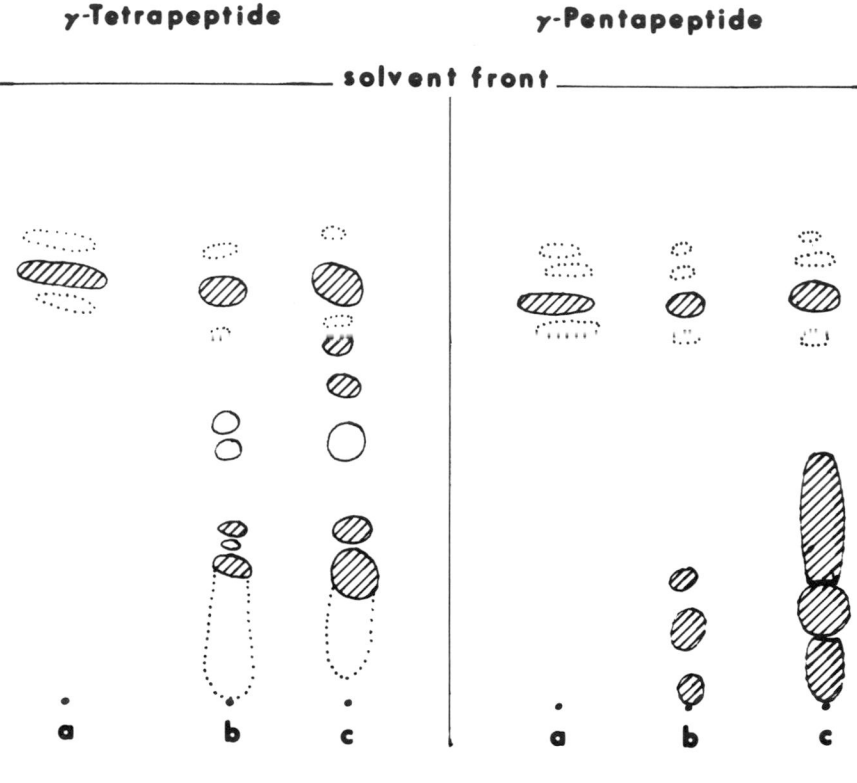

FIG. 4

TLC of fully protected glutamyl peptides treated with trifluoroacetic acid; (a) original peptide, (b) 2 hrs in TFA,
(c) 5 hrs in TFA. Solvent: chloroform - acetic acid, 95.5.

Electrophoresis on Whatman #1 and on DEAE cellulose

paper at pH 1.85 revealed a mixture with a predominant

decapeptide spot. One cannot use a Clorox spray on DEAE

cellulose sheets, but it is possible to do so on Whatman #1;

this reagent gave results identical to that obtained with

ninhydrin. If acetic anhydride can react with any amino

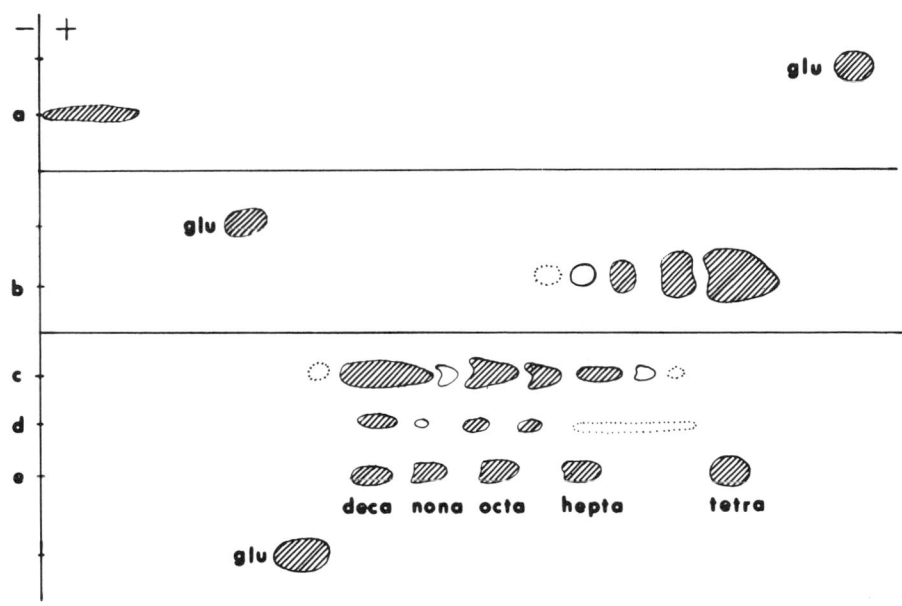

FIG. 5

Electropherogram of γ-glutamyl decapeptide preparation,
35 v/cm; (a) on DEAE cellulose, pH 3.5 (b) on Whatman #1,
pH 3.5; (c,d) on DEAE cellulose, pH 1.85, at two concentrations; (e) a mixture of γ-glutamyl peptides from anthrax
hydrolyzate.

groups that did not completely react in the coupling step,

acetylated peptides, especially acetylated shorter peptides,

should result from incomplete coupling. As the Clorox

spray is considerably more sensitive than ninhydrin, and

since both sprays gave identical patterns, this indicated

that the problems may be due to incomplete deprotection

rather than incomplete coupling. It was rather surprising

that the electrophoretic pattern of the byproducts did not

correspond to the expected pattern for a mixture of progressively shorter peptides from γ-decapeptide to the tetrapeptide, as obtained from hydrolysis of the anthrax polypeptide.

In order to get some insight into the efficienty of various conditions which can be used for solid phase synthesis, four γ-pentapeptides were synthesized. For all of these, the starting material and the same t-boc-glutamic acid α-p-nitrobenzyl ester was used for assembling the peptides. The deprotecting reagent and the carbodiimide were varied while other conditions were kept as identical as possible. The results of these syntheses are shown in FIG. 6 and it is impossible to draw any conclusions about the "best method", all of these products are about equally unsatisfactory. The same peptides are shown in FIG. 7 electrophoresed on Whatman #1 and, for example, the c preparation shows only two major products whereas on DEAE cellulose four major components were resolved.

FIG. 8 shows that pentapeptide preparation c(FIGS. 6 and 7) did not contain the expected shorter byproducts, i.e., γ-tetrapeptide or γ-tripeptide. Thus it seens that new additional products are formed. There is a distinct possibility that these products are the result of transpeptidation. Trans-peptidation reactions are known to occur with activated

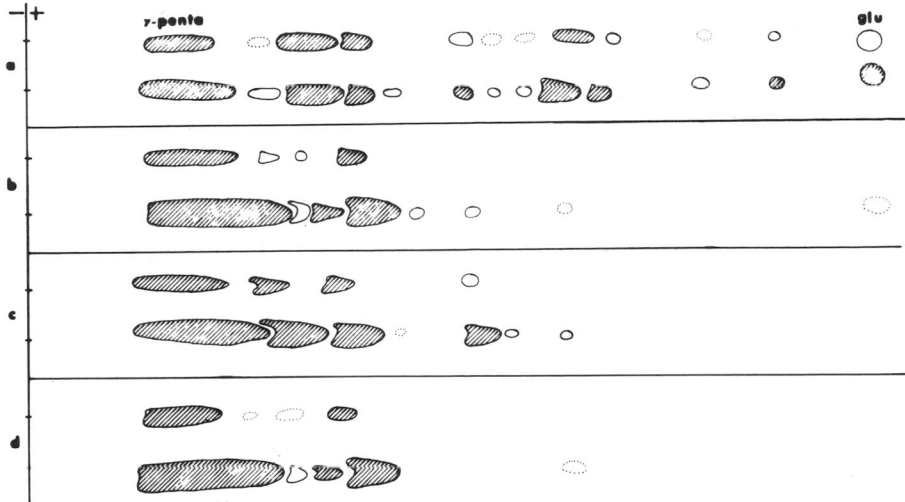

FIG. 6

Electropherogram of four preparations of γ-glutamyl pentapeptide shown at two concentrations each; on DEAE cellulose,
pH 3.5, 35 v/cm. Deprotection: (a, d) in 4N HCl/dioxane;
(b, c) in 1 N HCl/acetic acid. Coupling: (a, b) dicyclohexylcarbodiimide; (c, d) N-ethyl, N'-(3-dimethylaminopropyl)
carbodiimide.

carboxylic acid derivatives of glutamic acid[13]. It is very

likely that the acid treatment for removal of the t-boc group

removes to some extent the protective benzyl or nitrophenyl

ester groups. If this occurs, the free carboxylic acid could

react with the excess of carbodiimide used, and this interme-

diate may very well under transpeptidation (possibly via an

imide intermediate). The product of such a rearrangement

in effect would have one strong acid group (the free α-carboxyl)

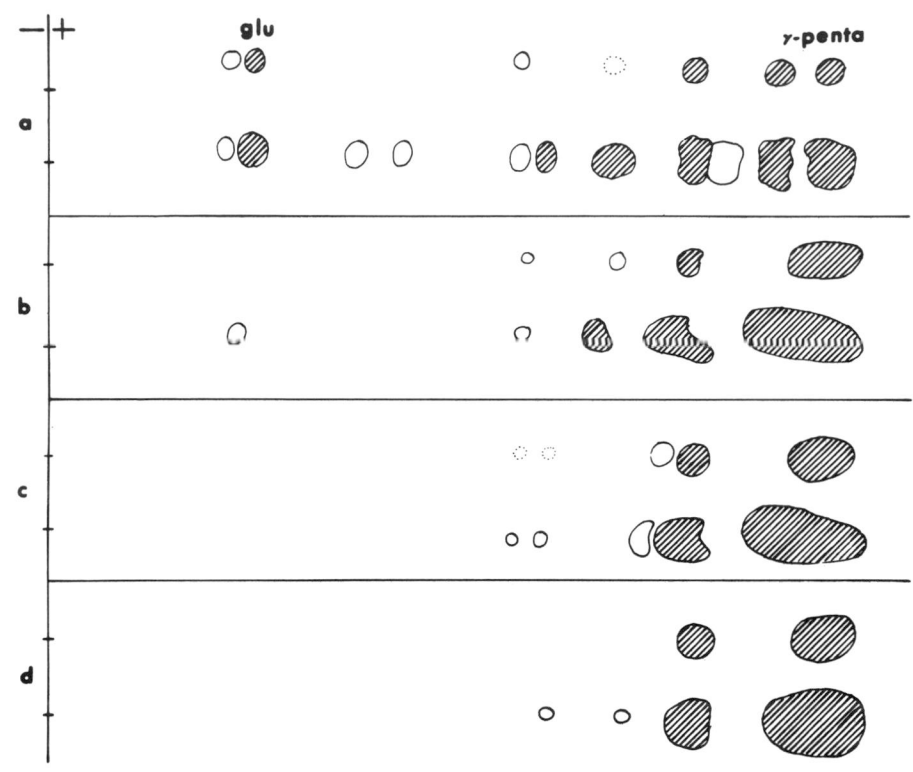

FIG. 7

Electropherogram of same materials as shown in Figure 6;
on Whatman #1, pH 3.5, 35 v/cm.

replaced by a much weaker acid group (the γ-carboxyl). This

could very well be detected by electrophoresis on DEAE

cellulose sheets since this medium is very sensitive to small

differences in charge under the conditions used. If trans-

peptidation can occur under these conditions, the conventional

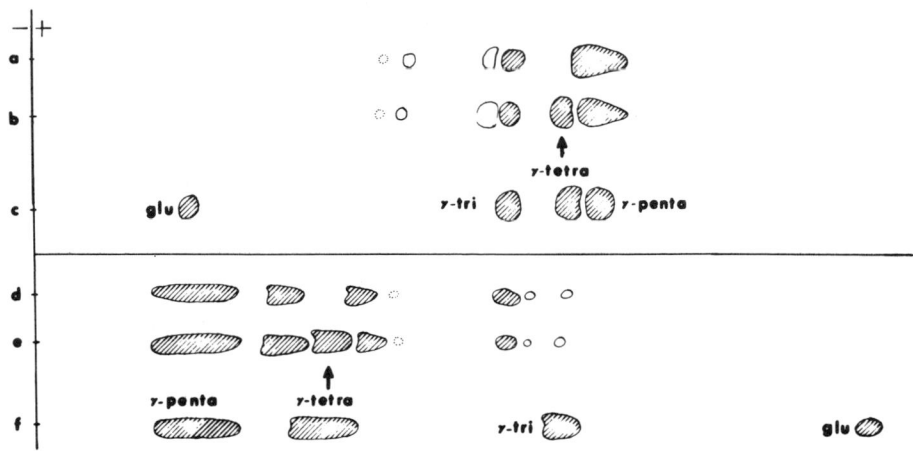

FIG. 8

Electrophoretic analysis of γ-pentapeptide preparation c
(FIGS. 6 and 7), 35 v/cm; (a, b, c) on Whatman #1, pH 3. 5;
(d, e, f) on DEAE cellulose, pH 3. 5; (a, d) preparation c;
(b, c) preparation c with γ-tetrapeptide added; (c, f) mixture
of γ-glutamyl peptides synthesized by classical methods.

solid phase method as applied here is not practical for the

synthesis of γ-glutamyl peptides of defined structure.

ACKNOWLEDGMENTS

The authors wish to acknowledge the skilled technical

assistance of Miss Inge Stoltenberg.

This investigation was supported by U. S. Public Health

Service Grant Nos. AI 05664 and AI 00299.

REFERENCES

1. E. A. Kabat, Ciba. Found. Symp. Chem. Biol. Mucopoly-saccharides, Little, Brown, Boston, 1957, p. 42.

2. J. W. Goodman, Immunochemistry, in press.

3. G. Ivanovics and V. Bruckner, Naturwissenschaften, 25, 250 (1937).

4. B. Bruckner, M. Kajtar, J. Kovacs, H. Nagy and J. Wein, Tetrahedron, 2, 211 (1958).

5. M. Torii, J. Biochem., 46, 189 (1959).

6. W. E. Hanby and H. N. Rydon, Biochem. J., 40, 297 (1946).

7. A. C. Chibnall, M. W. Rees and F. M. Richards, Biochem. J., 68, 129 (1958).

8. J. W. Goodman and D. E. Nitecki, Biochemistry, 5, 657 (1966).

9. D. E. Nitecki and J. W. Goodman, Biochemistry, 5, 665 (1966).

10. J. W. Goodman, D. E. Nitecki and I. M. Stoltenberg, Biochemistry, 7, 706 (1968).

11. E. Schroeder and E. Klieger, Ann., 673, 196 (1964).

12. J. W. Westley, Advan. Astronaut. Sci., 22, 213 (1967).

13. E. Schroeder and K. Luebke, The Peptides, Vol. 1, Academic Press, New York, 1965, pp. 188-190.

ON THE STERICALLY CONTROLLED SYNTHESES OF DIPEPTIDES AND THEIR STEREOCHEMICAL COURSES

Kaoru Harada and Kazuo Matsumoto

Institute of Molecular Evolution
University of Miami, Coral Gables, Florida

Several nonenzymatic syntheses of α -amino acids from α -keto acids have been reported. Erlenmeyer[1] first synthesized DL-phenylalanine from phenyl-pyruvic acid and ammonia by reductive amination. Later the method was developed by Knoop[2]. Platinum and palladium have been used for the catalytic reductive amination. Another method of synthesizing α -amino acids from α -keto acids is the reduction of oximes and phenylhydrazones of α -keto acid. DL-Alanine was first synthesized from pyruvic acid oxime by reduction with zinc and hydrochloric acid[3]. Most of the natural α -amino acids have been synthesized from α -keto acids by use of the above mentioned methods.

Asymmetric synthesis of α -amino acids has been studied recently. Knoop[4] and Herbst[5] synthesized isooctopine from L-arginine and pyruvic acid. In 1961, Hiskey and Northrup[6] published a method of asymmetric synthesis of α -amino acids from α -keto acids and optically active

α -methylbenzylamine by catalytic hydrogenation and
hydrogenolysis. A steric course for the asymmetric
synthesis has been proposed by Harada and Matsumoto[7].
The proposed mechanism was further confirmed by the
studies of the solvent effect[8]. Kanai and Mitsui[9] reported
phenylglycine synthesis from benzoylformic acid and
optically active α -methylbenzylamine, and proposed a
steric course for the optically active phenylglycine formation. A similar asymmetric synthesis of α -amino acids
from α -keto acids and optically active α -phenylglycine by
catalytic hydrogenation and subsequent hydrogenolysis in
aqueous solution has been carried out by Harada[10].
Optically active amino acids were also synthesized from
Schiff bases and oximes of α -keto acid l-menthyl esters
by catalytic hydrogenation[11].

In 1965, Hiskey and Northrop[12] published a description
of a stereoscopic synthesis of dipeptide from benzylamine
from benzylamine Schiff base of N-pyruvyl-S-alanine. If
the catalytic hydrogenation of the Schiff base was to follow
the "Prelog rule"[13], S-alanyl-S-alanine (IIa) would result
(FIG. 1).

However, the ratio of resulting dipeptides was found to
be R-ala-S-ala:S-ala-S-ala = 2:1. The results indicate
that the catalytic hydrogenation does not follow the Prelog
rule. In 1966, Kanai and Mitsui[9] suggested that the C=N

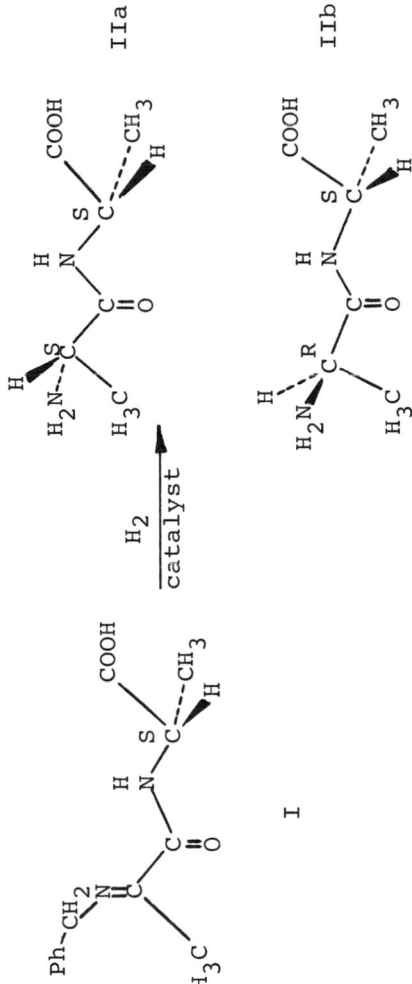

FIG. 1

Formal Application of the Prelog rule in the dipeptide synthesis

bond of the Schiff base and the C ⇌ O bond of the amide might
be in the cisoidal conformation. However, no reasons have
been given for the apparently unusual cisoidal conformation.

In order to clarify the steric course of the stereospecific
synthesis of dipeptides, series of reactions were carried out
in our laboratory. Oximes of N-(S)- and (R)-α -methyl-
benzylbenzoyl-formamide and N-(S)- and (R)-α -ethylbenzyl-
benzoyl-formamide were hydrogenated by the use of
palladium on charcoal in ethanol and the hydrogenated
products were hydrolyzed. When optically active (S)- or
(R)-α -methylbenzylamine was used, the configuration of
the resulting phenylglycine was (R) and (S), respectively[7],
which agreed with the results obtained by Hiskey[12]. However,
when (S)- or (R)-α -ethylbenzylamine was used, the resulting
phenylglycine was (S) or (R), which agreed with the configurations expected by the formal application of the Prelog
rule. The results are summarized in Table 1 and the possible steric courses are shown in FIG. 2.

It seems reasonable to assume that both structures III
and IV could take a cisoidal conformation as shown in
(FIG. 2). The amide bond has been regarded as a resonance
hybrid of the lactam $\left[-\underset{\underset{O}{\|}}{C}-NH- \right]$ and dipolar $\left[-\underset{\underset{O-}{|}}{C}=\overset{+}{N}H- \right]$
structures. Therefore the carbonyl group of the amide
could be adsorbed on the catalyst surface to form a five

TABLE 1

Formation of Phenylglycine from N-α-Alkylbenzylbenzoylformamide

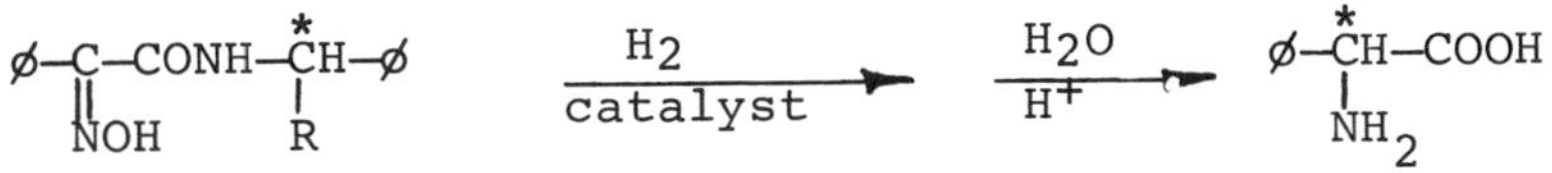

$$\phi-\underset{\underset{NOH}{\parallel}}{C}-CONH-\overset{*}{C}H-\phi \quad \xrightarrow[\text{catalyst}]{H_2} \quad \xrightarrow[H^+]{H_2O} \quad \phi-\overset{*}{C}H-COOH$$
$$\qquad\qquad R \qquad\qquad\qquad\qquad\qquad\qquad\qquad\qquad NH_2$$

R = Me, Et

Config. of amine	Yield, %	Config. of amino acid	Dinitrophenyl-phenylglycine, $[\alpha]_D^{25}$, deg. (c, AcOH)	Optical purity, %	Conformation of substrate
Me (S) – (–)	56	(R) – (–)	+6.1 (0.82)	5.5	A
Et (S) – (–)	52	(S) – (+)	–9.7 (0.35)	8.8	B
Me (R) – (+)	53	(S) – (+)	–5.4 (0.91)	4.9	A
Et (R) – (+)	48	(R) – (–)	+11.1 (0.37)	10.0	B

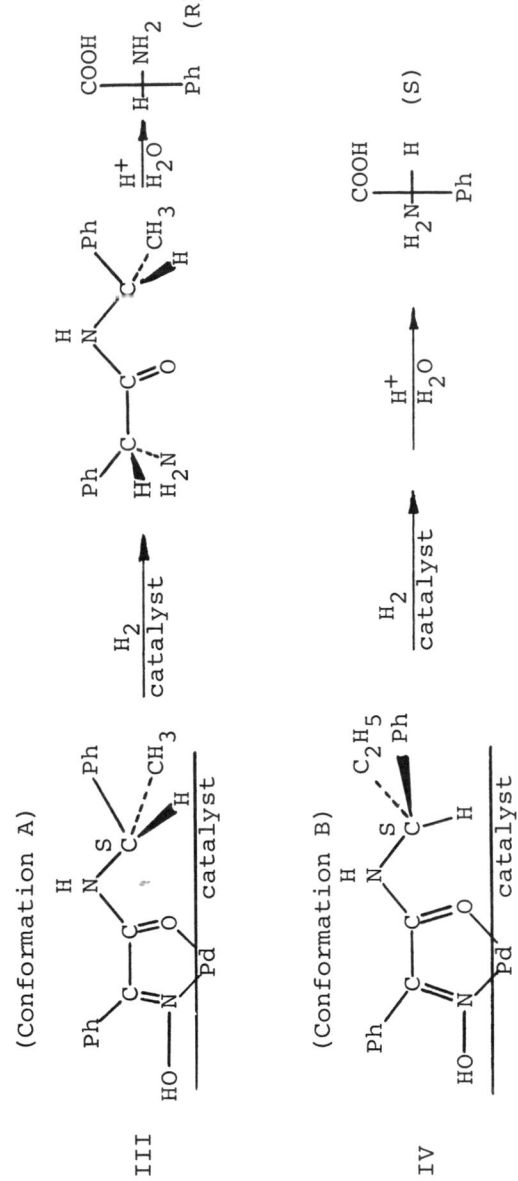

FIG. 2

Probable steric course for the formation of optically active phenylglycine membered ring structure. Then the cyclic complex could be adsorbed on the less bulky side of the molecule and the hydrogenation reaction would take place. When (S)-α - methylbenzylamine was used as a moiety of benzoylformamide, the conformation of the substrate could be structure (III) (conformation A). However, when (S)-α -ethylbenzylamine was used, the conformation of the substrate could not be the same as in the case of α -methylbenzylamine. Since the ethyl group is bulkier than the methyl group, the ethyl group could reach the catalyst surface if the substrate were to take on conformation A. Therefore the least bulky hydrogen atom might be situated closest to the catalyst surface because of the steric hindrance between the substrate and the catalyst. The most probable conformation is, therefore, structure IV (conformation B) when the R-group of the amine moiety is larger than the ethyl group. The results which were obtained by the use of α -ethyl-benzylamine, in appearance, agreed with the results expected by employing the Prelog rule. However, the substrate could take on structure B which has a cisoidal conformation.

In order to confirm further the proposed steric course of the synthesis, a series of dipeptide syntheses were carried out. When the benzylamine Schiff base of N-pyruvyl-(S)- alanine isobutyl ester was used, the configuration of newly formed alanine was (R), (R-ala-S-ala:S-ala-S-ala 82:18)[7].

Results are summarized in Table 2. These results agreed with the results obtained in the phenylglycine formation described earlier. The steric course of the reactions is shown in FIG. 3.

When the alkyl group is methyl, structure A could be the preferred conformation, and when the alkyl group is larger than the ethyl group, structure B could be the major conformation in the stereospecific syntheses of dipeptides. Optical purities of the newly formed alanine using valine and leucine isobutyl ester are larger than that of alanine obtained by the use of valine and leucine methyl ester. This finding may also support the fact that structure B could be the major conformation in these reactions.

If structure B is the preferred conformation when the R-group is larger than the ethyl group, we could make an order of effective bulkiness of the R-group in this reaction by the use of the optical purity of newly formed alanine. When R is phenyl, the optical purity of newly formed alanine is zero so that the effective bulkiness of the phenyl group and of the -COO-i-Bu group are almost the same. In the same way, the bulkiness of the benzyl group and of the $-CH_2COO-i-Bu$ group are almost the same. However, these are smaller than those of the phenyl or -COO-i-Bu groups. The order of effective bulkiness can be arranged as shown in FIG. 4.

TABLE 2

Sterically Controlled Synthesis of Alanyl Dipeptides

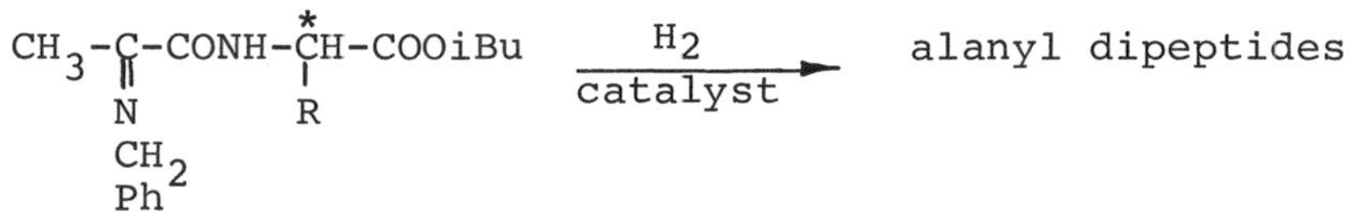

$$CH_3-C-CONH-CH-COOiBu \xrightarrow[\text{catalyst}]{H_2} \text{ alanyl dipeptides}$$

with N, CH_2, Ph (marked *), R

R	Asymmetric moiety	Yield of dipeptide, %	Ratio of diastereomeric dipeptides	Newly formed alanine Config.	Newly formed alanine Optical purity, %	Conform. of substrate
CH₃	(S)-ala-i-Bu	15	R-S:S-S=82:18	R	64	A
	(S)-ala-Me	25	76:24	R	52	A
Et	(S)-α-NH₂-n-Bu-i-Bu	16	29:71	S	41	B
i-Pr	(S)-val-i-Bu	11	34:66	S	32	B
	(R)-val-i-Bu	12	34:66	R	32	B
	(S)-val-Me	12	42:58	S	17	B
i-Bu	(S)-leu-i-Bu	19	32:68	S	35	B
	(S)-leu-Me	18	41:59	S	18	B
Benzyl	(S)-ph-ala-i-Bu	26	37:63	S	25	B
-CH₂COOiBu	(S)-asp-di-i-Bu	11	37:63	S	25	B
∅	(R)-ph-gly-i-Bu	27	50:50	±	0	B

459

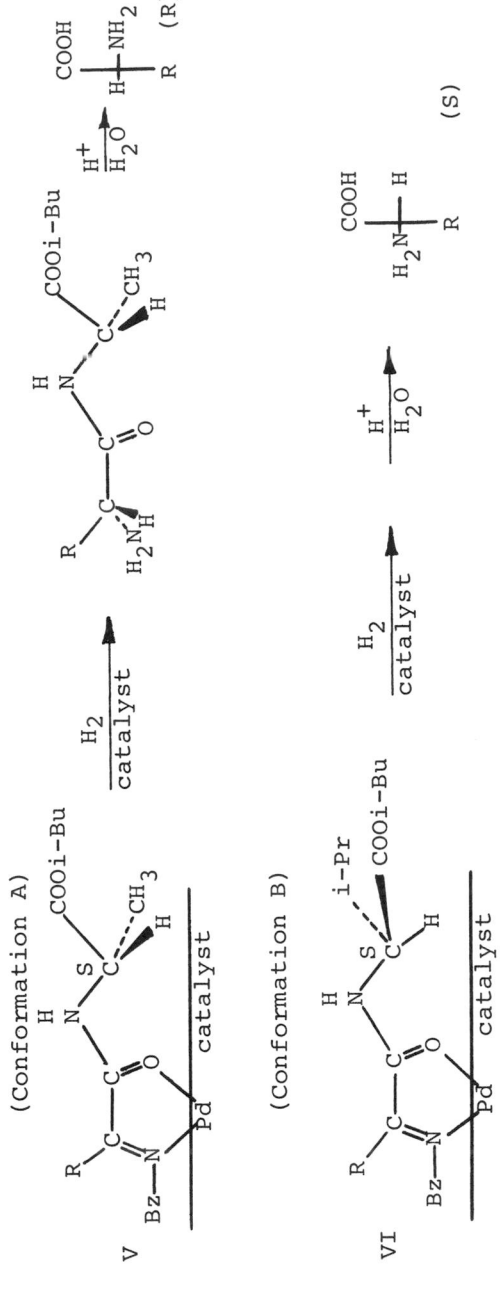

FIG. 3

Probable steric course for the sterically controlled synthesis of dipeptides.

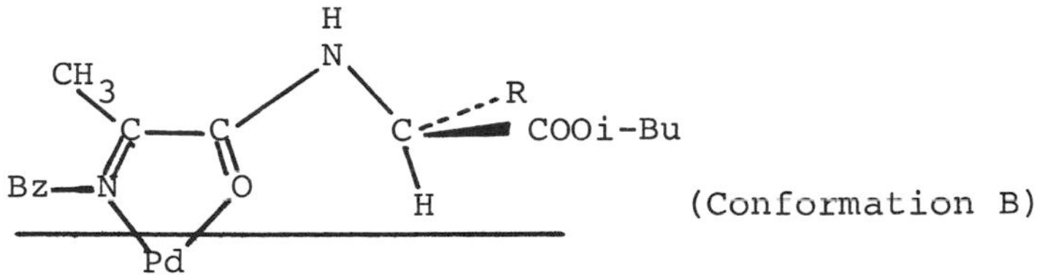

(Conformation B)

$$-COO-i-Bu \sim Ph > -CH_2 Ph \sim -CH_2 COO-i-Bu > i-Pr > i-Bu > Et$$

FIG. 4

Effective bulkiness of side chain in
the sterically controlled synthesis
of dipeptides

The order of bulkiness does not agree with the order of
the residue weight. In this order of effective bulkiness, the
phenyl group is larger than the benzyl group and also the
isopropyl group is larger than the isobutyl group. This
relationship can be explained on the basis that the phenyl
group is larger than the benzyl group and also the isopropyl
group is larger than the isobutyl group. This relationship
can be explained on the basis that the phenyl group and
isopropyl groups are rigid and branched and that these groups
also cannot be bent. On the other hand, benzyl and isobutyl
groups are flexible and these are not branched at the α -carbon
to which these groups are attached. Therefore, the effective
bulkiness of rigid and branched phenyl and isopropyl groups
is larger than that of the benzyl and isobutyl groups.

Table 3 describes α -aminobutyryl peptides. The reaction
products have all S-S and R-R structures. The R-groups

461

TABLE 3

Sterically Controlled Synthesis of α-Aminobutyryl Peptide

$$C_2H_5-\underset{\underset{CH_2\phi}{|}}{\overset{|}{C}}-CONH-\underset{R}{CH}-COOi\text{-}Bu \quad \xrightarrow[\text{catalyst}]{H_2} \quad \xrightarrow[H_2O]{H^+}$$

α-aminobutyryl amino acid

Asymmetric moiety	α-Amino n-butyric acid			Conform. of substrate
	Yield	Optical purity	Config.	
(R)-ϕ-gly i-Bu (oxime)	67	0	–	B
(S)-ϕ-ala-i-Bu	56	12	S	B
(S)-ϕ-ala-i-Bu (oxime)	65	9	S	B
(S)-asp-i-Bu	53	28	S	B

$$-COOi\text{-}Bu \sim \phi > -CH_2-\phi > -CH_2COOi\text{-}Bu$$

used are phenyl, benzyl, and $-CH_2-COO-i-Bu$. Therefore, structure B could be the major conformation in these reactions.

In order to prove further the chelation hypothesis in the dipeptide synthesis, benzoylformylamino acid esters were hydrogenated. Optically active mandelic acid was obtained after hydrolysis. Results are summarized in Table 4.

In the peptide synthesis described above, conformation of the substrate is that of structure A only when the R-group is methyl. Table 4 indicates that when (S)-ala was used, (R)-mandelic acid was obtained. However, when (S)-leucine

TABLE 4

Sterically Controlled Synthesis of Mandelic Acid

$$\emptyset\text{-CO-CONH-CH-COOi-Bu} \xrightarrow[\text{catalyst}]{\text{H}_2} \xrightarrow[\text{H}_2\text{O}]{\text{H}^+} \text{mandelic acid}$$
$$\overset{|}{\text{R}}$$

R	Asymmetric moiety	Yield	Optical purity	Config.	Conform. of Substrate
CH$_3$	(S)-ala-Me	66	3	R	A
	(S)-ala-i-Bu	40	14	R	A
	(R)-ala-i-Bu	40	13	S	A
i-Bu	(S)-leu-i-Bu	49	11	R	A
i-Pr	(S)-val-i-Bu	36	2	S	B

i-butyl ester was used, the resulting mandelic acid was still
R. Therefore, the conformation of the substrate in these
reactions could be that of structure A. The configuration of
the resulting mandelic acid was inverted when (S)-valine
isobutyl ester was used (conformation B). These results
imply that the amount of space between substrate and catalyst
is different from that of the space in the dipeptide syntheses.
Although the accurate bond distances of C=O and C=N of the
substrate are not known, these are approximately 2.5 Å in
each bonding. In the dipeptide synthesis, the nitrogen atom
of C=N bond combined with the hydroxy or benzyl group.
Therefore, one may assume that the whole substrate molecule
inclines to the catalyst side (FIG. 5). In the case of mandelic

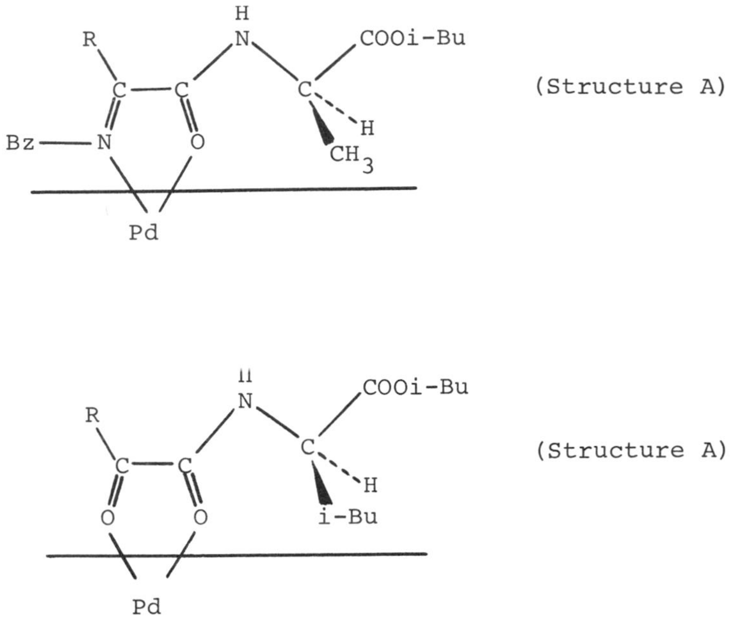

(Structure A)

(Structure A)

FIG. 5

Dimension of space between substrate and catalyst in the sterically controlled synthesis of dipeptide and N-mandelyl-α-amino acid

acid synthesis, there is no substituent such as a hydroxy or benzyl group. Therefore, the substrate does not incline to the catalyst side so that the dimension of the space between substrate and catalyst is larger than that in the dipeptide synthesis (FIG. 5). In the dipeptide synthesis only a methyl group can be allowed to take part in conformation (A). However, in the mandelic acid synthesis, the isobutyl group can occupy the space in the form of conformation (A) because of the larger space between substrate and catalyst. Thus the dimension of space between substrate and catalyst could be estimated by the use of chemical data obtained from the sterically controlled syntheses of dipeptides and mandelic acid.

SUMMARY

1. A chelation hypothesis in the stereospecific synthesis of dipeptides was proposed.

2. An order of effective bulkiness of side chains was discussed by the use of optical purity of the newly formed amino acids.

3. The dimension of the space between substrate and catalyst surface was discussed by the use of chemical data.

4. When the proposed stereochemical course was further established, it could be possible to determine the configurations of structurally unknown primary amines by the use of these results.

ACKNOWLEDGMENTS

The work was supported by Grant NsG-689 of the National Aeronautics and Space Administration. Contribution no. 115 of the Institute of Molecular Evolution.

REFERENCES

1. E. Erlenmeyer, Jr. and J. Kunlin, Ann., 307, 146 (1899).

2. F. Knoop and H. Oesterlin, Z. Physiol. Chem., 148, 294 (1925); 170, 186 (1927).

3. H. Gutknecht, Ber., 13, 1116 (1880).

4. F. Knoop and C. Martius, Z. Physiol. Chem., 258, 238 (1939).

5. J. B. Herbst and E. A. Swart, J. Org. Chem., 11, 366 (1946).

6. R. G. Hiskey and R. C. Northrop, J. Am. Chem. Soc., 83, 4798 (1961).

7. K. Harada and K. Matsumoto, J. Org. Chem., 32, 1794 (1967).

8. K. Harada and K. Matsumoto, J. Org. Chem., 33, in press.

9. A. Kanai and S. Mitsui, J. Chem. Soc. Japan, 89, 183 (1966).

10. K. Harada, Nature, 212, 1571 (1966); J. Org. Chem., 32, 1790 (1967).

11. K. Matsumoto and K. Harada, J. Org. Chem., 31, 1956 (1966).

12. R. G. Hiskey and R. C. Northrop, J. Am. Chem. Soc., 87, 1753 (1965).

13. V. Prelog, Helv. Chim. Acta, 36, 308 (1953). The Prelog rule was originally proposed for the homogeneous reactions. Catalytic reduction of α -keto acid esters of optically active alcohols has been studied and it was found that the catalytic reduction followed the Prelog rule [V. Prelog, Bull. Soc. Chim. France, 987 (1956)]. However, the Prelog rule might not be applicable for the catalytic hydrogenation of the Schiff base of α -keto acid amide. It is important to consider that the configurational agreement of the final product does not always mean that the conformation of the substrate follows the Prelog rule, because several possible conformations of the substrate would result in the specific configuration which is predicted by the Prelog rule.

FURTHER STUDIES WITH SELENIUM-CONTAINING AMINO ACIDS AND PEPTIDES

Roderich Walter

Department of Physiology,
Mount Sinai Medical and Graduate Schools
of the City University of New York
New York, N. Y.

and

The Medical Research Center
Brookhaven National Laboratory
Upton, N. Y.

The amino acid sequence of a peptide hormone provides all of the information required for evoking a particular physiological response in a given environment. Our task is to identify this information and to elucidate the mechanism whereby it is recognized and translated as a result of the hormone-receptor complex formation.

In this effort the synthetic approach has achieved a prominent position as the point of departure for studies which attempt to probe the mechanism of hormone action at the molecular level. Synthesis is the choice method for inaugurating structural changes at will at any designated locus in the peptide hormone; such changes can lead to the elucidation of functional and steric requirements for a particular hormonal activity. Essential for this kind of study are amino acids possessing maximally diverse structures. Some of these amino acids are readily available from natural sources; others are scarce or not known at all.

Searching for a sulfur replacement which differs electronically but retains in first approximation the steric properties of the sulfur moiety, we became interested in selenium-containing isologs of disulfide- and thioether-containing amino acids. Although many of these do occur in living organisms[1,2], their presence is limited to a low concentration or even trace amounts. Moreover, a complete separation from their corresponding sulfur derivatives has not yet been achieved on a preparative scale. From the experience accumulated to date it is apparent that with this class of compounds the direct synthetic approach has a distinct advantage over any isolation procedure. Therefore, the elaboration of synthetic routes for the preparation of optically active selenium-containing amino acids and for that matter any novel method for introducing selenium into a molecule are more than a mere academic exercise.

For example, in our experience the substitution of sulfur by selenium has already yielded valuable information bearing on the question of the functional equivalence or nonequivalence of the individual sulfur atoms in the disulfide bridge of peptide hormones[3,4]. Moreover, selenium isologs of neurohypophyseal hormones proved to be crucial during studies[5-9] culminating in the establishment of the absolute configuration of the cystine residue in oxytocin and its analogs.

Today I would like to direct your attention to some aspects of the synthesis of Se-benzyl-L-selenocysteine compounds, to present the preparation of a few naturally occurring selenium-containing amino acids as well as homoselenocysteine derivatives, to describe the synthesis of diselenooxytocin, and to cite some preliminary pharmacological studies with this oxytocin isolog. I would like also to call attention to some unsolved problems with regard to selenium-containing amino acids and to the usefulness of these compounds in biochemical studies.

Several years ago Zervas, Photaki and their collaborators[10-12] described the conversion of serine derivatives to the corresponding cysteine compounds. This method consists of the nucleophilic displacement of the O-tosyl group of serine by the sodium salt of an alkylated mercaptan.

Dr. Theodoropoulos et al.[13,14] adapted this procedure for the preparation of selenocysteine derivatives. The racemization encountered during the displacement of the O-tosyl moiety in serine derivatives with mercaptide was not observed during the displacement with the sodium salt of benzylse-lenol.   This advantageous finding is probably

due to the differences in basicity of the nucleophiles--the

thiolate ions are stronger bases than the corresponding

selenolate ions.   Thus one would expect the selenolate to

possess a decreased tendency to promote proton abstrac-

tion from the C_α.   Further experiments proved that not

only O-tosylated serine derivatives but also O- tosylated

serine-containing peptides could be readily transformed

to Se-benzylselenocysteine peptides under mild conditions

which do not affect the configuration of the serine

residue[13, 14]

More recently it became mandatory that we obtain an

N-protected derivative of L-selenocysteine possessing a

free carboxyl group suitable for peptide coupling by pro-

cedures other than the azide method.   Since the acidolysis

of the methyl and benzyl esters of N-carbobenzoxy-Se-

benzyl-L-selenocysteine met with difficulty[14], we attempted

to saponify the benzyl ester.   However, the base affected

the selenium-containing amino acid adversely; the acid

was isolated in low percentage and dibenzyldiselenid[15],

resulting from β -elimination of benzylselenol and subse-

quent oxidative dimerization, constituted a major reaction

product.   Once we had prepared the diphenylmethyl ester

of N-carbobenzoxy-Se-benzyl-L-selenocysteine,

Drs. Gordon and Theoporopoulos readily deprotected

the carboxyl group and then, after quantitative removal of

the byproduct diphenylmethyl chloride, crystalline N-

carbobenzoxy-Se-benzyl-L-selenocysteine was isolated in

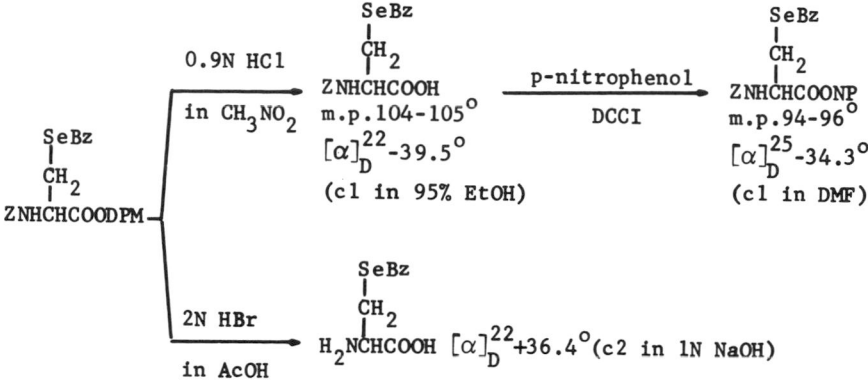

high yield. This product differed in its optical rotation

from the compound which Frank[16] prepared by an indepen-

dent method, in spite of identical melting points. Our

value for the optical rotation is substantiated by the fact

that treatment of the diphenylmethyl ester--the precursor

of N-carbobenzoxy-Se-benzyl-L-selenocysteine--with 2N

HBr yields Se-benzyl-L-selenocysteine of high optical

purity[14]. In addition, we converted the N-carbobenzoxy-L-

selenocysteine to its p-nitrophenyl ester, which exhibited

physical properties identical to those reported previously[16].

In order to obtain maximum utility for this displace-

ment reaction in the synthesis of selenium-containing

amino acids, Dr. Gordon investigated the possibility of

transforming an O-tosylated L-serine derivative with

sodium hydrogen selenide--instead of the benzylselenolate--
to the corresponding selenocysteine derivative. Such a
derivative with its free selenol function would provide a
key intermediate allowing the transformation to either the
diselenide by oxidation or selenides by alkylation. While
the former type of reaction would pave the way for the
synthesis of L-seleno-cysteine, the latter would offer a
route toward the synthesis of such amino acids as L-selenolanthionine and L-selenocystathionine, which possess a
selenocysteine moiety as the basic skeleton.

To examine the feasibility of the above compendium,
N-carbobenzoxy-O-tosyl-L-serine diphenylmethyl ester
was allowed to react with a stoichiometric amount of sodium
hydrogen selenide. In view of the ease with which aliphatic

$$TsOCH_2\underset{NHZ}{CHCOODPM} \xrightarrow[-TsO^-]{+HSe^-} \left[HSeCH_2\underset{NHZ}{CHCOODPM} \right] \xrightarrow{oxid.} \left(-SeCH_2\underset{NHZ}{CHCOODPM} \right)_2$$

$$\downarrow \begin{array}{l} 1.\ HCl/CH_3NO_2 \\ 2.\ (C_6H_{11})_2NH \end{array}$$

$$\left(-SeCH_2\underset{NH_2}{CHCOOH} \right)_2 \xleftarrow[\substack{2.\ HBr/AcOH \\ 3.\ pH\ 5}]{1.\ H_3O^+} \left(-SeCH_2\underset{NHZ}{CHCOO^-}(C_6H_{11})_2\overset{+}{NH}_2 \right)_2$$

m.p. 206°dec.
$[\alpha]_D^{23}$ -141.4°
(c1 in 5N HCl)

selenols oxidize, we did not attempt to isolate the N-car-
bobenzoxy-L-selenocysteine diphenylmethyl ester, but
instead converted the selenol in situ to the corresponding
diselenide, bis(diphenylmethyl) bis(N-carbobenzoxy)-L-
selenocystinate, which was isolated in more than 90%
yield. This ester was deblocked stepwise to yield ultimately L-selenocystine[17].

That the initial conversion reaction of N-carbobenzoxy-
O-tosyl-L-serine diphenylmethyl ester to the selenol proceeded with full retention of chirality was affirmed via the
synthesis of diphenylmethyl N-carbobenzoxy-Se-benzyl-L-
selenocysteinate by a new path:

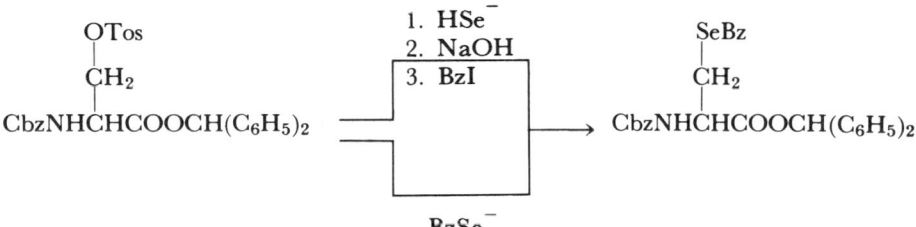

To prepare diphenylmethyl N-carbobenzoxy-Se-benzyl-
L-selenocysteinate the O-tosylated ester was treated with
sodium hydrogen selenide and the resulting selenol was
subsequently, without risk of racemization, alkylated in
situ with benzyl iodide. The physical properties of the
product were essentially identical with those reported
previously for this compound when obtained from the
O-tosylated ester in a single step with sodium benzylselenolate[14].

One of the more complex sulfur-containing amino acids
--thought to occur in nature--is lanthionine[18-20]. While
the DL- and meso-mixture of its seleno isolog is known[21],
the synthesis of L-selenolanthionine was yet to be achieved.
We therefore set out to prepare the L-enantiomer in a
further test of our method. The experimental path as
outlined below is self-explanatory:

$$\left[NaSeCH_2\underset{\underset{NHZ}{|}}{CHOODPM} \right] + TsOCH_2\underset{\underset{NHZ}{|}}{CHCOODPM} \longrightarrow Se\left(CH_2\underset{\underset{NHZ}{|}}{CHOODPM} \right)_2$$

m.p.114°

$[\alpha]_D^{22}$-31.7°(c1 in DMF)

1. HCl/CH_3NO_2

2. $(C_6H_{11})_2NH$

$$Se\left(CH_2\underset{\underset{NH_2}{|}}{CHCOOH} \right)_2 \xleftarrow[\substack{2.\ HBr/AcOH \\ 3.\ NH_4OH}]{1.\ H_3O^+} Se\left(CH_2\underset{\underset{NHZ}{|}}{CHCOO^-}(C_6H_{11})_2\overset{+}{NH}_2 \right)_2$$

m.p.230-270° dec.

$[\alpha]_D^{21}$+34.9°

(c1 in 5N HCl)

m.p.172-173°

$[\alpha]_D^{22}$-0.88°(c1 in MeOH)

So far we have focused on selenium-containing compounds which possessed a propionic acid skeleton as the
basic structure. I would now like to turn to the next higher
homolog in the series, to compounds with a homoselenocysteine skeleton. The problems encountered in this
ancillary program of research differed sharply from those
discussed above. While the chief task with O-tosyl-serine

derivatives was to avoid racemization during the conversion,
the major challenge with homoserine was to develop a
reaction path which would minimize lactone formation which
in the past hampered chemical work employing homoserine
per se instead of its lactone, e.g. [22, 23].

In pilot experiments Dr. Pande found that the p-toluenesulfonate of homoserine can readily be prepared and then
converted--according to Aboderin et al.[24]--to the diphenylmethyl ester. While the p-toluenesulfonate of homoserine
was stable, the ester underwent cyclization to the lactone
during repeated manipulations.

$$\overset{\overset{+}{N}H_3Tos^-}{HOCH_2CH_2\underset{|}{C}HCOOH} \xrightarrow{(C_6H_5)_2CN_2} \overset{\overset{+}{N}H_3Tos^-}{HOCH_2CH_2\underset{|}{C}HCOODPM}$$

m.p. 124-125°

$[\alpha]_D^{23} +6.8°$

(c2 in MeOH)

TosCl/Pyr

$$\overset{NHTos}{BzSeCH_2CH_2\underset{|}{C}HCOO^-}(C_6H_{11})_2\overset{+}{N}H_2 \xleftarrow[\substack{2.\ 0.9N\ HCl \\ 3.\ (C_6H_{11})_2NH}]{1.\ BzSe^-} \overset{NHTos}{TosOCH_2CH_2\underset{|}{C}HCOODPM}$$

m.p. 176-178°

$[\alpha]_D^{22} +42.4°$ (c1 in MeOH)

m.p. 132-133°

$[\alpha]_D^{22} -15.5°$ (c1 in DMF)

Therefore, no further attempt was made to isolate the
ester in crystalline form. Instead it was ditosylated in
the next step to yield the crystalline ditosyl-L-homoserine
diphenylmethyl ester which was subsequently transformed
to the N-tosyl-Se-benzyl-L-homoseleno-cysteine dicyclo-
hexylammonium salt.

Our next objective was to secure an Se-benzyl-L-homo-
selenocysteine derivative bearing amino- and carboxyl-pro-
tecting groups of such a nature that the nitrogen function

$$
\underset{\substack{\text{NHZ}\\|}}{\text{HOCH}_2\text{CH}_2\text{CHCOO}^-} \xrightarrow[\text{2. TosCl/Pyr}]{\text{1. TosNB}} \underset{\substack{\text{NHZ}\\|}}{\text{TosOCH}_2\text{CH}_2\text{CHCOONB}}
$$

m.p.114-115°

$[\alpha]_D^{23}$ -7.8°(c2 in DMF)

$\Big|$ BzSe$^-$

$$
\underset{\substack{\text{NH}_2 \cdot \text{HBr}\\|}}{\text{BzSeCH}_2\text{CH}_2\text{CHCOONB}} \xleftarrow[\text{AcOH}]{\text{2N HBr}} \underset{\substack{\text{NHZ}\\|}}{\text{BzSeCH}_2\text{CH}_2\text{CHCOONB}}
$$

m.p.116-117°　　　　　　　m.p.64-66°

$[\alpha]_D^{21}$ -18.4°(c1 in DMF)

could be deprotected selectively, thus allowing the incorporation of homoselenocysteine into a peptide as a C-terminal residue. For the preparation of such an intermediate,
N-carbobenzoxy-L-homoserinate was selectively esterified
with p-nitrobenzyltosylate[25] to yield p-nitrobenzyl N-carbobenzoxy-L-homoserinate. This ester was subsequently
tosylated to provide p-nitrobenzyl N-carbobenzoxy-O-
tosyl-L-serinate, which in turn was allowed to react with
the benzylselenolate giving p-nitrobenzyl N-carbobenzoxy-
Se-benzyl-L-homoselenocysteinate; subsequent decarbob-
enzoxylation yielded the hydrobromide of Se-benzyl-L-
homoselenocysteine p-nitrobenzyl ester.

The above reactions with homoselenocysteine are preliminary, and many additional problems will have to be investigated. Nevertheless, it appears that the nucleophilic displacement of the O-tosyl moiety of an appropriately protected homoserine is a most flexible method. There are, however, a few other procedures -- although more limited in scope -- for the synthesis of a -amino-γ -selenobutyric acid derivatives, such as the displacement of the ester oxygen of a -amino-γ -butyrolactone[26] or the alkylhalide in a -amino-γ -halobutyric acid[27, 28].

In defining the measure of responsibility of a particular group in the hormone molecule for binding or for the catalytic function or for both, we have become interested in the isosteric replacement of sulfur by selenium. We therefore embarked on a study of a series of neurohypophyseal hormone analogs such as 1-seleno- and 6-seleno-oxytocin, their deamino analogs and deamino-diseleno-oxytocin[3, 5, 6]. Perhaps the most logical member in the group of selenium-containing oxytocin analogs, viz. diseleno-oxytocin, is notably missing from this list. This is not without reason. In the course of long-standing studies specifically related to the preparation and the determination of physical and pharmacological properties of diseleno-oxytocin, we were confronted with the fact that this molecule is highly unstable, tending to dimerize and polymerize; this probably also explains why an initial attempt by Frank to synthesize

diseleno-oxytocin was unsuccessful[29].

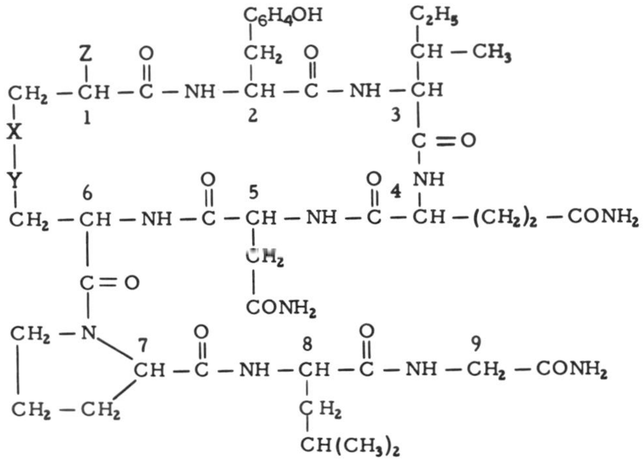

$$Z = NH_2 \text{ or } H$$
$$\text{I. } X-Y = S-S$$
$$\text{II. } X-Y = Se-S$$
$$\text{III. } X-Y = S-Se$$
$$\text{IV. } X-Y = Se-Se$$

FIG. 1

After we had secured N-carbobenzoxy-Se-benzyl-L-
seleno-cysteine in sufficient quantities by the method
discussed above, we returned to the synthesis of diseleno-
oxytocin. For this purpose the C-terminal octapeptide
amide, employed during the synthesis of hemi-6-seleno-
oxytocin and its deamino analog[5], was lengthened with
N-carbobenzoxy-Se-benzyl-L-selenocysteine p-nitrophenyl
ester, and the resulting nonapeptide was deprotected with
sodium in liquid ammonia as described for the synthesis

of oxytocin[30, 31]. After lyophilization and ampuling of

diseleno-oxytocin, tests for its avian vasodepressor[32]

and rat oxytocic[33] activities gave potencies far below our

expectations. This prompted us to study the effect of heat

sterilization and lyophilization on the biological properties

of crystalline deamino-oxytocin, deamino-1-seleno-oxytocin

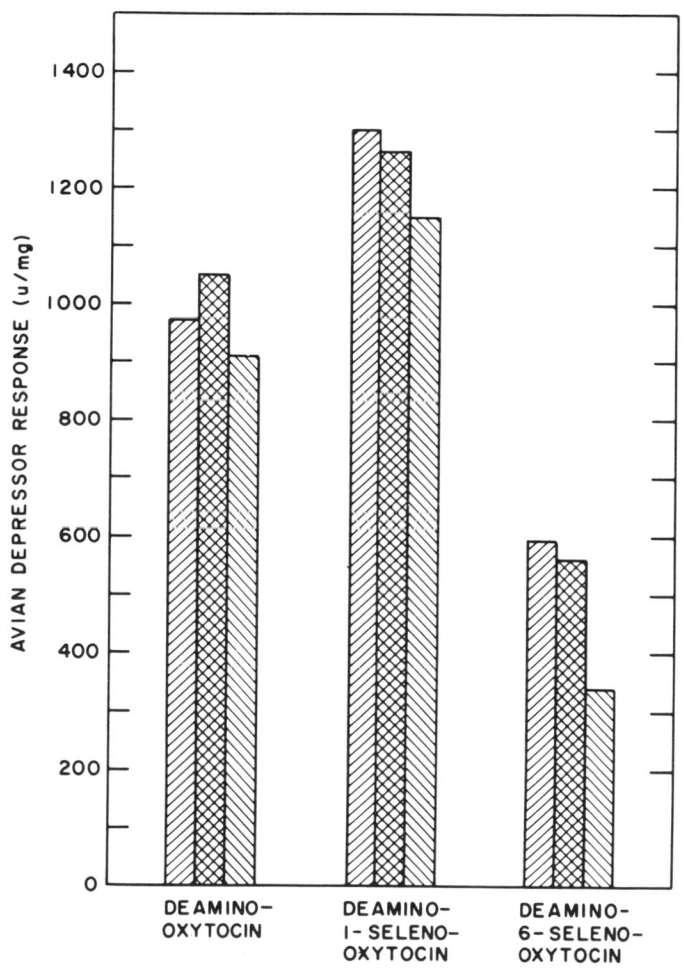

FIG. 2

and deamino-6-seleno-oxytocin. It was found that no
inactivation of the hormonal peptides occurs during heat
sterilization; however, lyophilization affected all peptides
negatively -- the disulfide, deamino-oxytocin, to a
lesser degree than both of the seleno-thiolates (FIG. 2,
compare second with third bar for each analog). In
addition, a study of the avian vasodepressor activities
of the crystalline analogs and the analogs obtained after
countercurrent distribution or partition chromatography
with omission of lyophilization, revealed that both groups
of compounds exhibit comparable potencies (FIG. 2,
compare first with second bar for each analog). We
therefore feel that direct assay after purification offers a
satisfactory alternative for determining the biological
activities of hormonal peptides, and with those analogs
which are too unstable to be isolated by means of
lyophilization this may be the only feasible procedure.
The concentration of hormone in the bio-assay solution is
determined in three ways: (a) quantitative amino acid
analysis after acid hydrolysis of an aliquot (labile amino
acids, such as tyrosine, are omitted during the calculations); (b) weight determination after lyophilization of
an aliquot; and (c) quantitative determination of the
tyrosine content by a spectrophotometric procedure at a
constant pH.

With these experiences as background we returned to diseleno-oxytocin and carried out bioassays on preparations which had not undergone lyophilization but instead were ampuled immediately following countercurrent distribution and evaporation of the organic layer. When the effect of diseleno-oxytocin on the avian blood pressure was now determined, a value of approximately 600 U/mg was found. These data suggest that the selenium isolog is slightly more potent than oxytocin, which possesses a potency of about 500 U/mg in this assay[34]. The last picture shows the effect of lyophilization on the avian vasodepressor activity of diseleno-oxytocin; the isolog lost approximately 85% of its original potency during this process. Similarly, the activity of deamino-diseleno-oxytocin was drastically reduced by lyophilization (FIG. 3).

In considering the future outlook for studies of the role of selenium in biology, we are confident it is now possible to readily secure optically active selenium-containing amino acids possessing almost any desired structure. It also can be anticipated that acid labile and selectively removable protecting groups will be applied for the protection of the selenol function, thus enabling the peptide chemist to initiate the synthesis of selenium isologs of more complex sulfur-containing peptide hormones such

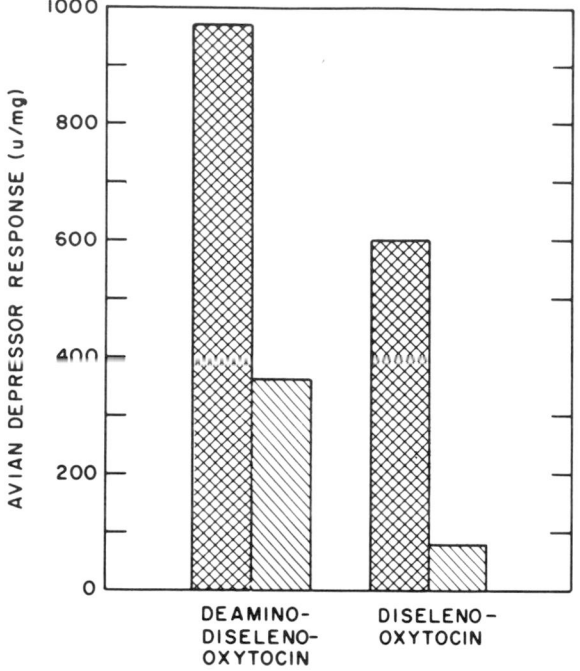

FIG. 3

as calcitonin, insulin, etc. These kinds of investigations should ultimately lead to the determination of the ionization, reactivity and stability properties of selenol and diselenide groupings in a physiological environment and of the degree to which the topography and, consequently, the biological activity of a peptidyl hormone or enzyme are affected by the replacement of sulfur by selenium. It is anticipated that the mild reaction conditions required to displace the O-tosyl moiety by a selenium nucleophile will lead to the isolation of an acyclic compound containing a mixed sulfur-selenium bond. Further, the high yield in which the O-tosyl moiety is replaced by a selenium nucleophile paves the way for the synthesis of ^{74}Se-enriched amino acids, thereby expanding the scope of their metabolic, distribution and diagnostic studies. Following irradiation by thermal neutrons (^{74}Se(n,γ)^{75}Se) the resulting ^{75}Se, which has a half-life of 127 days, is determined by standard counting procedures. Finally, selenium can serve as a heavy atom marker during the X-ray crystallographic elucidation of the three-dimensional structure of biologically important compounds^{35}.

ACKNOWLEDGMENTS

Consultation with Dr. I. L. Schwartz has been a privilege frequently exercised, much enjoyed, and greatly valued. I would also like to thank sincerely all who contributed to this project at its various stages.

This work was supported by U. S. Heal th Service Grants AM-10080 and AM-11580 and by the U. S. Atomic Energy Commission.

REFERENCES

1. I. Rosenfield and O. A. Beath, Selenium, Academic Press, New York, 1964.

2. J. Jaurequi-Adell, Adv. Protein Chem., 21, 387 (1966).

3. R. Walter and W. Y. Chan, J. Am. Chem. Soc., 89, 3892 (1967).

4. R. Walter and I. L. Schwartz in Pharmacology of
    Hormonal Polypeptides and Proteins (N. Back,
    L. Martini and R. Paoletti, eds.), Plenum Press,
    New York, 1968, p. 101.

5. R. Walter and V. du Vigneaud, J. Am. Chem. Soc.,
    87, 4192 (1965).

6. R. Walter and V. du Vigneaud, ibid., 88, 1331 (1966).

7. D. W. Urry, F. Quadrifoglio, R. Walter and
    I. L. Schwartz, Proc. Natl. Acad. Sci. U.S., 60,
    967 (1968).

8. W. Gordon, R. T. Havran, I. L. Schwartz and
    R. Walter, ibid., 60, 1353 (1968).

9. R. Walter, W. Gordon, I. L. Schwartz, F. Quadrifoglio
    and D. W. Urry, in Proc. of the 9th European Peptide
    Symposium (E. Bricas, ed.), North Holland Publishing
    Co., 1968, p. 50.

10. L. Zervas and I. Photaki, Chimia, 14, 375 (1960).

11. I. Photaki, J. Am. Chem. Soc., 85, 1123 (1963).

12. I. Photaki and V. Bardakos, ibid., 87, 3489 (1965).

13. D. Theodoropoulos, I. L. Schwartz and R. Walter,
    Tetrahedr. Letters, No. 25, 2411 (1967).

14. D. Theodoropoulos, I. L. Schwartz and R. Walter,
    Biochem., 6, 3927 (1967).

15. S.-H. Chu, W. H. H. Gunther and H. G. Mautner
    in Biochem. Prep., Vol. 10 (G. B. Brown, ed.),
    John Wiley and sons, New York, 1963, p. 153.

16. W. Frank, Hoppe-Seyler's Zeitschr. Physiol. Chem.,
    339, 202 (1964).

17. A. Fredga, Svensk Kem. Tids., 49, 124 (1937).

18. J. Stein, Chem. and Ind., 744 (1955).

19. W. O. Kermack and J. Stein, J. Biochem., 71, 648
    (1959).

20. D. R. Rao, A. H. Ennor and B. Thorpe, Biochem.
     Biophys. Res. Comm., 22, 163 (1966).

21. G. Zdansky, Ark. Kemi., 26, 213 (1961).

22. M. Flavin and C. Slaughter, Biochem., 4, 1370
     (1965).

23. J. S. Morley and J. M. Smith, J. Chem. Soc.,
     726, (1968).

24. A. A. Aboderin, R. G. Delpierre, and S. J. Fruton,
     J. Am. Chem. Soc., 87, 5469 (1965).

25. D. Theodoropoulos and J. Tsangaris, J. Org. Chem.,
     29, 2272 (1964).

26. H. Plieninger, Chem. Ber., 83, 265 (1950).

27. E. P. Painter, J. Am. Chem. Soc., 69, 232, 2009
     (1947).

28. H. D. Jakubke, J. Fischer, K. Jost and J. Rudinger,
     Coll. Czech. Chem. Comm., 33, 3910 (1968).

29. W. Frank, Z. Physiol. Chem., 339, 222 (1964).

30. V. du Vigneaud, C. Ressler, J. M. Swan,
     C. W. Roberts, P. G. Katsoyannis, and S. Gordon,
     J. Am. Chem. Soc., 75, 4879 (1953).

31. V. du Vigneaud, C. Ressler, J. M. Swan,
     C. W. Roberts, and P. G. Katsoyannis, ibid., 76,
     3115 (1954).

32. R. A. Munsick, W. H. Sawyer, and H. B. Van Dyke,
     Endocrinology, 66, 860 (1960).

33. R. A. Munsick, ibid., 66, 451 (1960).

34. W. Y. Chan and V. du Vigneaud, ibid., 71, 977
     (1962).

PENICILLIN POLYPEPTIDES AND THEIR RELEVANCE TO ALLERGENICITY

Norman H. Grant
Research Division, Wyeth Laboratories
Radnor, Pennsylvania

THE ALLERGENICITY PROBLEM

After a quarter of a century of clinical use, practically the only untoward effect of penicillins has been allergic hypersensitivity. The incidence is probably in the range of 0.3 to 5% of the population, although present statistics do not reflect experience with semi-synthetic penicillins introduced in the 1960's.

A full account of the investigations into penicillin allergenicity is inappropriate here, but even a casual look into the immunochemical mechanisms comes to focus on the peptide aspects. The evolving sequence of explanations has been: (1) antigenic impurities; (2) penicillenic acid formation, followed by acylation of proteins; (3) direct acylation of proteins; (4) impurities again; (5) polymerization.

Allergic reactions to penicillin first appeared when the product was recognized as still impure. Since proteins from microbial fermentation systems were known to be antigenic in in man, the origin of the allergenicity seemed clearly to be residual protein, plus, perhaps, impurities introduced in the vehicles[1].

PENICILLENIC ACIDS

With the emergence of very pure penicillin preparations the problem failed to vanish, and the idea of a penicilloyl hapten gained prominance. In 1961, Levine reported that the penicillenic acid rearrangement product (II) of benzylpenicillin (structure I; R= benzyl) is a strong sensitizer, and may

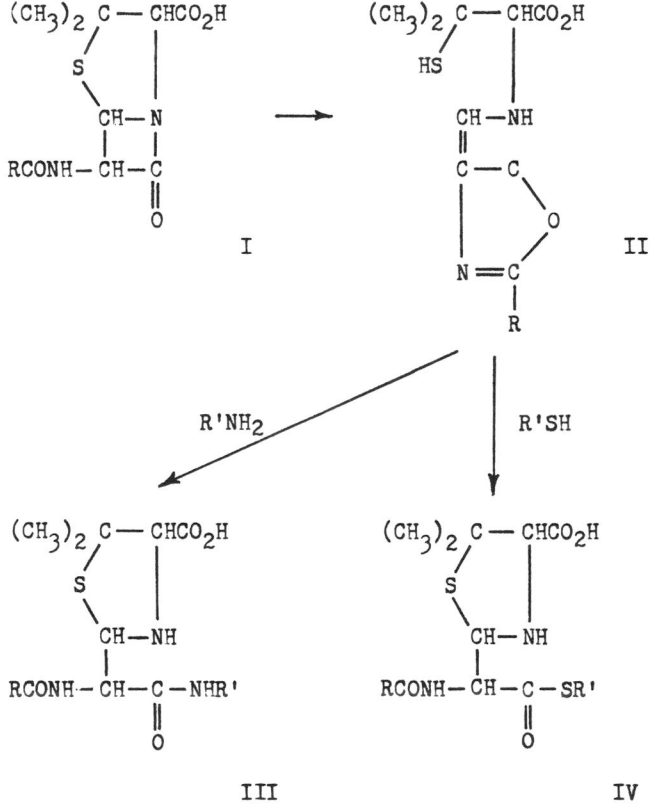

react with tissue or bacterial proteins in vivo to form the active allergens[2]. Reaction with ε-amino groups would give the novel peptide III. Reaction with sulfhydryl groups would give the corresponding thioester conjugate (IV)[3].

Where R^1 is part of a protein, III and IV admirably meet the requirements of haptenic conjugates. Such conjugates have proved, moreover, to be effective elicitors of wheal and erythema skin responses in allergic humans[4-6].

Although overwhelming evidence now points to the penicilloyl group as the principal antigenic determinant, the highly labile penicillenic acids compete with the parent penicillin as the precursor; i.e., the β-lactam is itself reactive enough to penicilloylate amines directly. To assess the role of penicillenic acids, then, one must ask whether it is possible to relate rate of penicillenic acid formation, rate of penicilloylation, and degree of antigenicity.

Researchers in Switzerland and England have failed to find such a relation. Schneider and de Weck concluded from a kinetic study that penicillenic acid formation could not be the rate limiting step in the aminolysis of benzylpenicillin by ε-aminocaproic acid[4]. Furthermore, they could find no correlation between penicillenic acid formation from various penicillins and either penicilloylation of polylysine or immunogenicity of the penicillins[5]. Batchelor and co-workers also studied several penicillins and could find no correlation between penicillenic acid formation and penicilloylation of serum albumin[6].

IMPURITIES

In 1967 two groups of workers again proposed macromolecular impurities as the principal factors in allergenicity[7-9]. These could arise from outside the penicillin -- from components of the fermentation system -- or from the penicillin itself. The evidence on extraneous antigens -- and its interpretation -- is presently conflicting; the preparations studied by Batchelor, Feinberg, and Stewart and their associates[7-9] contained substances which on hydrolysis gave amino acid not present in penicillins. On the other hand, Dursch[10] and de Weck and colleagues[11] reported that many parenteral preparations of commercial penicillins contain either no protein or amounts inadequate to account for hypersensitivity.

PENICILLIN POLYMERS

The other possible source of polymeric material is the penicillin molecule. In 1962 we showed that 6-aminopenicillanic acid (6-APA) could form polypeptides of about 7 to 9 units in length by reaction between the primary amino amino group on one molecule and the β-lactam of a neighboring molecule[12]:

No interferences were originally drawn suggesting a role for these polymers in allergenicity, but these implications became evident with the new interest in impurities. This was

$$\left[\begin{array}{c} (CH_3)_2 \underset{S}{C}\!-\!CHCO_2H \\ \quad \diagdown \quad | \\ CH\!-\!N \\ | \quad | \\ NH_2\!-\!CH\!-\!C \\ \qquad \| \\ \qquad O \end{array} \right]_{n\,+\,2} \qquad \longrightarrow$$

$$(CH_3)_2\underset{S}{C}\!-\!CHCO_2H \quad \left[(CH_3)_2\underset{S}{C}\!-\!CHCO_2H \right] \quad (CH_3)_2\underset{S}{C}\!-\!CHCO_2H$$

especially true because of complications which arose on trying
to separate preformed polymers from monomeric penicillin.
The very processes of prolonged dialysis or gel diffusion gave
rise to new macromolecular entities. And after initial
purification, changes continued to occur on standing. When
polymers of benzylpenicillin and 6-APA were tested for
antigenicity, they were found incapable of eliciting antibody
formation, but they were very antigenic when used as the
challenge in the passive cutaneous anaphylaxis test[7].

NORMAN H. GRANT

By what mechanisms could a non-amino penicillin, such as
benzylpenicillin, polymerize? Two may be suggested. The
formation of a trace of penicilloic acid under mildly alkaline
conditions would initiate a series of nucleophilic attacks by the
secondary amine:

where R is $C_6H_5CH_2$ for benzylpenicillin.

An alternative route not requiring any penicilloic acid
has been shown for non-penicillin β-lactams[13]:

It is noteworthy that this scheme results in a polymer possessing an intact terminal β-lactam in the R group; it would thus remain capable of acylating amino groups on small molecules and proteins.

In order to follow polymerization in solution, an unequivocal assay is needed, and this is readily available with the important group of semi-synthetic penicillins containing a primary amino group. These display 'broad-spectrum' antibacterial activity, i.e., they are effective against a large variety of gram-positive and gram-negative organisms. Two members of this group are α-aminobenzylpenicillin (generic name: ampicillin)[14] (V;R_1=phenyl, R_2=H) and 6-(1-aminocyclohexanecarboxamide) penicillanic acid[15] (V;R_1 and R_2 joined as cyclohexyl).

V

VI

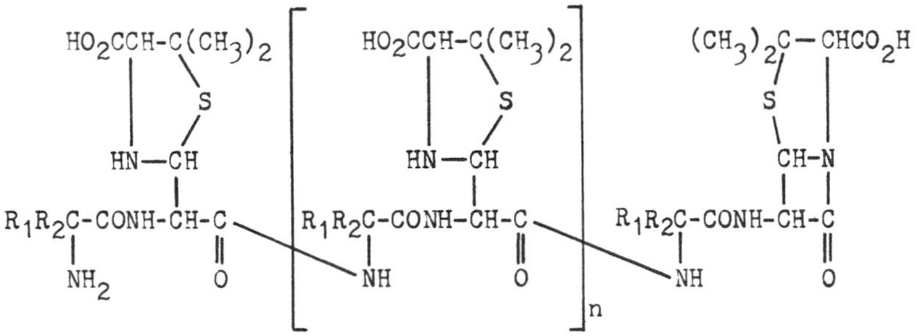

VII

NORMAN H. GRANT

Because of the free amino group, fresh solutions of the penicillin are very sensitive to the ninhydrin reaction, giving a linear response with concentration. A penicilloic acid (VI) or its decarboxylation product would be expected to give a higher color yield with ninhydrin, due to the uncovered secondary amino group. A polypeptide (VIII) and deketopiperazine would both give a lower ninhydrin response owing to binding of these formerly free amino groups.

TABLE 1. Hydrolytic and Polymerization Products of Ampicillin

	Ampicillin	Penicilloate	A	B	C
β -Lactam (relative)	100	0	30	24	0
Ninhydrin (relative)	100	115	59	49	20
Molecular Weight	367	385	750-900[a] 1211[b]	1210-1480[a] 1396[b]	-[c]

[a] From osmometric analysis.

[b] From β -lactam analysis by hydroxamate.

[c] Too insoluble for accurate molecular weight determination.

The data in Table 1 supports this hypothesis for ampicillin. The reaction products described in this table were prepared by incubating saturated ampicillin solutions for 11 days at 22°, after which they were dried without fractionation. Initial and final pH's were 7.5 and 6.7 for system A and 7.7 and

6.8 for system B (to which a trace of pyridine was added as catalyst); a third product C, was the precipitate which formed from system B. Several lines of evidence indicate that under such experimental conditions ampicillin polypeptides predominate over the diketopiperazine and penicilloate. Titration curves for A and B indicate the presence of a primary amine ($pK_3 = 7.5$) not present in the diketopiperazine. Infrared patterns of ampicillin and the three ampicillin products of Table 1 all show NH stretching bands near 3300 cm^{-1} and amide II bands near 1525 cm^{-1}, while the simplest diketopiperazine, glycine anhydride, does not absorb at those frequencies. Finally, increases in number-average molecular weight to values corresponding to a trimer or tetramer accompanied the decrease in ninhydrin reactivity. Similar analyses for 6-APA also showed a correlation between polypeptide formation and ninhydrin changes[12].

In solution, polymerization and hydrolysis can proceed simultaneously, and the ninhydrin changes reflect the net effect. Direct comparison of the amino penicillins revealed striking divergence in their degradative pathways.

Table 2 shows that a saturated solution of ampicillin at pH 8.0 lost most of its ninhydrin reactivity, while at each assay period the 1-aminoalicyclic penicillin had a net gain. In harmony with this finding, dialysis of the reaction mixture led to significantly more nondialyzable ampicillin product.

TABLE 2. Polymerization and Hydrolysis at pH 8. 0 and 22°

	Ampicillin[a]	Aminocyclohexane Penicillin[a]
β - Lactam (% change)		
2 days	-25	-7
5 days	-50	-25
7 days	-50	-30
Ninhydrin (% change)		
2 days	not assayed	+2
5 days	-56	+15
7 days	-69	+21
Dialysis (% retained)	12	4

[a]Saturated solutions of the anhydrates.

Alterations in 6-APA properties were compared with those of the amino penicillins.   Incubation at 37° for 6 days at pH 7. 4 (Table 3) led to quantities of nondialyzable or slowly dialyzable products which fixed the comparative polymerizing tendency of the three materials as follows: ampicillin > 6-APA > 6-(1-aminocyclohexanecarboxamide)penicillanic acid.   Again, if we view polymerization as tying up primary amino groups (in turn, lowering ninhydrin reactivity) and hydrolysis as liberating secondary amino groups (enhancing ninhydrin reactivity), all

the ninhydrin analyses confirm this order. Exclusion chromatography, using Sephadex G-10, further confirmed this order;
incubated ampicillin systems possessed by far the most material
of molecular weight greater than 700.

TABLE 3. Polymerization and Hydrolysis at pH 7.4 and 37°

	6-APA[a]	Ampicillin[a]	Aminocyclo-hexane Penicillin[a]
β-Lactam (% change)	-78	-86	-82
Ninhydrin (% change)	+5	-46	+39
Terminal dialysis (% retained)	11	31	5

[a]Penicillins initially purified by dialysis. Incubation conditions:
all compounds 10.8% w/v in 0.06 M potassium phosphate
buffer, 6 days. Precipitate formed in ampicillin system.

The role of penicillin polymers in clinical hypersensitivity
remains to definitively established. The present study,
comparing two highly active broad-spectrum penicillins,
shows that a strong tendency toward polymerization may not
be an inherent property of such compounds.

ACKNOWLEDGMENTS
I am indebted to Dr. Harvey E. Alburn for valuable discussions and to Misses Catherine Parrott and Betsy Hamblin
for their skilled technical assistance.

REFERENCES

1. Antibiotics (H. W. Florey, E. Chain, N. G. Heatley, M. A. Jennings, A. G. Sanders, E. P. Abraham, and M. E. Florey, eds.), Vol. 2, Oxford Univ. Press, Oxford, 1949, pp. 1200-1221.

2. B. B. Levine, Arch. Biochem. Biophys., 93, 50 (1961).

3. E. S. Wagner, W. W. Davis, and M. Gorman, Division of Organic Chemistry, 155th Meeting, American Chemical Society, San Francisco, California, April, 1968.

4. C. H. Schneider and A. L. deWeck, Helv. Chim. Acta, 49, 1695 (1966).

5. C. H. Schneider and A. L. deWeck, Nature, 208, 57 (1965).

6. F. R. Batchelor, J. M. Dewdney, and D. Gazzard, Nature, 206, 362 (1965).

7. F. R. Batchelor, J. G. Feinberg, J. M. Dewdney, and R. D. Weston, The Lancet, 1175 (1967).

8. G. T. Stewart, The Lancet, 1177 (1967).

9. E. T. Knudsen, O. P. W. Robinson, E. A. P. Croyden, and E. C. Tees, The Lancet, 1184 (1967).

10. F. Dursch, The Lancet, 1005 (1968).

11. A. L. deWeck, C. H. Schneider, and J. Gutersohn, Int. Arch. Allergy, 33, 535 (1968).

12. N. H. Grant, D. E. Clark, and H. E. Alburn, J. Am. Chem. Soc., 84, 876 (1962).

13. H. Bestian, Angew. Chem. Internat., 7, 278 (1968)

14. F. P. Doyle, J. H. C. Nayler, H. Smith, and E. R. Stove, Nature, 191, 1091 (1961).

15. H. E. Alburn, D. E. Clark, H. Fletcher, III, and N. H. Grant, Antimicrobial Agents and Chemotherapy, 586 (1967).

METHODS FOR PRODUCING OCTADECATONIC ANHYDROPOLYMERS OF AMINO ACIDS

S. W. Fox, C. -T. Wang, T. V. Waehneldt,
T. Nakashima, G. Krampitz, T. Hayakawa,
and K. Harada

Institute of Molecular Evolution
and Biochemistry Department
University of Miami, Coral Gables, Florida

INTRODUCTION

One emphasis in the polymerizations in our laboratory differs from those in more traditional polyamino acid and polymer laboratories. This departure consists of the simultaneous condensation of 18 monomers. We have been drawn to this newer emphasis because of a great respect for the selective advantages which in general have fueled the evolutionary process.

The results obtained have underlined the benefits accruing from polymers containing a large variety of monomers, each with its own kind of reactive side chain. Both proteins and models of protein which contain 18 kinds of amino acid are seen to permit a wide array of finely and subtly tuned specificities in the individual macromolecules. These have become, more vividly than before[1], the material basis for biological variety in specificity. In pursuing the objective

499

of studying polymers of 18 kinds of monomer, we have come
to realize that copolymerization often yields results which
could not have been predicted from homopolymerization
experiments.

Moreover, the total results suggest that hydrocarbon side
chains of different types contribute significantly to specific
interactions. The resultant reactivity is beyond that of the
more chemically overt side chains such as those bearing
carboxylic and amino groups. When the exponentially increased
number of possibilities due to interactions of side chains of
various types within the same macromolecule is recognized,
a molecular basis for specificity and evolved specialization
becomes yet clearer.

Another point of view emerging from such studies is that
the fundamental structure-function relationship is that of the
relative positioning of the reactive side chains as they are
constrained by the macromolecule. This three-dimensional
relationship is the significant basis at the molecular level.
The sequences of amino acid residues[2] are, in this view,
only a means to an end. The relative contributions of sequence
or of conformed composition can be tested in polymers.

A disadvantage of the polymerization approach to peptide
formation is that the processes do not yield sequences such
as are prespecified by the chemist when he synthesizes the
kinds of peptide which are the main subject of this symposium.

Extensive studies on one of the three methods to be reviewed here, the thermal, shows however that predetermined sequences are obtained. The information fed into the peptides formed is in this case not from the chemist primarily; it is information furnished by the reacting amino acids.

Another disadvantage of the thermal method is that it yields polymers in which reacted L-α -amino acids are largely, albeit not entirely, racemized. This finding of partial optical activity is valuable in understanding the evolution of primordial proteins to yield the sequences with which peptidechemists are predominantly concerned. The confused consequences are, however, disturbing for the step- wise synthesist. This result points to another consequence of cocondensation of 18 monomers. When successful, such methods generate new questions for which many years are required to accumulate the answers.

The term octadecatonic in the title is designed to indicate polymers composed of 18 or more kinds of amino acid. Octadecamer has been suggested, but this signifies size of polymer, not number of types of monomer.

Thermal Condensation

FIG. 1 demonstrates the result of the pyrocondensation of amino acids, which is the method most studied for achieving the objectives indicated[3]. This work has been aided particularly by Drs. Harada, Krampitz, and Waehneldt, and Mr. Wang.

501

FIG. 1

Results of heating amino acids above boiling point of water.
Left--indiscriminate mixture of amino acids. Center--
pigmented polymer from heated mixture containing sufficient
dicarboxylic amino acid. Right--polymer freed of pigment.

The tube on the left illustrates the result often encountered by peptide chemists in indiscriminate heating of amino acids. If, however, one employs sufficient proportions of aspartic acid, glutamic acid, or lysine, polymers of genuine peptide nature result. The amino acids are initially heated dry. In this case they consisted of one part of aspartic acid, one part of glutamic acid, and one part of the 16 other amino acids, common to protein, present in equimolar proportions in that part[4]. The amino acids were heated to 170° for 6 hours. The product was not a dark forbidding material, but rather a light amber colored material which upon granulation and purification yielded the lightly pigmented material shown, a 1:1:1-proteinoid. This simple process invariably produces the pigment, which is tenaciously held. Many experiments, some conducted recently by Mr. A. Weber, emphasize that the principal contributor to the color is the amino acid glycine. (When polyphosphoric acid is added to the reaction mixture much coloration ensues easily.) On the right is seen a preparation in which the polymer has been freed of pigment by fractional crystallization. This can be managed in other ways. Recently we have learned that this pigment is a photosensitizing pigment[5]. The pigmented proteinoid greatly accelerates in visible light some of the reactions catalyzed under other conditions by proteinoid. The molecular weights of these polymers are many thousands, typically in the range

of 4,000-10,000. Some proportion of each of the amino
acids common to protein is found in the polymers; cystine,
serine, and threonine suffering substantial decomposition.
The heating of amino acids in the dry state overcomes the
free energy barrier which stands in the way of coupling free
amino acids in aqueous solution[6].

The evidence that these polymers are essentially polypeptides is essentially the evidence that has been accumulated
for the peptide nature of proteins[3]. The polymers give biuret
tests. They show the same infrared absorption spectra except
that the acid proteinoids have also imide groups. These latter
easily hydrolyze in aqueous solution to peptide bonds. The
initial products show little or no ninhydrin color but upon
complete hydrolysis they give the ninhydrin-reactive amino
acids. The polymers are split by proteolytic enzymes, although
in some cases less rapidly, or far less rapidly, than is true
for proteins. This susceptibility is increased by treatment with
urea in aqueous solution[7]. Rohlfing has shown that when these
are heated in aqueous solution, a change in conformation of
the whole macromolecule results[8]. While this change is not
identical to denaturation, inasmuch as covalent bonds are
broken, the evidence indicates that the molecule as a whole is
unfolded.

The heating of amino acids has produced polymers that are
sharply limited in their heterogeneity[9]. This finding was

somewhat unexpected by some. One of the earlier kinds of

result which pointed to limited heterogeneity was that in which

a 2:2:3-proteinoid was purified from hot water by cooling,

whereupon it separated, much in the fashion of a recrystal-

lization. The amino acid analyses of such material were

very similar[10] (Table 1).

TABLE 1. Composition of Hydrolyzates (110°, 4 Days) of
2:2:3-Proteinoid Following One and Two
Purifications

Amino Acid	Unpurified	Purified	Repurified
	%	%	%
Lysine	5.1[a]	5.4	5.4
Histidine	1.8	2.0	2.0
Ammonia	8.6	8.1	6.9
Arginine	2.0	2.3	2.4
Aspartic acid	51.7	50.2	51.1
Glutamic acid	10.7	11.6	12.0
Proline	0.7	0.6	0.6
Glycine	2.7	3.1	2.8
Alanine	4.0	4.3	5.5
Half-cystine[b]	4.5	3.5	3.4
Valine	1.2	1.2	1.2
Methionine	1.8	1.9	1.7
Isoleucine[c]	1.2	1.3	0.9
Leucine	1.3	1.2	1.1
Tyrosine	2.0	1.9	1.7
Phenylalanine	1.8	1.7	1.5
Total recovery[d]	84.8	97.5	100.0

[a]Values are given in gram residues of amino acid/total gram residues.

[b]Half-cystine values may be partly other material.

[c]Isoleucine includes alloisoleucine.

[d]Total recovery = total residues of amino acid/wt. of polymer.

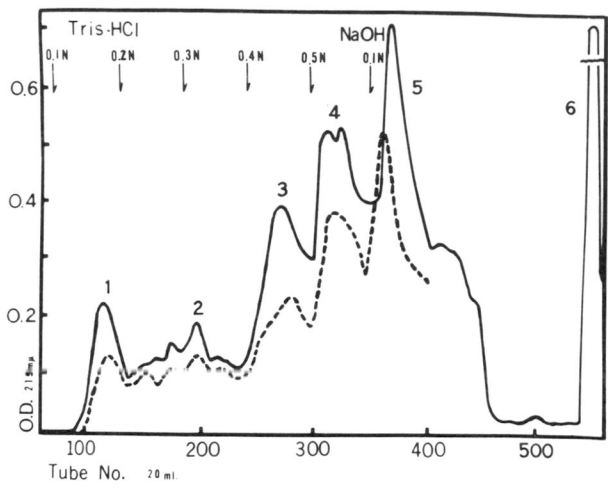

FIG. 2

Elution pattern of 1:1:1-proteinoidamide from DEAE-cellulose.

    The curves of FIG. 2 were obtained by elution from
DEAE-cellulose of a 1:1:1-proteinoid amidated in liquid
ammonia. (The 1:1:1 signifies proportions in the reaction
mixture of 1 aspartic acid:1 glutamic acid:1 basic-neutral
amino acids referred to in the previous figure.) Five major
fractions are removed from the column; a sixth is separated
by the use of sodium hydroxide solution. The fractionation
has been carried out seven times with substantial similarities
in each fractionation. The broken line indicates the elution
pattern on the second run. The saddle which appears from
the first experiment was found on that occasion only. While
this is a discontinuous elution interrupted by changes in concentration of the tris buffer, gradient elutions give essentially

the same pattern. Instead of a random distribution of macro-molecules, as would be indicated by a horizontal line, one sees these five or six major peaks. These and other data indicate that the macromolecules segregate into a small number of types as judged in standard ways. The total number of kinds of evidence, all of which point in the same direction, are seven or eight[9].

FIG. 3 shows the results obtained in analyses of hydroly-zates of fractions from the DEAE-cellulose following further purification. In the three upper chromatograms of FIG. 3 are seen the total hydrolyzates of fractions 3, 4, and 5 from the DEAE-cellulose column. The principal differences are found in the leucine area. The composition is quite highly uniform among these three fractions, which represent 38% of the total material. A chromatogram of the hydrolyzate of the crude material is similar in appearance.

In the lower three chromatograms of FIG. 3 we see partial (mineral acid) hydrolyzates of the material from the same three peaks obtained from the DEAE-cellulose column. These are, thus, "fingerprints" from the amino acid analyzer. The partial hydrolyzates are virtually indistinguishable one from the other, as was observed also in two dimensional chromatograms. Each chromatogram has 40 peaks in the original. Fifteen of these are ascribable to amino acids, the others being peptides. That they are peptides was demonstrated

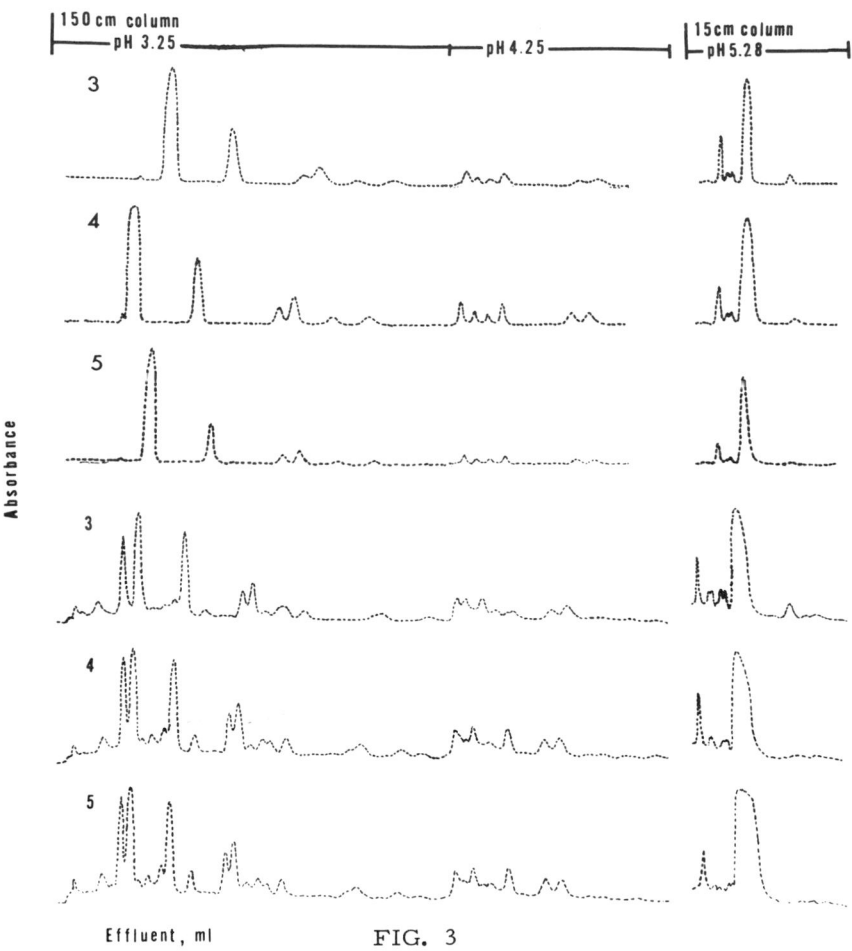

FIG. 3

Chromatograms of hydrolyzates of fractions 3, 4, and 5 from DEAE-cellulose. Top three are for complete hydrolyzates, bottom three are for partial hydrolyzates.

by the fact that further hydrolysis showed increased ninhydrin reactivity. We are led by these results to the thought that not only is the composition quite highly uniform throughout the polymer; the sequences appear also to be.

A more rigorous treatment of this last question is found
in other studies by Dr. Nakashima. He has pyrocondensed
glutamic acid, glycine, and tyrosine. The resultant polymer,
which has a molecular weight in the range of 4000-8000, has
been partially hydrolyzed by mineral acid, fragments have
been isolated, and some of the sequences have been assigned.
A principal fragment has the sequence indicated in FIG. 4.

Pyroglutamylglycyltyrosyl-α -glutaminyl-
tyrosylglycine

FIG. 4

Dominant hexapeptide derivative isolated from partial
hydrolyzate of pyro (glutamic acid, glycine, tyrosine).

This sequence represents at least 9% of the total
polymer. According to calculations based on an a priori
random distribution of amino acids, this hexapeptide derivative could be present only to 1%. When all of the assumptions
are recognized the occurrence would be an order of magnitude
lower. We thus again observe internal ordering effects in
the reactions of the amino acids. The reacting amino acids
are determining or specifying their sequences, as indicated
by this fraction, 4-2, from the polymer. Fraction 4-3,
present to 12%, has the pentapeptide sequence corresponding
to the C-terminal pentapeptide of the hexapeptide. The
methods used for determining these sequences have included
dinitrophenylation[11], subtractive Edman degradation[12], and

509

the use of carboxypeptidase, and of leucine aminopeptidase. The evidence from the action of leucine aminopeptidase on the hexapeptide indicates that both glutamic acid residues are present entirely in the α linkage.

Table 2 describes some of the thermal polymers obtained in the latest compositional studies[13]. This set is a group of polymers in which the compositions of histones have been mimicked. This and other similar sets each required 7 days or less for their preparation. The simplicity of the method is indicated by the relative ease with which a precisely varying set of proteinoids can be produced. In this table may be seen analyses of proteinoids containing less than 5% aspartic acid. In earlier preparations[4] larger proportions of aspartic acid were used in the reaction mixture, with the result that larger proportions of aspartic acid appeared in the polymer. A 1:1:1-proteinoid, for example, would contain 50-55% of aspartic acid[4]. No. 55 in the new study, for example, was produced from equimolar proportions of all amino acids. In the resultant polymer, a relatively small proportion of aspartic acid is found. This fact supports interpretations of earlier studies on acid types of proteinoids, in which infrared analysis indicated that the amount of branching could not be major[14]. In some proteinoids of Table 2, the percent of aspartic acid is so small that the question of a major amount of side chain branching through aspartic acid side chains does not arise.

TABLE 2

Amino Acid Composition of Hydrolyzates of Proteinoids 50-60 (in mole %)

Amino Acid	Proteinoid No.										
	50	51	52	53	54	55	56	57	58	59	60
Ala	4.38	5.21	5.64	6.34	7.01	6.79	5.59	5.81	5.02	4.59	4.22
Arg	3.85	4.47	4.90	5.27	4.75	5.15	3.93	4.01	3.99	3.81	3.46
Asp	40.34	30.08	20.31	13.72	7.25	6.26	5.71	4.91	4.12	3.56	3.65
Glu	13.91	13.78	12.12	10.45	8.57	7.78	8.79	8.85	8.07	7.78	7.45
Gly	5.88	7.33	8.26	9.41	10.97	10.70	9.74	9.13	8.00	7.35	6.97
His	3.87	4.28	5.04	5.33	4.75	5.19	4.29	4.75	4.59	4.44	4.03
Ile	2.07	2.59	3.07	4.03	6.17	6.86	4.75	3.88	2.90	2.38	2.25
Leu	4.75	5.25	6.67	7.88	10.95	11.18	9.54	8.13	6.53	5.83	5.33
Lys	6.67	9.72	12.72	14.33	14.04	15.23	26.38	36.29	39.62	44.36	47.05
Pro	1.90	2.26	3.02	3.28	3.82	3.63	3.35	3.68	3.70	2.87	2.56
Val	4.83	5.38	6.40	7.72	9.97	9.80	8.19	7.37	5.37	5.06	4.81
aIle*	2.07	2.51	3.05	3.54	5.05	5.03	3.89	3.19	2.45	2.11	2.04
NH	5.77	6.87	8.60	8.27	6.23	7.13	5.15	5.75	5.35	4.62	5.46
Basic (B) (%)	14.39	18.47	22.66	24.93	23.59	25.57	34.60	39.05	48.20	53.21	54.54
Acidic (A) (%)	54.25	43.86	32.43	24.17	15.82	14.04	14.50	13.76	12.19	11.34	11.40
B/A	0.27	0.42	0.70	1.03	1.49	1.82	2.39	2.84	3.95	4.69	4.91
Yield of soluble polymer (%)	1.43	1.78	1.53	1.29	1.05	1.15	0.73	0.95	1.00	0.89	0.64
Yield of insoluble polymer (%)	8.10	6.15	3.58	0.50	0.00	0.00	0.00	0.00	0.00	0.00	0.00

*allo-Isoleucine

One functional aspect of these histone-like proteinoids is their ability to form particulate units with polynucleotides[15]. One inference is that a ratio of basic amino acid to acidic amino acid in excess of 1.0 is necessary for such particulate units to form. The primary reaction in such formation is the neutralization of opposite charges in lysine-rich proteinoid and in polyanionic polynucleotide. Such results are modified by other copolymerized amino acids, such as the "neutral" amino acids. These experiments, therefore, tell us much more than do reactions of polynucleotides with homopolylysine. Once again, also, we find a special consequence in products resulting from copolymerization rather than merely from homopolymerization.

One example of catalytic activity in proteinoids is a progress curve for the decarboxylation of pyruvic acid in the presence of 2:2:1-proteinoid (FIG. 5). While this rate is orders of magnitude slower than the reaction catalyzed by pyruvic acid decarboxylase of the contemporary type, it is quite noticeably more rapid than the uncatalyzed reaction. The control is observed in the lower part of the graph. The hydrolyzate of the proteinoid, or the amino acids in the proportions found in the analysis of the proteinoid show little or no effect above that of the control.

Catalytic activities of the kind illustrated have now been found in at least six laboratories and recorded in more than

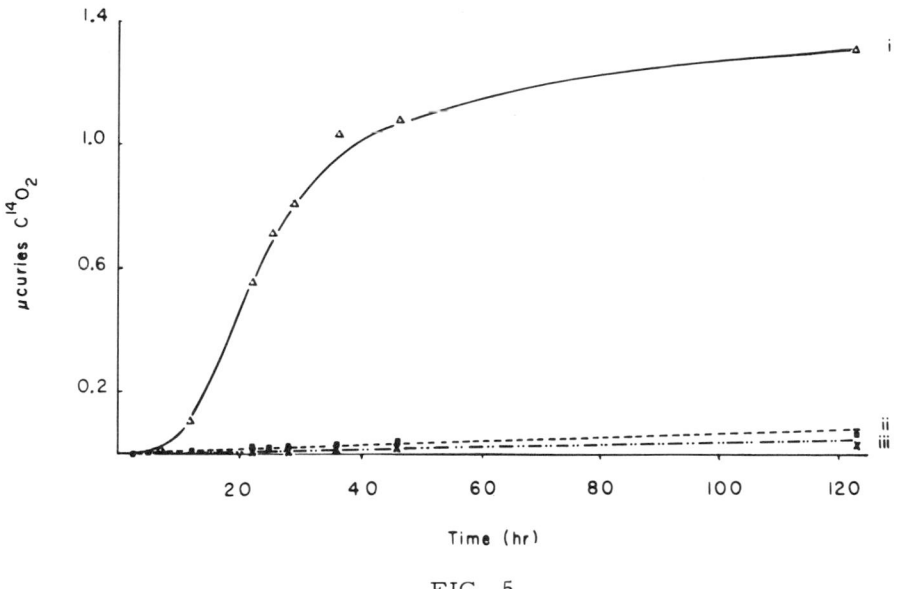

FIG. 5

Progress curve for decarboxylation of pyruvic acid.
Controls without proteinoid, and with amino acid
mixtures replacing proteinoid.

14 publications[8,16] and biblios. These are summarized in

Table 3. Some four kinds of reaction have so far been estab-

lished as catalyzed by proteinoids. These include hydrolysis,

decarboxylation, amination, and a type of deamination.

Adherence to Michaelis-Menten kinetics has been observed

in a number of these cases. The beginning of a basis for

metabolism can be constructed conceptually by placing

sequentially the catalyzed reactions of oxaloacetic acid, of

pyruvic acid to acetic acid or to alanine. Moreover, these

reactions are attended by specificities. One step in this

sequence is catalyzed almost exclusively by basic proteinoids[17],

FOX ET AL.

another is catalyzed more strongly by acidic proteinoids than by basic proteinoids[18], and the third requires Cu^{++} as a cofactor[16].

TABLE 3. Catalytic Activities Identified in Proteinoids and Other Thermal Polyamino Acids

Substrate and Reaction	Authors and Year	
Hydrolysis		
p-Nitrophenyl acetate	Fox, Harada, and Rohlfing	1962
	Rohlfing and Fox	1967
	Noguchi and Saito	1962
	Usdin, Mitz, and Killos	1967
p-Nitrophenyl phosphate	Oshima	1968
ATP (by Zn salt)	Fox	1965
Decarboxylation		
Glucuronic acid	Fox and Krampitz	1964
Pyruvic acid	Krampitz and Hardebeck	1966
	Hardebeck, Krampitz, and Wulf	1968
Oxaloacetic acid	Rohlfing	1967
Amination		
α-Ketoglutaric acid	Krampitz, Diehl and Nakashima	1967
	Krampitz, Baars-Diehl, Haas, and Nakashima	1968
Deamination		
Glutamic acid	Krampitz, Baars-Diehl, Haas, and Nakashima	1968

TABLE 4.   Contribution of Basic Amino Acids in Deletion
Studies of Acid Proteinoids for the Hydrolysis of
p-Nitrophenyl Acetate

Basic Amino Acid Omitted	Relative Activity per Unit Weight of Polymer
None	1.00
Arginine	1.14
Lysine	0.87
Histidine	0.13
Arginine and lysine	1.03
Histidine and lysine	0.44
Arginine and histidine	0.20
All basic amino acids	0.05

In Table 4 are seen the effects of deleting the amino acid

histidine and other amino acids from polymers active in

accelerating the hydrolysis of p-nitrophenyl acetate. These

polymers have come to be called "deletion polymers." They

represent a way in which one may modify such complex

polymers to derive information about the essentiality of any

one amino acid for a given function. The kind of information

obtained from deletion polymers can be used to supplement the

information available from oligotonic polymers, as in Table

5, which deals with polymers active on pyruvic acid.

In FIG. 6 is seen the result of thermally copolymerizing

the 6 amino acids which have been implicated as part of the

center of the active site in melanophore stimulating hormone[19]

These amino acids are glutamic acid, glycine, arginine,

histidine, phenylalanine, and tryptophan.

TABLE 5. Relative Activity (d. p. m.) in Decarboxylation
          of Pyruvic Acid

Polymer	Relative Activity
1:1:1-Proteinoids (5)	33,000-40,000
Hydrolyzate	4900
Trypsin	2700
Copoly (Glutamic acid, Isoleucine)	1500
Copoly (Glutamic acid, Leucine)	29,000
Copoly (Glutamic acid, Threonine)	45,000
Glutamic Acid	3000
Threonine	2500
Leucine	2600

FIG. 6a shows normal pigmentation in the frog skin. FIG. 6b shows lack of pigmentation due to hypophysectomy of the frog. The pigment granules are present but they have not matured. In FIG. 6c one sees the effect of treating the hypophysectomized frog with natural hormone. The pigment granules have in this case now been stimulated and have extended. Quite a similar result is found when the synthetic polymer is employed (FIG. 6d). The activities observed with the polymer are typically 10^3-10^4 units per gram whereas the activity in the natural hormone is 10^9-10^{10} units per gram.

In Table 6 may be seen the effect of deletion polymers on such activity.

Leuchs Polymers

We turn now to a second type of heteropolymerization of amino acids through the Leuchs' anhydrides. This was developed

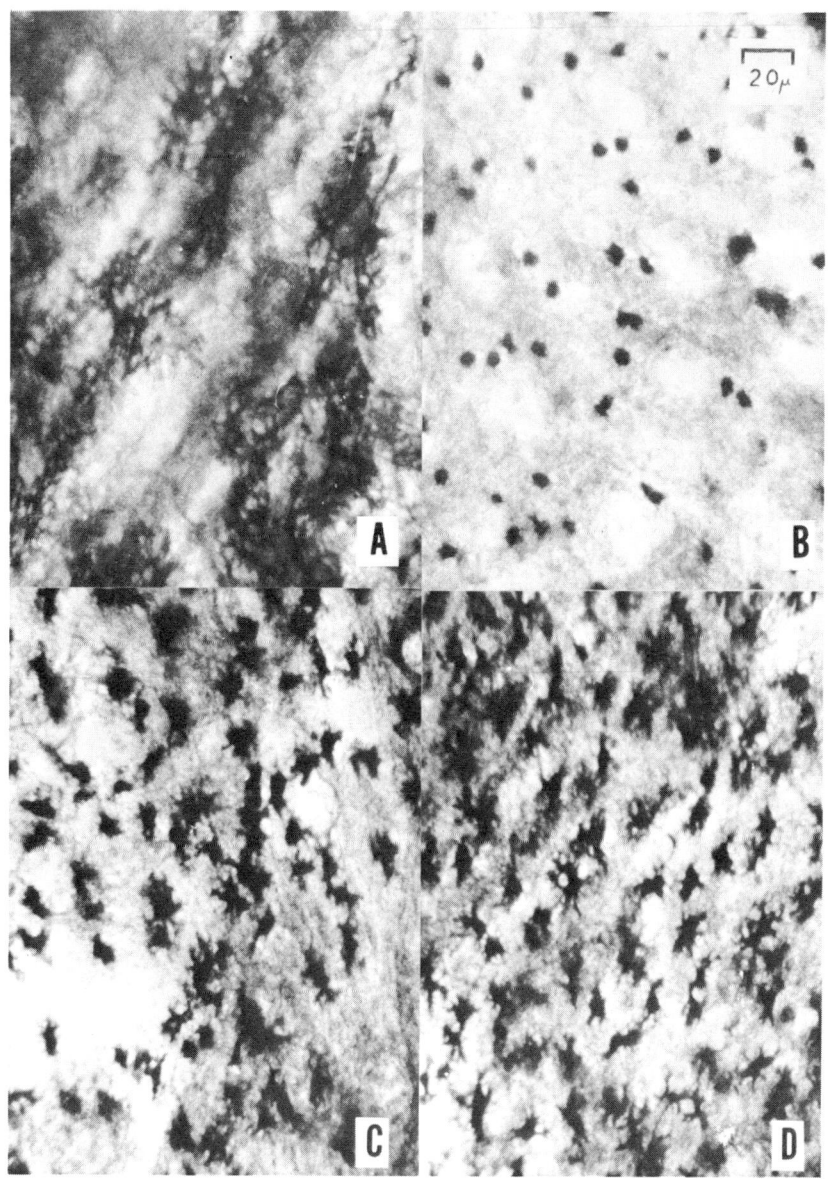

FIG. 6

a--Normal frog skin.   b-- Skin of hypophysectomized frog.
c--Skin of hypophysectomized frog treated with natural
α -MSH.   d--Same as c except thermal polymer used instead
of α -MSH.

517

FOX ET AL.

TABLE 6. Effect on Melanocyte Stimulating Acitivity of Amino
Acid Deletions from Amino Acid Polymers

	Amino Acids Present (X)					Active (+) or Inactive (0)
Arg	Glu	Gly	His	Phe	Try	
X	X	X	X	X	X	+
X	X	X	X	X		+
X	X	X	X		X	0
X	X			X	X	+
X	X		X	X	X	+
X		X	X	X	X	0[a]
	X	X	X	X	X	0
X	X	X		X		+

[a]This product essentially not a polymer, due to absence of glutamic acid in mixture

first by Dr. Hayakawa[20]. The intricate procedure requires making Leuchs' anhydrides of the 18 common amino acids, 9 of which have to be especially protected. These were all protected by substituting groups which were simultaneously removeable by hydrogenolysis[20].

One of the proteinoids to be made this way, a so-called natural ratio Leuchs' proteinoid, is presented in FIG. 7. The first and third chromatograms placed in sequence represent a typical amino acid profile for a protein hydrolyzate. For comparison was used the first comparable graph found in the literature when this work was completed. This was the amino acid profile of the hydrolyzate of the α -amylase of Bacillus stearothermophilus[20]. The great similarity is obvious. Only in the synthetic polymer is found some proportion of one artifact, which is absent from the natural.

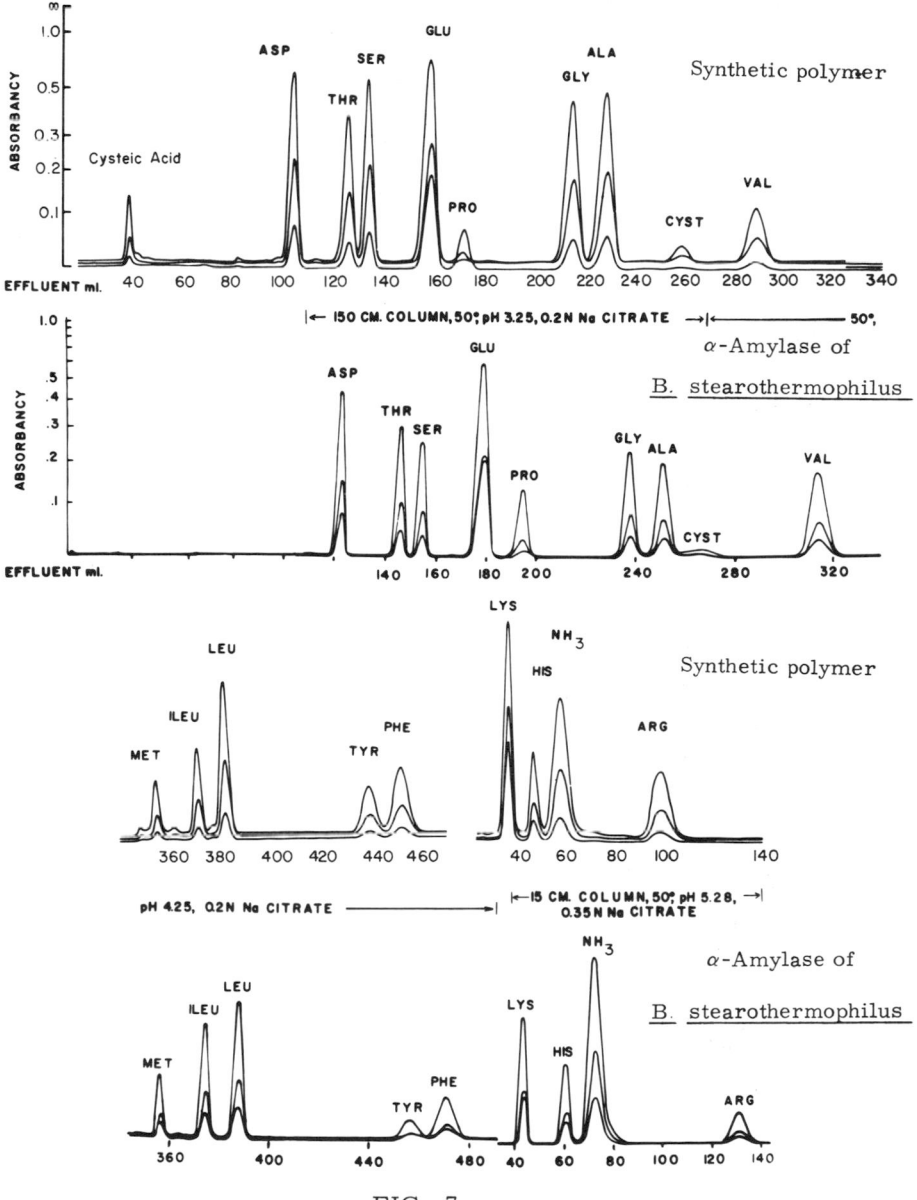

FIG. 7

Interdigitated chromatograms, of hydrolyzates of Leuchs'
proteinoid and of α-amylase of Bacillus stearothermophilus.

Molecular weights of these polymers are in the range of 2500-7000. In this case no racemization has occurred and the optical activity of hydrolyzates of such polymers shows the same value as the equivalent mixture of L-amino acids.

In Table 7 are again seen the effects of deletion. When histidine is omitted from the reaction mixture of a Leuchs' proteinoid much less activity on p-nitrophenyl acetate is the result.

TABLE 7. Influence of Various Forms of Histidine on Rate of Hydrolysis of p-Nitrophenyl Acetate

Compound	Conc. compound/ liter	Conc. histidine/ liter	Rate relative to that of histidine
L-Histidine	10 mg	10	1.0
NRLP[a]	441	10	2.9
(2:2:3) LP[b]	415	10	1.7
ERLP[c]	173	10	2.7
Histidine-free ERLP 200		-	0.5
Histidine-free ERLP 200 plus histidine	10	10	2.1

[a]Natural Ratio Leuchs' Proteinoid

[b]Leuchs' Proteinoid

[c]Equimolar Ratio Leuchs' Proteinoid

Condensation of Amino Acid Adenylates

We turn now to the third method of panpolymerization, which employs the amino acid adenylates for condensation.

This method is of particular interest in the evolutionary context inasmuch as contemporary organisms use amino acid adenylates for the synthesis of protein[21]. The literature reveals only a few papers on chemical studies of amino acid adenylates. In no case did we find that anyone had copolymerized two or more adenylates. For the reasons given in the introduction, however, Dr. Krampitz undertook the simultaneous copolymerization of the 18 amino acid adenylates. FIG. 8 demonstrates that when the amino

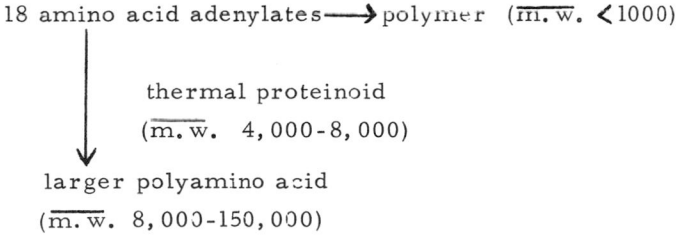

18 amino acid adenylates ⟶ polymer ($\overline{m.w.}$ < 1000)

thermal proteinoid
($\overline{m.w.}$ 4,000-8,000)

larger polyamino acid
($\overline{m.w.}$ 8,000-150,000)

FIG. 8

Flow sheet of condensation of amino acid adenylates with and without thermal proteinoid.

acid adenylates made from the mixture of the 18 common amino acids are brought together in aqueous solution they yield mainly a very small polymer. When they are brought together in aqueous solution in which thermal proteinoid is already dissolved, they produce a larger polymer.

Table 8 shows the analysis of the small polymer obtained.

521

FOX ET AL.

TABLE 8. Analysis of Hydrolyzates of Condensation Product
of Adenylates of Methionine, Phenylalanine,
Serine, and Tryptophan

Amino Acid	Mole %
Methionine	34.6
Phenylalanine	46.4
Serine	17.9
Unidentified peaks	1.1*

*On leucine equivalent basis

Table 9 presents an analysis of a neutral proteinoid of
the histone-like type which has been modified by the adenylate
reaction. The underlines indicate those amino acids which
are ordinarily absent from histones and which are present,
however, in some measure in the modified proteinoid.

FIG. 9 shows the effect of pepsin on lysine-rich proteinoid
modified by the adenylate reaction. Pepsin of course does
not act upon the lysine-rich proteinoid itself. As the
chromatogram shows, it acts to split the adduct peptide
portion of the larger molecule. This is a first evidence of
some linearity in the adenylate portion. Further investigations will examine the question of how much linearity is to
be found in the various modified proteinoids in general.
Also, the question of what other properties may be modified
by the reaction with adenylates is to be investigated. We
know already that the tendency of such polymers to assemble
themselves into particulate units[22] is improved in these
new polymers.

TABLE 9

Compositions of Neutral Proteinoid Before and After
Coupling with Amino Acid Adenylates

Amino Acid	Hydrolyzates of		
	Polymer of Adenylates Alone*	Neutral Proteinoid	Neutral Proteinoid Modified by Adenylates
Lysine	2.9%	17.1%	18.1%
Histidine	1.1	5.2	4.7
Ammonia	53	7.3	6.9
Arginine	1.9	5.6	5.1
Aspartic acid	4.6	9.5	10.4
Threonine	2.2	0.0	0.1
Serine	1.9	0.0	0.2
Glutamic acid	4.3	9.3	7.5
Proline	2.3	4.8	4.7
Glycine	5.0	15.0	15.8
Alanine	6.4	8.4	8.4
Half-cystine	– **	0.0	1.0
Valine	3.3	7.0	6.6
Methionine	0.3	0.0	0.3
Isoleucine	2.0	1.9	1.8
Leucine	4.3	7.3	6.8
Tyrosine	0.0	0.0	0.1
Phenylalanine	2.0	0.0	0.3
Alloisoleucine		0.0	0.9
Unidentified peaks	2.7***	0.9***	0.4***

*Det'd on purified fraction

**Amino acid not included in reaction

***On basis of leucine equivalent

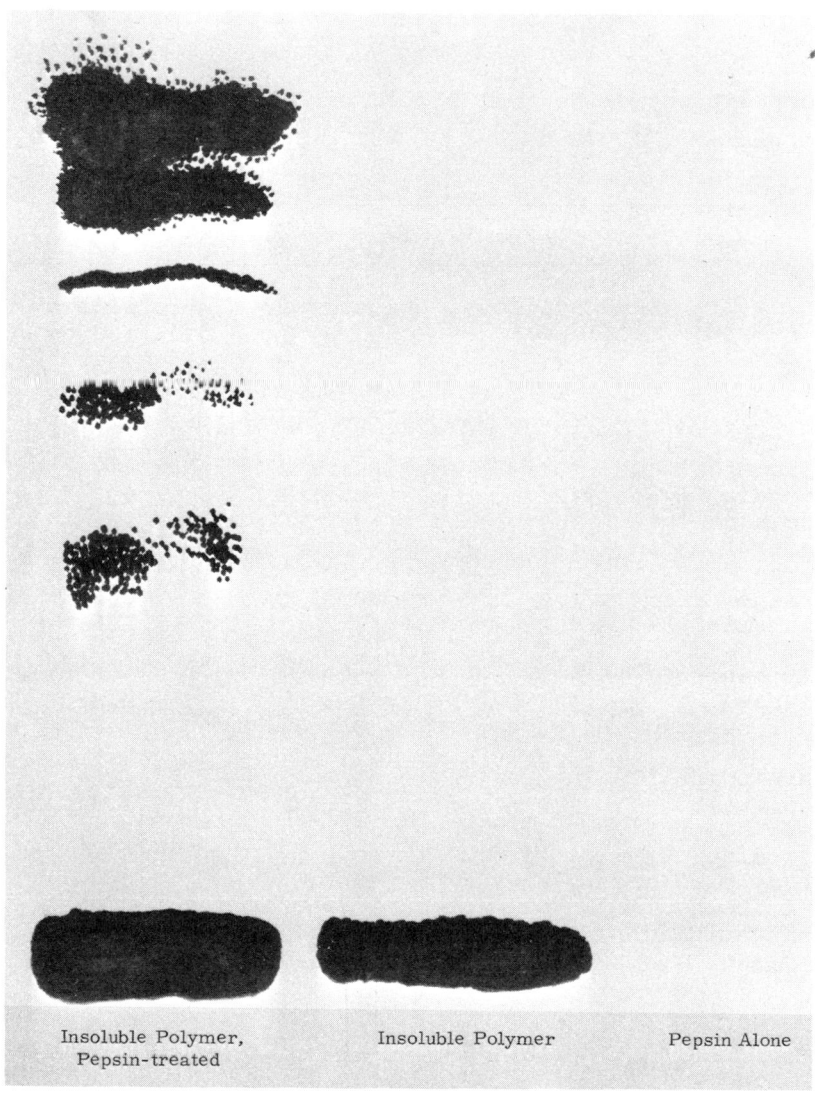

FIG. 9

Effect of pepsin on proteinoid formed by reaction of lysine-rich thermal proteinoid with mixed 18 amino acid adenylates.

SUMMARY

By way of summary, three methods of producing octadecatonic polymers or polymers containing more than 18
monomers have been described. Secondly some of these,
particularly the thermal polymers, have been extensively
characterized. Finally, all of the studies emphasize that
copolymerization of reacting amino acids or reactive amino
acid derivatives give results which could not be predicted from
attempts to homopolymerize such compounds. The scope of
these enhanced results is enlarged by the copolymerization
of as many as 18 monomers, the approximate number which
has played a large role in evolution.

ACKNOWLEDGMENTS

We thank Mr. C. R. Windsor for numerous analyses.
We thank the National Aeronautics and Space Administration
for Grant NsG-689. Contribution no. 116 of the Institute of
Molecular Evolution.

REFERENCES

1. A. E. Needham, The Uniqueness of Biological Material,
   Pergamon Press, Oxford, 1965.

2. S. W. Fox, Advances Protein Chem., 2, 155 (1945).

3. S. W. Fox, Nature, 205, 328 (1965).

4. S. W. Fox and K. Harada, J. Am. Chem. Soc., 82,
   3745 (1960).

5. A. L. Weber, A. Wood, H. C. Hardebeck, and S. W. Fox, Federation Proc., 27, 830 (1968).

6. S. W. Fox, A. Vegotsky, K. Harada, and P. D. Hoagland, Ann. N. Y. Acad. Sci., 69, 328 (1957).

7. G. Krampitz, unpublished information.

8. D. L. Rohlfing and S. W. Fox, Arch. Biochem. Biophys. 118, 127 (1967).

9. S. W. Fox and T. Nakashima, Biochim. Biophys. Acta., 140, 155 (1967).

10. S. W. Fox, K. Harada, K. R. Woods, and C. R. Windsor, Arch. Biochem. Biophys., 102, 439 (1963).

11. F. Sanger and E. O. Thompson, Biochem. J., 53, 353 (1953).

12. S. W. Fox, T. L. Hurst, and C. Warner, J. Am. Chem. Soc., 76, 1154 (1954).

13. S. W. Fox and T. V. Waehneldt, Biochim. Biophys. Acta, 160, 246 (1967).

14. S. W. Fox, in Polyamino Acids, Polypeptides, and Proteins, (M. Stahmann, ed.), University of Wisconsin Press, Madison, 1962, p. 54.

15. T. V. Waehneldt and S. W. Fox, Biochim. Biophys. Acta, 160, 239 (1968).

16. G. Krampitz, S. Diehl, and T. Nakashima, Naturwissenschaften, 19, 516 (1967).

17. D. L. Rohlfing, Arch. Biochem. Biophys., 118, 468 (1967).

18. H. G. Hardebeck, G. Krampitz, and L. Wulf, Arch. Biochem. Biophys., 123, 72 (1968).

19. S. W. Fox and C.-T. Wang, Science, 160, 547 (1968).

20. T. Hayakawa, C. R. Windsor, and S. W. Fox, Arch. Biochem. Biophys., 118, 265 (1967).

21. J. M. Buchanan, in The Origins of Prebiological Systems, (S. W. Fox, ed.), Academic Press, New York, 1965, p. 101.

22. S. W. Fox, Encyclopedia of Polymer Science and Technology, (H. Mark, N. E. Gaylord, and M. M. Bikales, eds.), 9, 284,(1968).

ENZYMATIC DIGESTION OF C-TERMINAL ^{3}H-LABELED PEPTIDES AND ITS POSSIBLE USEFULNESS FOR THE STRUCTURAL STUDY OF PROTEINS

Hisayauki Matsuo[1] and Hiroshi Matsubara

Department of Entomology and Space Sciences Laboratory
University of California, Berkeley, California

Selective tritiation of the C-terminal amino acids in polypeptide chains has recently been proposed by one of the present authors (H. Matsuo) as a new method for identifying the C-terminal amino acids in proteins[2-6]. As shown in FIG. 1, proteins are selectively tritiated at their C-terminal amino acids through racemization mechanism via oxazolone formation by the action of acetic anhydride and pyridine in a medium containing ^{3}H$_2$O.

This new method has successively been applied in the C-terminal determination of several proteins, such as ferredoxins (Scenedesmus[7] and Chromatium[8]), glutamic acid-oxaloacetic acid transaminase (mitochondrial[9] and supernatant[9]) and ovine-luteinizing hormone[10], as well as beef insulin[3], lysozyme[4], ribonuclease T$_1$[4], clupein Z[11], beef cytochrome c[11], and human haemoglobin[9].

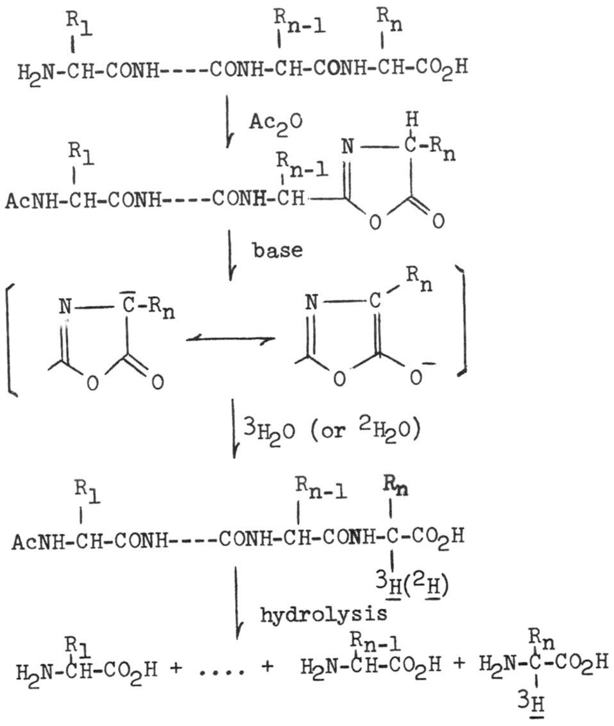

FIG. 1

Tritiation of c-terminal amino acids.

Moreover, the application of this method to DNP-protein resulted into the simultaneous determination of N- and C-terminal amino acids[5].

The present study describes the enzymatic digestion of C-terminal tritiated peptides which were readily obtained by the above method. This facilitates the detection of C-terminal fragments in enzymatic digests by radioactivity.

Our investigations were carried out with Scenedesmus ferredoxin and a peptide derived from it during the course of structural studies of Scenedesmus ferredoxin, whose primary structure has recently been established by the group of one of the present authors (H. Matsubara)[7,12].

The results indicate the usefulness of tryptic and chymo-tryptic digestion of the tritiated peptides in identifying C-terminal fragments.

C-TERMINAL DETERMINATION BY TRITIATION REACTION

Protein (10 - 50 nonamole) was dissolved in a mixture of 0.1 ml of ^3H_2O (0.1 - 10mC) and 0.2 ml of pyridine. Acetic anhydride (0.05 ml) was added to the solution under ice-cooling and the whole was kept at room temperature for several hours. After evaporation in vacuo below 40°, addition of ordinary water, followed by evaporation, was repeated several times to remove completely the washable radio-isotope. The C-terminal tritiated protein thus obtained was hydrolyzed in 6 N HCl at 110° in an evacuated tube for 24 hours.

After removal of HCl in a vacuum desiccator, the resulting amino acid mixture was separated by an appropriate method such as paper chromatography, electrophoresis or their combination. The radio-active spot from the map was easily detected by the scintillation spectrometric measurement of all spots which were cut out of the amino acid map. For the characterization of radioactive amino acid, the radio-gas chromatography was also useful[6]: In the case of C-terminal determination of Scenedesmus ferredoxin, the use of water-soluble carbodiimide (1-ethyl-3-(3-dimethylaminopropyl)carbodiimide) in place of acetic anhydride has given satisfactory ^{3}H-incorporation into C-terminal phenylalanine.

All C-terminal amino acids except proline can be easily determined by this method under mild conditions and in a microscale.

TRYPTIC DIGESTION OF C-TERMINAL TRITIATED PEPTIDE

As shown in FIG. 2, the peptide (C-V), one of the C-terminal fragments obtained by chymotryptic digestion of carboxymethylated Scenedesmus ferredoxin, has one lysine residue whose peptide linkage is susceptible to trypsin. To protect the free amino group of lysine from acetylation which might occur during subsequent tritiation reaction, 0.337 μmole of peptide C-V was treated with F_3CCOSEt and 1 N NaOH at pH 9.8 as described by Goldberger and Anfinsen[13]. This yielded the corresponding N-trifluoroacetyl peptide (TFA-C-V). Purification was carried out on a small Dowex 1-X2 column equilibrated with a buffer containing 0.124 M pyridine and 0.003 M acetic acid by successive elutions with the same buffer and 30% acetic acid. Lyophilization of the fraction eluted by acetic acid gave a pure peptide, TFA-C-V (ninhydrin: -, Pauli: +), which was subjected to tritiation reaction by the

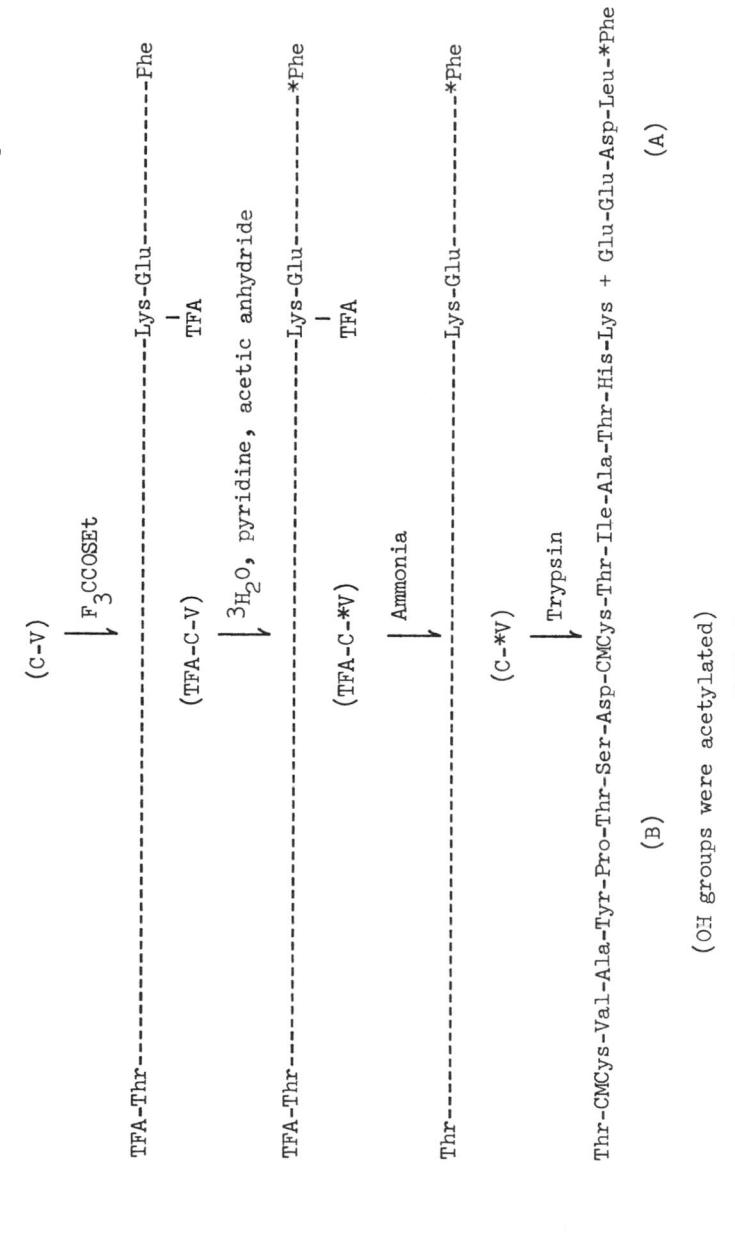

FIG. 2

Schematic representation of trifluoroacetylation, tritiation, and trypsin digestion of C-terminal fragment of Scenedesmus ferredoxin.

533

method described by Matsuo et al. [3] as follows: Peptide TFA-C-V was dissolved in 0.1 ml (10 mC) of ^3H_2O and pyridine (0.2 ml), and acetic anhydride (0.05 ml) was added. The solution was allowed to stand at room temperature overnight to yield the corresponding radioactive peptide (TFA-C-*V), which gave only one spot (+15 cm, ninhydrin: -, Pauli: +) on electrophoresis (pH 6.5, 2000V, 1 hr.). The removal of the TFA group was carried out by exposing the peptide to ammonia in an evacuated desiccator by the method of Perham and Jones [14]) to produce a ninhydrin-positive peptide (C-V), with free NH_2-groups and acetylated hydroxyl groups. The structure of peptide C-*V was confirmed by amino acid analysis and radioactivity measurement of the hydrolysate, which indicated that only the C-terminal phenylalanine residue was tritiated. The radioactive peptide (C-*V: 0.168 µmole) was dissolved in 0.2 ml of 0.1 M Tris-HCl buffer at pH 8.0 and digested overnight with 0.05 mg of trypsin at 40°.

The digest was lyophilized and subjected to preparative electrophoresis (pH 6.5, 2000V, 1 hr.). A guide strip gave two spots, A (+19.5 cm., ninhydrin:+, Pauli: -) and B(+3 cm, ninhydrin: +, Pauli: +). Radioactivity measurement of spots A and B by liquid scintillation spectrometer showed that only A was radioactive. Peptides corresponding to spots A and B were extracted from the ionogram with 30% acetic acid. The amino acid compositions of peptides A and B (Table 1) showed that radioactive peptide A was precisely derived from C-terminal portion of peptide C-V by tryptic cleavage at the Lys-Glu linkage as expected, while peptide B was from the N-terminal portion. The results showed that the tritiated peptide underwent tryptic digestion smoothly and the C-terminal fragment was easy to detect by its radioactivity.

TABLE 1. Amino Acid Composition of Peptides Obtained by Enzymatic Digestion

Amino acid	(A)	(B)	(C)
Lysine		1.02(1)	0.69(1)
Histidine		1.04(1)	0.63(1)
Cysteic acid			1.31(2)
S-Carboxymethylcysteine		1.49(2)	
Aspartic acid	1.07(1)	1.03(1)	2.07(2)
Threonine		3.69(4)	2.63(4)
Serine		1.07(1)	0.82(1)
Glutamic acid	1.97(2)		1.98(2)
Proline		1.15(1)	0.96(1)
Alanine		2.07(2)	1.79(2)
Valine		0.94(1)	1.14(2)
Isoleucine		0.92(1)	0.84(1)
Leucine	1.02(1)		1.68(2)
Tyrosine		0.60(1)	0.71(1)
Phenylalanine	0.97(1)		0.81(1)

CHYMOTRYPTIC DIGESTION OF SCENEDESMUS FERREDOXIN

Scenedesmus ferredoxin (0.87 μmole) was tritiated by treatment with ^3H_2O (0.2 ml: 100 mC), pyridine (0.3 ml) and acetic anhydride (0.05 ml) to yield radioactive N, O-acetyl ferredoxin (0.8 mole). The tritiated protein (0.1

μmole) was hydrolyzed with HCl and subjected to paper chromatography (butanol: acetic acid: water = 200: 30: 75). The radioactivity of the ninhydrinpositive spots was measured as described above and only C-terminal phenylalanine was found to be radioactive, coinciding with the result obtained by carboxypeptidase A[15].

Radioactive N, O-acetyl-ferredoxin (0.7 mole) was digested with chymotrypsin (0.5 mg) in 0.05 M Tris-HCl buffer (pH 8.0) at 40° overnight. After lyophilization, the digest was subjected to two-dimensional paper chromatography (butanol: pyridine: acetic acid: water 15: 10: 3: 12) and electrophoresis (pH 6.5, 2000 V, 1 hr.). The radioactive spot from the map was easily detected by scintillation spectrometric measurement of all 15 spots which were cut out of the peptide map. The spot corresponding to the radioactive peptide (Rf 0.53; 11.0 cm) was cut out of another map and extracted with 30% acetic acid to obtain the radioactive peptide fragment (C). The amino acid composition of peptide C (Table 1) agreed well with the theoretical value for the C-terminal peptide which is presumed to be derived by cleavage at the Phe-Val linkage[12].

The C-terminal tritiated peptides were easily obtained by the same method as that used routinely for C-terminal amino acid determination. These peptides smoothly underwent enzymatic digestion and the resulted radioactive peptide fragments could be unambiguously characterized as C-terminal peptides.

Tritiation procedure using acetic anhydride for oxazolone formation result in simultaneous acetylation of hydroxyl groups. This hinders the direct comparison of peptide maps after enzymatic digestion with those of non-tritiated peptides, because acetylation changes the behavior of peptide fragments in chromatography or electrophoresis.

Attempts at reversible masking of hydroxyl groups, and use of other oxazolone formation reagents in place of acetic anhydride have given encouraging results that are being investigated.

ACKNOWLEDGMENTS

The authors wish to express their thanks to Dr. T. H. Jukes and Dr. J. E. Casida for their support and interest in this work, to Dr. K. Sugeno for helpful suggestions and discussions, and to Mrs. D. Tsuchiya for skillful technical assistance.

This work was support by Grant NsG479 from the National Aeronautics and Space Administration and Grant NIH HE-11553 from the National Institutes of Health.

REFERENCES

1. Present address: The Institute of Physical and Chemical Research, Komagome, Tokyo, Japan.

2. H. Matsuo, Y. Fujimoto and T. Tatsuno, Tetrahedron Letters, 3465 (1965).

3. Idem.: Biochem. Biophys. Res. Commun., 22, 69 (1966).

4. H. Matsuo, Kagaku, 26, 244 (1966).

5. H. Matsuo, Y. Fujimoto and T. Tatsuno, Chem. Pharm. Bull., 15, 716 (1967).

6. H. Matsuo, Y. Fujimoto, T. Tatsuno and N. Ikekawa, Abstr. of 7th International Congress of Biochemistry, Tokyo, 1967, p. 954.

7. H. Matsubara and K. Sugeno, Fed. Proc., 27, 392 (1968).

8. H. Matsubara, R. M. Sasaki and D. K. Tsuchiya, in preparation.

9. H. Kagamiyama, T. Watanabe, and H. Wada, Biochem. Biophys. Res. Commun., 32, 678 (1968).

10. G. L. Holcomb, S. A. James and D. N. Ward, Biochemistry, 7, 1291 (1968).

11. H. Matsuo, unpublished data.

12. K. Sugeno and H. Matsubara, Biochem. Biophys. Res. Commun., in press.

13. R. F. Goldberger and C. B. Anfinsen, Biochemistry, 1, 401 (1962).

14. R. N. Perham and G. M. T. Jones, European J. Biochem., 2, 84 (1967).

15. H. Matsubara: J. Biol. Chem., 243, 370 (1968).